QUANTITATIVE
APPROACHES
TO MANAGEMENT

Richard I. Levin, Ph.D.

C. A. Kirkpatrick, D.C.S.

Both of the Graduate School of
Business Administration
University of North Carolina

McGraw-Hill Book Company

New York
St. Louis
San Francisco
Toronto
London
Sydney

QUANTITATIVE

APPROACHES

TO MANAGEMENT

Quantitative Approaches to Management

Library of Congress Catalog Card Number: 64-24603

37366

III

PREFACE

This book is exactly what its title implies: an introduction to some of the quantitative techniques which today are playing an increasing role in decision making by management. It was written because of the need for an approach to these quantitative methods that is clear and understandable, yet sound and respectable. Because this book demands only a modest background in mathematics, it will have little appeal for the professional mathematician. Nor was it designed for the scientist whose interest is in pushing back the frontiers of knowledge. It was written, instead, for people in college and in business who want an understanding (or a *better* understanding) of some of the quantitative methods management uses.

When examining other texts in this area, we often were irritated; we always were disappointed. Prefaces boasted, "Only college algebra is needed." On one occasion, however, we had read fewer than ten pages before being confronted by complex notation. Certainly we hold no grudge against notation; we recognize that it is the accepted language of mathematicians. But in our opinion, the villain discouraging so many students in their attempt to grasp the fundamentals of operations research is the complexity of notation—not the complexity of the subject matter.

Our book contains none of the usual notation found in operations research texts. Nor does it resort to rigorous mathematical proofs: The proofs developed and used are heuristic—they are commonsense extensions of what the reader already knows. With the mathematical tools thus developed, not only can he use the new quantitative techniques—he can, indeed, understand how and why they work as they do.

Chapter 1, as is customary, is a general opening unit. It is followed by a two-chapter introduction to quantitative concepts. Chapter 2 deals with breakeven analysis, one of the early quantitative techniques—old but still quite useful. This look at costs and cost behavior is an appropriate start for a book concerned with the minimization of costs and the maximization of profits. Chapter 3 discusses probability, one of management's most effective guides when coping with uncertainty. A somewhat unusual feature is the clear handling of Bayes' theorem.

Chapters 4 and 5 are application chapters. The former bridges the gap between the theory of probability and the operational use of probability in dealing with uncertain demand for products. In Chapter 5, the traditional concept of economic order quantity is developed without any use of calculus. The problem of quantity discounts and the statistical determination of reorder points are included.

Chapters 6 and 7 form a mathematical unit. They treat determinants, vectors, and matrix algebra without the usual complex notation. They point up the usefulness of these mathematical tools in the solution of business problems.

Linear programming is the subject of Chapters 8 and 9. The wide potential application of linear programming is demonstrated in Chapter 8 using nothing more than simple two-dimensional graphs and high school algebra. Chapter 9 goes beyond the traditional simplex maximizing algorithm into an easily grasped development of the problem of minimization. A strong feature of the chapter is a method of using the simplex algorithm to solve allocation problems.

In Chapter 10, solutions for two-person zero-sum games are approached from four different directions: arithmetic, algebra, matrix algebra, and graphing. Solutions to games involving more strategies are illustrated by the use of linear programming.

The orientation of Chapter 11 is marketing management. Particular attention goes to the matter of brand loyalty.

The concluding chapter, Chapter 12, examines waiting-line behavior without reference to complex statistical distributions. It throws light on managerial decisions about the staffing of service facilities.

Our graduate students have been most generous to us. Many valuable ideas and helpful suggestions came, in particular, from Rudy Lamone, John Beverly, Jim Gentry, Geoff Churchill, and Al Newman.

We should like to thank the reviewers of our manuscript, Prof. Edwin B. Cox, Boston University, Prof. Oliver Galbraith, III, San Diego State College, and Dean Harold Feldman, Farleigh Dickinson University, for their many helpful suggestions.

Richard I. Levin

C. A. Kirkpatrick

CONTENTS

chapter two   BREAKEVEN ANALYSIS   17

chapter **INTRODUCTION**
one

Because the quantitative methods we shall be studying are based on scientific methodology, our first job is to get a grasp of the nature of the scientific method. The scientific method involves the following five phases.

THE SCIENTIFIC METHOD

1. Observation

The scientific method starts with the observation of a phenomenon; this can be an item, an object, a situation, a process, or a fact. Isaac Newton was "observing" under a tree when, according to history, an apple dropped and hit him on the head. Observation can be a casual glance— or a concentrated, detailed, lengthy analysis. For a scientist engaged in pure research, observing can be nothing more than the reluctant admission that there is something he does not understand fully.

The purpose of observation is to identify problems. A manager's major responsibility is to make decisions, and decisions involve problems. And, of course, a problem cannot be dealt with until its existence is known. Smart managers, therefore, work at developing an "observing" attitude; they try to stay always alert and sensitive to the presence of problems.

The detection of problems can be a most difficult, uncertain undertaking. Much time can elapse before the presence of a problem is suspected. Even then, what the manager observes may well be a symptom of the basic problem rather than the problem itself.

Here is a hypothetical example which will be carried through the five phases of the scientific method. Suppose a manufacturer of flashlight batteries visits 100 retail hardware stores and finds that only 4 have flashlight batteries displayed for sale on their counters. This is the manufacturer's observation of a situation—an observation which obviously suggests to him that a problem exists.

2. Definition of the problem

In phase two, the manager clarifies the problem and recognizes it for exactly what it is. He defines it in specific and detailed terms. He sees clearly what the critical issue—the key issue—consists of. By so doing, the manager avoids spending time, effort, and money on trying to solve some *wrong* problem.

Pinpointing the problem can involve several steps. Suppose a manager notes from profit and loss statements that profits last year were less than for the previous year. In step 1, he asks *why*, and discovers that a decrease in sales volume (rather than an increase in costs) was responsible. In step 2, the manager again asks *why*, and determines that his products were not responsible, that his prices were not responsible, but that his *promotion* does seem to be responsible. In step 3, he concludes that his sales department and staff are not to blame, but that his *advertising* does seem to be the explanation. Assuming this to be the case, in step 4 the manager examines the advertising variables (amount of money spent, media used, advertising theme, timing and scheduling, etc.) in order to identify the culprit.

Isaac Newton may have asked, "Why did that apple fall *down* rather than *up*?" He could have considered the weight, surface texture, and shape of the apple; the density, temperature, humidity, and viscosity of the air; the mass, shape, and spin of the earth. Fortunately for students of physics, he managed to combine or eliminate most of these variables. Many management problems involve a great number of relevant variables, but as in the case of Newton's apple, most of these variables can be combined or eliminated until only a small number of important ones remain.

Our manufacturer of flashlight batteries has little difficulty in defining his problem. It can be expressed in these words: How can he get more retail hardware stores to display batteries for sale on their counters?

3. Formulation of a hypothesis

Once his problem has been defined, the manager reviews what he and others have done earlier when facing similar or related circumstances. He confers with associates and perhaps with others. He examines, he scrutinizes, he analyzes. He calls on his creative and imaginative powers for approaches to *new* solutions. He studies the strengths and the weaknesses of every course of action deserving consideration.

What the manager is going through is the formulation of a hypothesis. What is a hypothesis? A solution to a problem. *The* solution—

the *one best* solution, the manager hopes. Often the hypothesis takes the form of a *model*. And what is a model? A model is a representation, an abstraction of an actual object or situation. A model is anything that shows the relations and interrelations of action and reaction—of cause and effect—in operational situations. Models are used in forecasting; they are used when management is trying to predict what will take place if a certain decision is made and a certain course of action adopted.

Photographers' models and model airplanes are examples of *iconic* models. An iconic model is a physical representation of some real-life object, either in more or less idealized form (the photographer's model) or on a different scale (the airplane model).

Our main interest is in *symbolic* (rather than iconic) models. Whereas the iconic model is concrete, the symbolic model is abstract. A simple demand curve in economics is a symbolic model predicting buyers' behavior at different price levels. Equations are a type of mathematical model commonly used in operations research. Another common model, one familiar to business managers, is the profit and loss statement. Here on one sheet of paper, the entire year's operations of a company are summarized in a manner which measures the success of those operations. The statement does not re-create every action that took place during the year; it does, however, show the net result of all activities. It is worth noting that *last* year's profit and loss statement and the budget for *next* year are both models.

A pie chart showing what a company did with the typical dollar of sales revenue is also a model—a graphic model. A drawing of what might happen if your automobile were in a collision and your seat belt not fastened is a pictorial model. A firm's organization chart—showing, perhaps, the vice-president of production reporting to the executive vice-president and the sales manager reporting to the vice-president of marketing—is another kind of model.

The symbolic models of interest to us usually take the form of figures, symbols, and mathematics. Mathematical models have many desirable qualities. They are concise and precise. They are not easily misconstrued. Their symbols are easier to manipulate than words are. They are easier to "see" than words are: 273/146 is much more quickly grasped than "two hundred seventy-three divided by one hundred forty-six."

Our manufacturer of flashlight batteries settles on this premise or hypothesis: If he can design an effective counter display container—one acceptable to a great proportion of retail hardware merchants—more batteries will be exposed and available on retail counters for purchase by consumers.

4. Experimentation

Here the manager tests his hypothesis; here he confirms it or he finds it unsound. If he has two possible solutions, he compares.

Our battery manufacturer did a two-way experiment in that he designed two counter containers, model A and model B, and placed 250 of each in the hands of typical retailers. Model A was a flat counter tray, colorful and attractive. But model A was not well received by the 250 retailers who got it. It turned out to be too wide, it took up too much space, and it became somewhat of a catchall for various other products. Model B was a slant pack which could be fashioned easily from the shipping case. This case contained 24 small polyethylene bags each of which held 2 batteries. Model B was narrower than model A, it would fit any basic store fixture, and its slant resulted in greater display. Model B was well received and widely used.

5. Verification

In this final phase of the scientific method, the manager verifies (or is *unable* to verify) the conclusion drawn from experimentation. Experimentation is often on a limited basis; often it is applied only to a sample, as in the case of the counter display containers. Verification, in such instances, can involve the entire group—the total population, as statisticians might say.

Such physical sciences as physics, geology, and chemistry are generally thought of as areas in which research is scientific. Why? Conditions in a laboratory can be controlled; the same experiments worked out in one laboratory can be duplicated in other laboratories because the variables involved can be controlled. The business area is different. Here managers deal with individuals, and individuals are *not* standardized and uniform, as is a ton of steel. Action by government, reaction by competitors, and consumer buying behavior are examples of variables which cannot be predicted as accurately or controlled as effectively as physical variables in a laboratory.

Our manufacturer of flashlight batteries offered model B to all his retailers; acceptance and use were overwhelming.

Summary

We have looked at the five phases which constitute the scientific method. First, the business manager observes an object or a situation for the purpose of identifying any problems which may be adversely affecting his operations. Second, if a problem is detected, it is verified, clarified, and defined. Third, one or more promising solutions to the problem are designed; these solutions are referred to as hypotheses or premises. Fourth, the manager experiments; he quickly discards unpromising courses of action and compares the courses of action remaining. Fifth and finally, the manager moves to verify his choice of solution.

EARLY WORK IN MANAGEMENT

Much of man's progress in the last few centuries can be traced to the application of the scientific method to problems where custom, inertia, and tradition had ruled previously. Scientific methodology, prominent earlier in the natural sciences, is now being applied more and more to management—to the planning, organizing, and controlling of operations.

Industrial engineering was born when the scientific method was applied to management problems, but the date of birth is not certain. Individual instances in which the essence of scientific method appears to have been used to solve management problems have been found in writings thousands of years old. Moses' father-in-law, Jethro, is credited with a treatise on organization principles in Chapter 18 of the Book of Exodus. Much more recently (1832), Charles Babbage wrote *On the Economy of Machinery and Manufactures,* showing much industrial engineering insight.

In the late nineteenth century, Frederick W. Taylor converted industrial engineering into a profession and can, with some justification, be considered the father of Scientific Management. Taylor's famed shovel study is an excellent example of the application of the scientific method to a management problem, namely, the productivity of men shoveling ore. Management had always assumed that the largest shovel a man could fill and carry was the size to maximize output. Even though this seems to be a reasonable assumption, Taylor questioned it and designed a series of experiments to prove or disprove it. After testing all variables that seemed relevant, Taylor determined that only one variable was really significant, namely, the combined weight of the shovel and its load. Too much weight on the shovel, and the worker tired easily and moved slowly. Too little, and he had to make too many trips. For a "first-class man" the proper load turned out to be about 20 pounds. Since the density of ores differs greatly, a shovel was designed for each ore so as to assure the proper weight when the shovel was correctly filled. Productivity rose substantially after this change.

Another man of the early Scientific Management era was Henry L. Gantt, best known perhaps for his work in scheduling production. Most work-scheduling methods prior to Gantt were rather haphazard. A machining job, for instance, might run through one stage of its production with no trouble and then wait for days for acceptance in the next machine center. Gantt mapped each job from machine to machine, allowing for and minimizing every delay. It is possible to plan machine loadings months in advance with the Gantt procedure and to quote delivery dates quite accurately. While Taylor was interested in the "one best way" to accomplish a single task, Gantt took a broader point of view; he looked at the various phases or steps in the complete operation.

This shift of interest away from the minutiae of management toward broader considerations was actually a transfer of emphasis from industrial engineering to operations research. It can be said that operations research emerged as a separate field when (1) industrial engineers became interested in the overall operations of the firm, and (2) natural and social scientists became interested in management problems.

EARLY OPERATIONS RESEARCH

As early as World War I, Thomas Edison was doing work that would now be called operations research. His problem, presented to him by the Navy, was to find out which of the possible maneuvers of merchant ships would be most effective in minimizing shipping losses to enemy submarines. In doing this work, he used a "tactical game board"; he did not risk ships in actual experimentation.

Another early work which could be considered operations research led to the solution of a telephone problem in 1917 by the Danish mathematician A. K. Erlang. His formulas even now are almost universally employed in planning circuit facilities and traffic flows in telephone exchanges. Erlang's early work is the foundation of many of the mathematical techniques now used in solving problems which involve the planning of facilities.

Horace C. Levinson provides the best pre-World War II example of a natural scientist who applied his analytic abilities to problems of management. Originally an astronomer, he went to work for L. Bamberger and Co. in the 1930s. He performed numerous experiments on customer reactions and often applied sophisticated mathematical models to great amounts of data which would otherwise have been totally unmanageable.

One of his best-known studies involved customers' refusals to accept C.O.D. packages ordered from a small mail-order house. These rejections averaged over 30 per cent of gross sales and were having, for reasons both obvious and not so obvious, bad effects on profits. Two variables turned out to be significant. First, as would be expected, the more expensive orders were more frequently refused. Another factor proved easier to deal with than this, however. Analysis of a very large sample of orders revealed that the time between receipt of the order and shipment of the merchandise was quite important. It was so important, in fact, that shipment 5 days after the placement of the order was not worthwhile; on the average, orders older than 5 days did not break even. From this point, of course, it was relatively easy to compare the cost of rejections with the cost of faster shipping and thus determine the optimum shipping effort.

It was not until World War II that the groups of researchers were formed which gave the activity its present name of operations research. In the late 1930s a number of scientists were working, separately and together, for Britain's RAF on radar and on its integration with ground observers. In 1939 the superintendent of the Telecommunication Research Establishment brought a small number of scientists together into a research section. This is said to be the nucleus of the first operations research group.

Not long after this beginning, the Anti-Aircraft Command Research Group was formed to study antiaircraft aiming problems. This group of eleven scientists represented a broad spectrum of disciplines and was soon known as "Blackett's Circus." The group, which solved a number of military problems, expanded and split into an army and a navy group. Thus, early in the war, all three of Britain's military arms had operations research groups actively engaged in military research. Other Allied nations, including the United States, soon saw the effectiveness of such groups and borrowed the idea. One of the more interesting wartime applications of operations research was in the deployment of merchant marine convoys to minimize losses from enemy submarines.

After the war, civilian operations research caught on much faster in Britain than in the United States. The British economy was in poor shape; equipment was badly worn, factories had been bombed, and the balance of payments was precarious. Management consulting had never become popular in Britain. Consequently, British managers were willing to try something new to raise productivity and profits; they turned to the newest approach in their country, operations research.

The reaction was much different in the United States. Management consulting in this country dated back at least to F. W. Taylor, and managers had seen many fads come and go. Communication between managers and scientists (in contrast to communication between managers and consultants) was quite difficult because neither spoke the other's language. What little message the scientists could get across to managers sounded like no innovation at all. And managers were inclined to turn to established consulting firms to get done the research recommended by the scientists. Furthermore, to some managers the scientists did not seem completely reliable or respectable.

It was not until a few of our bolder companies tried operations research with considerable success, and word began to leak out about the World War II accomplishments of operations research, that civilian operations research began to make any real headway in the United States. Scientists and managers began to learn how to achieve two-way communication.

OPERATIONS RESEARCH TODAY

The term operations research today refers to the application of scientific methodology to problems related to the functioning or operating of some unit—business, governmental, or institutional. Management asks operations research to provide *quantitative* bases for decisions, bases which will permit management to make the best operating decisions and to determine the best solutions to operating problems. Briefly, operations researchers are expected by managers to analyze managerial problems which involve the operations of systems, to gather essential data, to interpret those data, to build one or more models, to manipulate and experiment with those models, and finally, to predict and make recommendations about future operations.

The operations research specialists have not replaced managers, nor have they taken over the decision-making responsibility. The proper role of the operations research specialist is to help the manager make better decisions. If the specialist and the manager are to work together most effectively, the manager needs some understanding of the quantitative tools specialists use—he needs enough understanding to be able to describe a problem and then provide pertinent data for its solution. It is *not* necessary that the manager be familiar with the intricacies of the mathematics used by operations researchers.

Two features of operations research demand brief notice: the team approach and the breadth of scope.

1. Team approach. In operations research, problem solving is approached by a heterogeneous team rather than by one researcher or even a group of homogeneous researchers. An operations research team would not be unusual if it included a statistician, a mathematician, a psychologist, an accountant, and an engineer. Composition of the team changes in response to the nature of the problem at hand and the purpose of the research. By drawing from different fields, management increases the number and the sources of analytical techniques which can be applied to problems. And it is a fact that models from other areas can be profitably adapted to the area of business management. Because men from different disciplines cross-fertilize and sharpen their thinking on each other's thinking, they can always be *developing* analytical techniques and can come closer to fitting the best technique to each problem than would otherwise be possible. Researchers are always searching for better models.

Some managers are suspicious of operations research *teams* on two counts. (1) Some assume that these teams function as committees and consequently suffer from all the defects and weaknesses of committees. (2) Some fear that teams actually make managerial decisions, thus jeopardizing the manager's stature and even threatening to take over the manager's job. Neither of these suspicions is warranted.

Other managers are suspicious of operations research *scientists*, fearing that they are completely theoretical and totally indifferent to sales volume, costs, and profits. On the contrary, these researchers *are* concerned with the practical, the functional, the pragmatic. Operations research is an *applied* science—applied to operating problems.

2. Breadth of scope. Where possible, operations research adopts the *firm* or the *company* point of view. This is in contrast to the department or even the division point of view. Operations research focuses on and views the unit in question as a single system with one group of overall goals, not as an assortment of departments or divisions which work together in a more or less cooperative manner. In other words, operations research is concerned with what is best for the company—not what is best for the sales department or the production department.

The industrial engineering approach to production problems was something like this:

Our customers have ordered X amounts of Y types of products. What is the fastest, cheapest, best way to make them?

The operations research approach goes like this:

We can make A, B, and C types of products. Each unit requires a known portion of our capacity, involves known variable inputs, and sells for a known price. What is the most profitable combination of A, B, and C to make and sell?

Hypothetical crankshaft problem

Here is an example of the type of problem confronting managers. Suppose we are managing a machine shop and a manufacturer of small engines is interested in buying crankshafts from us. He is buying for inventory and will accept up to 175 power lawnmower crankshafts, up to 65 motor scooter crankshafts, and up to 160 golf cart crankshafts. He will pay $15.75 each for lawnmower crankshafts, $24.50 each for motor scooter crankshafts, and $20 each for golf cart crankshafts.

Our estimate is that material costs for the three kinds, in order, are $1, $6, and $5.50. These crankshafts would pass through three machine centers for which we expect no other orders in the near future. The first is the forge, which has 360 hours available. Here direct labor costs are $2.25 per hour. The next center is the lathe section, in which 240 machine hours are available; here direct labor costs amount to $2.50 per hour. Finally, there is the grinding department. Direct labor costs in this department are $1.50 per hour; 480 machine hours are available here.

From past experience with these crankshafts, we know the machine time needed for each type. A lawnmower crankshaft requires 3 hours in the forge, 2 hours' lathe time, and 1 hour of grinding. A motor scooter crankshaft requires 4 hours of forge work, 1 hour of lathe time, and 3 hours of grinding. A golf cart crankshaft requires 2 hours in each of these three departments. The problem? What *one* combination of the three types of crankshafts will net us the greatest profit?

With traditional mathematical and statistical tools, this crankshaft problem is time-consuming because there are so many variables and combinations. Our customer will not buy more of each type than stated. Our profit on each of the three types is different. We have a limited amount of time in each of the three machine centers, and each of the crankshaft types has its own needs for machine time. And, of course, there are three products rather than one. How can we approach a solution? Through the use of linear programming, a procedure explained in Chapters 8 and 9.

Hypothetical transportation problem

Another successful application of operations research in decision making has been in the area of transportation costs. Problems in this area arise from the fact that a company may produce in several factories and ship in turn to several warehouses. Shipping costs from each factory to each warehouse are different; hence the problem becomes one of minimizing total shipping costs in view of the total capacity of the factories and the total needs of the warehouses. Figure 1-1 is typical of situations of this type. The capacity for the forthcoming week is given for each factory, and the weekly needs for each of the three warehouses are also given. The company transportation manager must then decide which factory will supply which warehouse if costs are to be minimized.

Table 1-1

Possible shipping combinations				
Factory	Capacity	Shipping cost to R	Shipping cost to S	Shipping cost to T
A	100 tons	$4/ton	$7/ton	$3/ton
B	50 tons	$2/ton	$4/ton	$5/ton
C	70 tons	$8/ton	$6/ton	$1/ton
Needs this week		40 tons	80 tons	100 tons

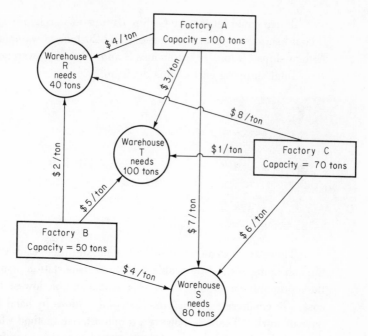

Figure 1-1 **Possible shipping combinations.**

The relationships between capacity, needs, and costs for shipment can be expressed as in Table 1-1. As you have noticed, the number of possible combinations of warehouses and factories is very large. Each different shipping combination involves a different total shipping cost for the coming week. Let us look at two of the many possible solutions to the problem facing the transportation manager.

1. He could let factory A supply warehouse T's needs; he could then let factory B ship 40 tons to warehouse R and 10 tons to warehouse S; factory C would then ship all its output to warehouse S.

Total shipping cost of this decision:

100 × $3	$300
40 × $2	80
10 × $4	40
70 × $6	420
	$840

2. He could let factory C ship 70 tons to warehouse T; then factory B could ship 30 tons to warehouse T and 20 tons to warehouse S; factory A then ships 60 tons to warehouse S and 40 tons to warehouse R.

Total shipping cost of this decision:

70 × $1	$ 70
30 × $5	150
20 × $4	80
60 × $7	420
40 × $4	160
	$880

There are, of course, many other possibilities, each with a different total shipping cost. The problem of the transportation manager is to find the optimum combination—in this instance, the lowest total shipping cost. To enumerate all the possible combinations by hand would require days of work. There is, however, a quantitative method which will yield the optimum answer in a very few minutes: linear programming, Chapter 9.

QUANTITATIVE METHODS TO BE TREATED

A brief comment about each of the quantitative methods to be covered in this text may indicate more specifically some of the types of analyses available and some of the problems to which they can be applied.

Breakeven analysis involves the variables which determine whether a firm makes a profit or incurs a loss. These variables consist of fixed costs, variable costs, selling price per unit of product, and number of units sold.

Probability theory is useful in the reduction of uncertainty. Bayesian statistics develop, from a single theorem, ways of predicting the future when only a minimum of information is available.

Inventory models aid in controlling total inventory costs. These costs consist of ordering costs and carrying costs.

Vectors, determinants, and *matrix algebra* are mathematical tools necessary for the understanding and use of linear programming.

Linear programming is an analytical method of finding, from a large number of possible combinations, the optimum combination of several limited resources to achieve a given objective. Problems are described by algebraic equations and are solved by algebraic manipulation of these equations.

Games and *competitive strategies* provide important insight into situations of conflict; they provide one approach to the determination of optimum solutions in certain competitive situations.

Markov analysis permits one to predict competitive changes over time when brand loyalties and current market shares are known.

Waiting lines consist of random arrivals at a servicing or processing facility of limited capacity. Models allow management to calculate (1) lengths of future waiting lines and (2) average time spent in line by a person awaiting service or a part awaiting processing.

QUESTIONS

1-1 Was Taylor's shoveling experiment an example of the application of the scientific method to a management problem? Relate each phase of his experiment to its corresponding phase of the scientific method. Do you think this experiment can be called an example of the application of operations research? Why?

1-2 Does the fact that operations research takes the organizational point of view instead of the individual problem-centered point of view appear to generate any constraints on its increased usage?

1-3 It appears that some early managerial decision making actually used an operations research approach. To what do you attribute the fact that it has taken about fifty years for operations research to come into accepted usage in industry?

BIBLIOGRAPHY

H. Bierman, L. E. Fouraker, and R. K. Jaedicke, *Quantitative Analysis for Business Decisions* (Homewood, Ill.: Richard D. Irwin, Inc., 1961).

R. W. Cabell and A. Phillips, *Basic Operations Research Methods* (New York: John Wiley & Sons, Inc., 1961).

C. W. Churchman, R. L. Ackoff, and E. L. Arnoff, *Introduction to Operations Research* (New York: John Wiley & Sons, Inc., 1957).

E. A. Johnson, "The Executive, the Organization, and Operations Research," *Operations Research for Management* (Baltimore: The Johns Hopkins Press, 1954).

E. A. Johnson, "The Long-range Future of Operational Research," *Operations Research,* vol. 8, no. 1, January–February, 1960.

P. M. Morse and G. E. Kimball, *Methods of Operations Research* (New York: John Wiley & Sons, Inc., 1951).

chapter **BREAKEVEN**
two **ANALYSIS**

The modern approach to the study of management concentrates on *decision making*. Because a firm's profits (or losses) are determined by the relationship between total revenue and total costs, the managerial decisions of interest to us are those which affect revenue and costs. Most decisions a manager makes do, of course, affect those two figures.

A manager's major responsibility is to run a profitable operation. Unless that operation *is* profitable, his firm will not survive. And the *amount* of the profit his firm makes is without doubt the one most important measure of the firm's performance.

Is there some way for a manager to determine, in advance and with at least a worthwhile degree of accuracy, the effects certain decisions might have on total revenue and total costs? Is there some device which will throw some light on what might happen to the profit figure if a certain course of action is adopted? *Yes.* Breakeven analysis and breakeven charts provide one such managerial tool.

CONCEPT OF BREAKEVEN

A manufacturer expects his revenue for the year (his income from the year's sales) to be large enough to cover or to take care of four items: (1) the costs of producing the products he makes—shoes or soap, automobiles or airplanes (example: the cost of raw materials); (2) the costs of marketing those products (example: the cost of advertising); (3) the general costs of administering the firm (example: the president's salary); and (4) the amount of profit he hopes to make during the year. Wholesalers and retailers differ from manufacturers in only one respect—they *buy* rather than manufacture the items they sell. Sellers of services are equally at the mercy of the revenue-cost relationship.

For manufacturers, for wholesalers, for retailers, and for sellers of services, total revenue is expected during most years to equal or to be greater than total costs. Whenever total revenue just equals (1) cost of goods made or bought, plus (2) cost of marketing those goods, plus (3) administrative costs of a general nature, then the firm has neither *made* any money nor *lost* any money. It has just broken even. For the year, the firm can be said to have operated at the breakeven point.

The breakeven point, then, is the volume or level of operation at which total revenue and total costs are exactly equal. Had the firm operated at a level *higher* than this point—had it sold just one *more* item —the firm would have showed a profit. Conversely, had the firm operated at a level *lower* than it did—had it sold just one *less* item—there would have been a loss for the period.

Volume or level of operation can be expressed in three ways. One is the number of units of product made or sold. Another is the dollar volume of sales. Third, volume can be expressed as a percentage of plant capacity being utilized. Revenue, of course, is the number of dollars of income from sales.

REVENUE AND COST ASPECTS

Total revenue from sales

The most important budget for a firm is its sales income or sales revenue budget. This budget reflects the sales forecast for the coming period, which is usually the calendar year. This estimate of the dollars to come in from the sales of products or services is the first budget figure to be established and the most basic figure.

One seller may multiply the number of units he expects to sell by the unit selling price to get the revenue figure. Another may multiply units by the *average* selling price he hopes to get. Still another seller may take last year's dollar total and adjust it upward or downward as seems indicated.

Total revenue from sales does *not* include fixed income or nonoperating income.

Variable costs

This group of costs consists of *direct* costs which can be charged directly and specifically to the products a firm makes or sells. Two concepts of variable costs are involved.

1. *Variable costs per unit* are assumed to be constant or fixed per unit regardless of the level of volume or output. For example, if the production of one desk requires 10 board feet of lumber at 40 cents per foot, then the production of two desks requires a total of 20 board feet ($8) or a variable cost per unit for lumber of $4.

2. *Total variable costs* must and do vary in amount as volume or output changes. At zero volume, total variable costs amount to zero.

A manufacturer's costs classified as *variable* include direct materials, direct labor, packaging, freight out, fuel, supplies, fabricating materials, and sales commissions.

Fixed costs

These are indirect costs.   Only one concept is involved, and that is of total fixed costs, expressed, of course, in dollars.   Fixed costs tend to remain constant in total dollar amount regardless of level of volume or output.   At zero volume and at 100 per cent volume, the total dollar amounts are the same.   Consequently, fixed costs must and do vary per unit of product, decreasing per unit as volume or output increases.

A manufacturer's costs classified as *fixed* include rent, interest on investment, property taxes, property insurance, executive salaries, allowance for depreciation, and lump sums spent for advertising.

Volume or output

Total revenue and total costs are tied to, and in a real sense are determined by, volume or output.   Because this is true, a change in volume or output can and does affect a firm's breakeven picture.   If a retailer's dollar sales rise from $350,000 to $400,000—a volume or output change—his showing could change from one of *loss* to one of *profit*.   If a manufacturer's sales in units drop from 700,000 to 600,000, his showing would change in the opposite direction.   If a firm is operating at a loss at 65 per cent of capacity, it is possible that a rise to 70 per cent would cause the firm to break even and that a further rise to 75 per cent of capacity would result in some profit.   See Table 2-1.

Contribution

The concept of contribution is a basic element in breakeven analysis. Suppose a manufacturer sells one unit of the product he makes and gets $5 for it.   Suppose the variable costs of that unit amount to $3.   After these variable costs have been paid, $2 remains as a *contribution* toward paying off the total fixed costs.   Each unit the manufacturer sells under these conditions provides an identical contribution for this purpose.   Obviously, as soon as enough $2 contributions have been accumulated to equal the fixed cost total, the manufacturer has reached his breakeven point.   If he then sells one *more* unit, the $2 from it is profit.

Table 2-1

Breakeven table for a manufacturer

Revenue from sales	$50,000	$60,000	$70,000
Total variable costs	25,000	30,000	35,000
Total fixed costs	+ 30,000	+ 30,000	+ 30,000
Total costs	$55,000	$60,000	$65,000
Profit or loss	($5,000)	0	$ 5,000
	Loss	BEP	Profit

Assumptions:	Selling price per unit	$10
	Variable cost per unit	$ 5
	Total fixed costs	$30,000

This table shows how an increase in sales can change a loss into a profit.

At a sales volume of $60,000, the manufacturer covers his total variable costs of $30,000 (6,000 units × $5) and has $30,000 left—just the amount of his total fixed costs.

Here is an example:

Selling price per unit	$1.00
Variable costs per unit	−0.70
Contribution	$0.30

Assume a sales volume of 1,000,000 units.
Assume a fixed cost total of $200,000.

Then, Total revenue	$1,000,000
Total variable costs	− 700,000
Contribution	$ 300,000
Total fixed costs	−200,000
Profit	$ 100,000

Now see Table 2-2.

Table 2-2

Breakeven table for a retailer

Sales	$275,000	$300,000	$325,000
Cost of goods sold	− 192,500	− 210,000	− 227,500
Gross margin	$ 82,500	$ 90,000	$ 97,500
Total variable costs	− 55,000	− 60,000	− 65,000
Contribution to cover			
total fixed costs	$ 27,500	$ 30,000	$ 32,500
Total fixed costs	− 30,000	− 30,000	− 30,000
Profit or loss	($2,500)	0	$ 2,500
	Loss	BEP	Profit

Assumptions: Net sales = 100%; cost of goods = 70%; gross
margin = 30%

Retailer's variable costs = 20% of net sales

Retailer's fixed costs = $30,000; this amounts to 10% of
net sales when sales volume is $300,000

This retailer pays out to suppliers (manufacturers and wholesalers) 70¢
of every dollar he takes in from his customers. This leaves a gross margin of 30%. Of this, two-thirds (20%) approximates his total variable
costs, and one-third (10%) approximates his total fixed costs in these
particular circumstances.

At a sales volume of $300,000, the retailer breaks even exactly.
A sales volume of $275,000 causes a *loss* of $2,500.
A sales volume of $325,000 causes a *profit* of $2,500.

Refinements

In order to be realistic, we must recognize and admit that there are certain *semi*variable costs and certain *semi*fixed costs. Some variable costs
per unit can and do change sometimes when volume changes. Here are
two hypothetical examples. (1) Suppose the cost of the major raw ma-

terial going into a product jumps sharply. (2) Or suppose that in a year of expanding volume, a larger quantity discount is earned on purchases made after midyear. In example 1, variable costs per unit rise; in example 2, they drop. See Figure 2-1.

Certain fixed costs also can and do change in total when volume changes. These show up on a breakeven chart as "stairsteps." Here are two possibilities. (1) Suppose planned advertising expenditures for the year are $1 million. But at some point within the budget period, management decides to cut advertising expenditures back so that the year's total will not exceed $800,000. (2) Suppose that at midyear, the president's salary is raised from the original budget figure of $40,000 to a new annual rate of $50,000. In example 1, the fixed cost total drops; in example 2, it rises. See Figure 2-2.

We generally disregard *semi*variable and *semi*fixed costs. Because breakeven charts are useful only in short-run forecasting and planning, management is usually justified in separating *all* costs into variable costs and fixed costs. This clear-cut division is the one we make.

Figure 2-1 **Increases in variable costs per unit. In this chart, the fixed cost total has remained constant regardless of volume. Variable costs per unit, however, increased on two occasions. The first increase took place at *one*-third of maximum volume, the second at *two*-thirds of maximum volume. *Total costs* had to rise at steeper rates after each of those points.**

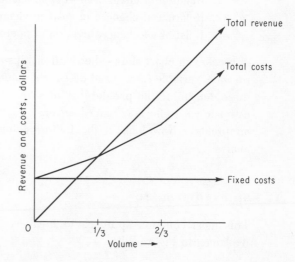

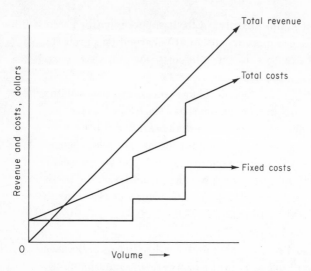

Figure 2-2 **Increases in fixed costs. In this chart, variable costs per unit did not change. The fixed cost total, however, increased on two occasions— at two different volumes. Because of these changes, the *total cost* line had to rise immediately and by the same amount.**

APPROACHES TO BREAKEVEN ANALYSIS

A breakeven chart is a graphic device helpful to management when management is making decisions about:

1. Relation of changes in sales to changes in profits
2. Relation of changes in costs to changes in profits
3. Relation of changes in scale of operation to changes in profits

A breakeven chart shows the relationships among these four variables: revenue, variable costs, fixed costs, and volume or output. It shows how these determine the profitability of a firm. The chart helps managers estimate what effects certain decisions and courses of action would have on profits. Now look at the following four approaches to breakeven analysis.

1. Standard graphic

This most common approach to breakeven analysis is illustrated and explained in Figure 2-3.

The mathematics of breakeven analysis are simple.

Let   TR = total revenue in dollars
       TC = total cost in dollars
       TVC = total variable costs
       TFC = total fixed costs
       x = volume or output in units
       v = variable cost per unit in dollars
       p = selling price per unit in dollars
       BEP = breakeven point

Figure 2-3   **Standard graphic approach. This is a typical representation of breakeven. Fixed costs are a rectangular base supporting a wedge of variable costs. Revenue and costs in dollars are plotted on the vertical or *y* axis. Volume or output in units is plotted on the horizontal or *x* axis. The intersection of the total revenue line with the total cost line locates the breakeven point. Here, total revenue is exactly equal to total variable costs plus total fixed costs.**

The fixed cost total does not change regardless of volume. The variable cost total increases as volume increases from left to right.

Any vertical distance between the total revenue line and the total cost line *to the right* of the breakeven point measures *profit* at that volume. *To the left* of the breakeven point, any vertical distance between those two lines measures negative profit or *loss*.

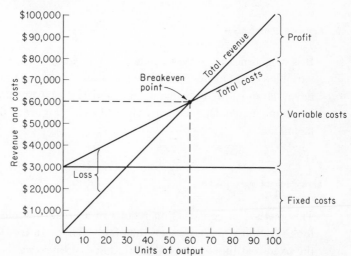

Now, total revenue must equal the volume in units multiplied by the selling price per unit: TR $= xp$. And total cost must equal total variable costs plus total fixed costs: TC $=$ TVC $+$ TFC, or TC $= vx +$ TFC.

To determine the BEP in units, simply equate TR to TC and solve for the volume figure. For example, assume TFC are \$10,000 for the year, v amounts to \$2, and p is \$4. Setting up the equation TR $=$ TC, we get

$$x(\$4) = \$10,000 + x(\$2)$$
$$\$2x = \$10,000$$
$$x = 5,000$$

5,000 units multiplied by \$4 gives the BEP in dollars: \$20,000.

Here are the formulas for BEP in units, in dollars, and in per cent of capacity utilized. (These are expressed graphically in Figure 2-4.)

$$\text{BEP, units} = \frac{\text{TFC}}{p - v} \tag{2-1}$$

$$\text{BEP, \$} = \frac{\text{TFC}}{1 - v/p} \tag{2-2}$$

$$\text{BEP, \% capacity} = \frac{\text{TFC}}{(p - v)(\text{tot. capacity in units})} \times 100\% \tag{2-3}$$

3. Gross graphic

It is sometimes possible to construct a breakeven chart even though the variable cost figure per unit is not known. In order to do this, we must have (1) an estimate of fixed costs and (2) total revenue and total cost for some percentage of capacity utilized. Figure 2-5 illustrates this technique.

4. Inverted graphic

This method of construction results in a breakeven chart that does not look like those we have seen thus far. Why? In this fourth approach, the fixed cost line is *above* the variable cost line—*not* below it. Note in

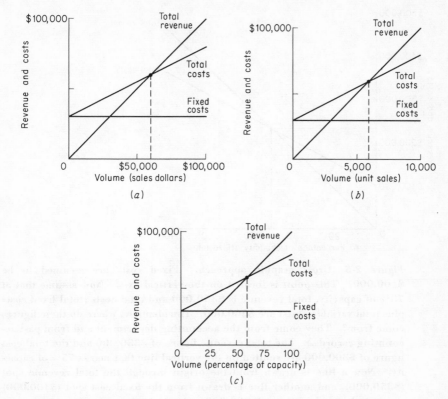

Figure 2-4 **BEP in dollars, units, and per cent.** **(a) Breakeven point—$60,000; (b) breakeven point—6,000 units; (c) breakeven point—60% of capacity.**

Selling price	**$10 per unit**
Variable costs	**$5 per unit**
Fixed costs	**$30,000 per year**
Capacity	**10,000 units**

Figure 2-6 that the wedge of variable costs rests on the horizontal or *x* axis. Note, too, that there is a total revenue line and a total cost line and that their intersection, as in the conventional charts, is the breakeven point.

In some types of manufacturing, the variable costs and the selling price of the product (chairs, for example) are relatively stable. In such cases, a major factor influencing profits is the ability to control overhead —a fixed cost. The effect of greater overhead on the BEP and conse-

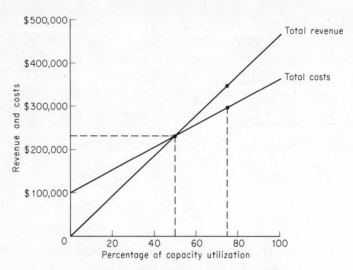

Figure 2-5   **Gross graphic approach.   Fixed costs are assumed to be $100,000.   This point is located on the vertical axis.   Now assume that at 75% of capacity, total revenue is $350,000 and total costs (total fixed costs plus total variable costs) are $300,000.   (Incidentally, where do these figures come from?   They come from the accounting department and from past accounting records.)   The total revenue figure of $350,000 and the total cost figure of $300,000 are spotted on the vertical line that marks 75% of capacity.   Now a line is drawn from the origin through the total revenue spot ($350,000), and another line is drawn from the fixed cost spot ($100,000) through the total cost spot ($300,000).**

The intersection of these two lines determines the breakeven point. The figure is 50% of capacity.

quently on profit is more easily seen on this type of chart than on the conventional chart.   Why?   Because the contrast between the two levels of fixed costs is more obvious.

THREE VARIABLES AFFECTING PROFITS

Total dollar profits for a firm are determined by the interactions of revenue, fixed costs, and variable costs.   Thus, each of these developments can cause a change in the profit figure:

a. A change in the selling price of each unit or in the number of units sold

b. A change in the fixed cost total

c. A change in the variable costs of each unit

For a simple and somewhat unrealistic example of change *a*, assume that a manufacturer is able to raise the unit selling price of his product from $1 to $1.25. Assume further that no other variable (sales volume in units, for example) changes in any significant amount. The immediate and pleasing effect on breakeven is that this manufacturer reaches his BEP sooner (at a smaller sales volume) at $1.25 than at $1. In actuality, this type of price increase is both attractive and unattractive to sales managers. It is attractive in that a smaller number of units must be sold in order to reach the BEP. It is unattractive in that selling a product for $1.25 is practically always more difficult than selling it for $1. See (*a*) in Figure 2-7.

The area of advertising supplies an example of change *b*. A manufacturer starts the calendar year with an advertising budget of $100,000. Assume that during the second quarter this manufacturer becomes convinced that his circumstances call for a greater advertising effort. He buys $50,000 worth of additional advertising during the second half of

Figure 2-6 **Inverted graphic approach. This chart differs from conventional breakeven charts in that fixed costs are *over* variable costs—not *under*. When fixed costs are at $40,000, the BEP is 400 units. When fixed costs rise to $50,000, the BEP rises to 500 units. Profit is greater at the lower level; profit line *AB* is longer than profit line *CD*.**

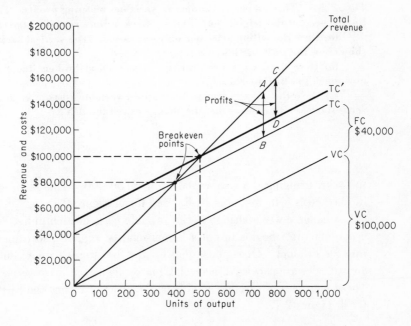

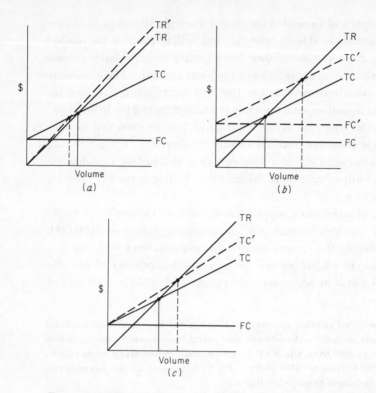

Figure 2-7   **Three separate changes in variables affecting profits.   The solid lines represent the original conditions.   Broken lines represent the changes.**

(*a*) **Here the selling price per unit was raised.   The vertical broken line shows how the BEP was lowered.**

(*b*) **Here fixed costs were raised.   The vertical broken line shows by how much the BEP increased.**

(*c*) **Here the change was an increase in variable costs.   As in (*b*), the vertical broken line shows that the change raised the BEP.**

the year, bringing the year's total up to $150,000.   This is an increase in fixed costs.   It raises the BEP.   See (*b*) in Figure 2-7.

Change *c* was a change in the variable costs of each unit.   Suppose a manufacturer begins to put a higher-quality, higher-priced ingredient into his product.   Or suppose that for the first time, 15 per cent of his annual sales are packaged in special, more expensive Christmas packages. These increases in variable costs have the effect of raising the BEP.   See (*c*) in Figure 2-7.

Illustrative problem—single product

Parts (*a*), (*b*), and (*c*) of Figure 2-7 have one feature in common—each shows how the change of just one variable can affect the breakeven point. A more interesting situation is that in which two or even all three variables change simultaneously. Figure 2-8 represents a situation in which all three change at the same time.

Let us start with some original conditions and plot them with solid lines in Figure 2-8. Now picture the company as (1) thinking about buying a machine which will reduce the number of production workers needed, and (2) at the same time, considering cutting the selling price of the product it makes. The purpose of the price cut is to increase sales volume. This, clearly, is a realistic problem in decision making.

Now make three assumptions: (1) Assume the new machine will in-

Figure 2-8 **Three simultaneous changes in variables affecting profits.**

Original assumptions (solid lines)		Later assumptions (broken lines)	
TFC	$30,000	TFC	$40,000
VC per unit	$500	VC per unit	$400
Selling price per unit	$1,000	Selling price per unit	$900
BEP in units	60	BEP in units	80
Profit at 80-unit volume	$10,000	Profit at 90-unit volume	$5,000

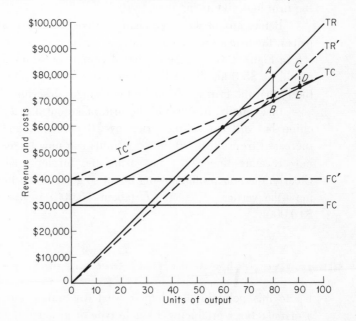

crease fixed costs by $10,000, largely because it increases the deprecia-
tion expense item.   (2) Assume a drop of 20 per cent in variable costs,
largely because of cuts in the number and wages of production workers.
(3) Assume a 10 per cent reduction in the selling price of the product.

Now plot these changes with broken lines.   The new fixed cost total
(FC′) is $40,000 ($30,000 plus $10,000).   The new variable cost per
unit is $400 ($500 less 20 per cent).   The equation for the total cost line
becomes TC′ = $40,000 + $400x, and the revenue line equation becomes TR′ = $900x.   These relationships are shown by the broken lines
in Figure 2-8.

See what these changes do if they are made at a time when 80 units
of production is the volume or output figure.   Revenue, which has been
$80,000, now drops by 10 per cent to $72,000.   The variable cost total,
which has been $40,000, now drops by 20 per cent to $32,000.   The
fixed cost total, which has been $30,000, now rises by $10,000 to
$40,000.   At this point, what has happened is that the BEP has gone up
from 60 units of production to 80 units.   Revenue is $72,000.   Total
costs are $72,000 ($32,000 plus $40,000).

But the 10 per cent reduction in selling price was intended to cause
an increase in the number of units sold.   Suppose the sales department
predicts that the reduction will cause the volume or output figure to rise
from 80 units per period to 90 units.   What will the profit position of
the firm look like then?

Before any of the three changes (fixed costs, variable costs, selling
price), the firm's profit on 80 units was $10,000, shown by the solid line
AB in Figure 2-8.   At the predicted volume of 90 units, the firm's profit
would be $5,000, shown by the broken line *CD*.   Thus it hardly seems
likely that the firm would make the changes described.

Incidentally, how would the firm make out if it *did not* buy the machine but *did* cut selling price by 10 per cent, and if volume then
increased from 80 to 90 units?   Profits can now be measured using the
new revenue line (TR′) but using the former total cost line (TC).
Clearly, the new profit showing is not so good as the former profit showing—the vertical distance *CE* (about $6,000) is less than *AB* (about
$10,000).

Illustrative problem—multiproduct manufacturer

Up to this point in the chapter we have limited our examples to (1)
a manufacturer producing a single type of product or (2) a retailer sell-

ing a single type of product. Why? For purposes of simplification. Most manufacturers, as you know, make more than one type of product; similarly, most retailers sell many types of products.

Look first at the circumstances of a manufacturer who makes and sells tables, lamps, and chairs. The variable cost figures come from the cost accounting department; the sales volume breakdown comes from sales department records.

Product	Selling price per unit	VC per unit	% of dollar sales volume
Tables	$4	$3	20
Lamps	5	4	30
Chairs	7	5	50
			100

Capacity of firm: $1,500,000 total sales volume
Annual fixed charges: $200,000

We first note that each table contributes $1 toward fixed costs, each lamp contributes $1, and each chair contributes $2. Converting these to percentages of selling prices, we have

Table: $\dfrac{\$4 - \$3}{\$4} \times 100\% = \dfrac{\$1}{\$4} \times 100\% = 25\%$

Lamp: $\dfrac{\$5 - \$4}{\$5} \times 100\% = \dfrac{\$1}{\$5} \times 100\% = 20\%$

Chair: $\dfrac{\$7 - \$5}{\$7} \times 100\% = \dfrac{\$2}{\$7} \times 100\% = 28\%$

The basic formula just used is

$$\text{Contribution} = \frac{\text{selling price} - \text{VC}}{\text{selling price}} \times 100\% \qquad (2\text{-}4)$$

Now we multiply each of the contributions by the percentage of sales volume for that particular product and then add the figures we get.

What we get is the total contribution per sales dollar for the tables, lamps, and chairs.   Here are the figures:

	Contribution		% of sales		
Tables	25%	×	20%	=	5%
Lamps	20%	×	30%	=	6%
Chairs	28%	×	50%	=	14%
					25%

This 25 per cent is the total contribution per overall sales dollar at the present product-sales mix.   Here are sales for two weeks:

2,100 tables × $4 = $ 8,400 (20%) $ 8,400 × 25% = $ 2,100
2,520 lamps × $5 = $12,600 (30%)   12,600 × 20% =   2,520
3,000 chairs × $7 = $21,000 (50%)   21,000 × 28% =   5,880
$42,000 (100%) $42,000 $10,500

$10,500 is 25% of $42,000

The BEP of this firm may be calculated as follows:

$$ BEP = \frac{\text{fixed costs}}{\text{price} - \text{variable costs}} $$

$$ = \frac{\text{fixed costs}}{\text{contribution}} $$

$$ = \frac{\$200,000}{25\%} $$

$$ = \$800,000 \tag{2-5} $$

Calculation of profit or loss at various volumes is no more complicated than in the single-product problem.   For example, the profit for this company at 80 per cent of capacity (assuming the same product mix) can be found in this way:

Profit = total revenue − total costs
    = 80% ($1,500,000) − fixed costs − variable costs
    = $1,200,000 − $200,000 − 75% ($1,200,000)
    = $1,200,000 − $200,000 − $900,000
    = $100,000

Suppose an analysis of a men's clothing store revealed these facts:

Product lines	Markup on selling price	% of dollar sales
Shirts	40%	30%
Slacks	30	10
Suits	35	40
Accessories	50	20

Assume the retailer's TFC to be $50,000 and his TVC to approximate 12 per cent of net sales. Note that the retailer's cost of goods sold for shirts is 60 per cent of what the retailer gets for his shirts. Likewise, the retailer pays suppliers 70 per cent of retail for slacks, 65 per cent of retail for suits, and 50 per cent of his selling prices for accessories. What the retailer grosses on each line (40, 30, 35, 50 per cent) is available to defray his variable costs and fixed costs. Any dollars remaining are profit.

Our calculation resembles that for the multiproduct manufacturer:

	Gross margin		% of sales		
Shirts	40%	×	30%	=	12%
Slacks	30%	×	10%	=	3%
Suits	35%	×	40%	=	14%
Accessories	50%	×	20%	=	10%
					39%

Thus, 39 per cent is the overall gross, as a percentage of selling price, with the product lines assumed. After we subtract 12 per cent to cover the retailer's variable costs, we have 27 per cent as contribution. BEP is determined in this manner:

$$BEP = \frac{\text{fixed costs}}{\text{contribution}}$$

$$= \frac{\$50,000}{27\%}$$

$$= \$185,185$$

Here is the way to determine how much profit this retailer will make on a sales volume of $200,000:

Total revenue − cost of goods sold = gross margin
    $200,000 − (61% × $200,000) = $78,000

Profit = gross margin − (fixed costs + variable costs)
    = $78,000 − ($50,000 + 12% × $200,000)
    = $78,000 − ($50,000 + $24,000)
    = $78,000 − $74,000
    = $4,000   (2-6)

Notice that any change in the product-sales mix (for example, the sale of a greater proportion of shirts or the sale of a smaller proportion of suits) will change (1) the BEP and (2) the dollar profit figure.

BREAKEVEN ANALYSIS AND DECISION MAKING

Breakeven analysis is not the sole determinant of which decisions management should make. Such analysis is, however, helpful enough to be worth doing in many situations. It constitutes one of management's planning tools; it is an aid to decision making. Management, of course, wants to do *more* than break even—it wants to maximize dollar profits. This means that breakeven charts are actually "profit planning" charts. Now let us look at certain decision-making areas in which breakeven analysis is worthwhile.

Product planning

Various product-planning decisions, sometimes referred to as "merchandising" decisions, lend themselves to breakeven charting. Immediately there come to mind the "drop and/or add" decisions. Should a contemplated new product be added, in the light of its estimated revenue and cost? Should some item be dropped from the product line, with resulting effects on revenue and cost? Also related is the matter of packaging. If a more (or less) expensive package is adopted and new machinery is a consideration, variable costs and fixed costs are certainly affected—revenue and volume too, in all probability.

Think of a manufacturer who is wondering whether he should drop one item from his product line and replace it with another. Here are his present cost and output data:

Product	Price	Variable costs per unit	% of sales
Bookcases	$ 6	$ 4	30%
Tables	10	6	20
Beds	20	12	50

Total fixed costs per year: $75,000
Sales last year: $250,000

The change under consideration consists in dropping the line of tables and replacing it with a line of cabinets. If this drop-and-add change is made, the manufacturer forecasts the following cost and output data:

Product	Price	Variable costs per unit	% of sales
Bookcases	$ 6	$ 4	50%
Cabinets	16	6	10
Beds	20	12	40

Total fixed costs per year: $75,000
Sales this year: $260,000

Does this change look attractive?

Profit on the present product line is computed in this manner:

$$\frac{\$6 - \$4}{\$6} \times 30\% = 0.10$$

$$\frac{\$10 - \$6}{\$10} \times 20\% = 0.08$$

$$\frac{\$20 - \$12}{\$20} \times 50\% = \underline{0.20}$$
$$0.38 \text{ contribution}$$

$250,000 \times 0.38 = \$95,000$ contribution

$95,000 - \$75,000 = \$20,000$ profit

Profit on the proposed product line looks like this:

$$\frac{\$6 - \$4}{\$6} \times 50\% \quad = 0.17$$

$$\frac{\$16 - \$6}{\$16} \times 10\% \quad = 0.06$$

$$\frac{\$20 - \$12}{\$20} \times 40\% = \underline{0.16}$$
$$\phantom{\frac{\$20 - \$12}{\$20} \times 40\% = } 0.39 \text{ contribution}$$

$260,000 \times 0.39 = \$101,400$ contribution
$101,400 - \$75,000 = \$26,400$ profit

The proposed change appears to be attractive.

Pricing

A seller's prices certainly affect his total revenue and his volume or output. In turn, his prices are certainly affected by his variable costs and his fixed costs. There is the problem of setting original prices; there are the problems of raising and lowering prices. Demand and demand schedules play a basic role in pricing. The sole source of operating profit is gross margin.

Suppose an inventor develops a new type of product. His capital is limited. Competitors sell an inferior product at approximately $6. Our inventor assumes a fixed cost total of $50,000. His variable costs are

Price to consumer	$10.00	$7.50	$4.95
Functional discounts to wholesalers and retailers	−5.00	−3.75	−2.48
Amount inventor gets	$ 5.00	$3.75	$2.47
Variable costs	−1.50	−1.50	−1.50
Contribution to TFC	$ 3.50	$2.25	$0.97
BEP in units (TFC/contribution)	14,285	22,222	51,546

$1.50. He wonders how he would make out if he set consumer price at $10, at $7.50, at $4.95. See table at bottom of page 38.

At $4.95, the inventor must sell 51,546 units in order to break even; at $10, the BEP is only 14,285 units.

Equipment selection and replacement

A firm's initial selection of equipment can have a lasting effect on its profitability. Equipment affects costs, volume, and revenue. Sooner or later, improved equipment becomes available, making older equipment obsolete or at least quite expensive. Newer equipment may save labor, save on materials, permit greater output, or raise product quality. Newer equipment may lower the firm's breakeven point.

Here is a simplified illustration. A manufacturer has three choices of the type of machine to be installed in his factory. (1) An *automatic* machine will add $10,000 a year to his fixed costs but will permit variable costs per unit to be only 20 cents. (2) A *semiautomatic* machine will add $4,000 a year to his fixed costs; variable costs per unit with this machine will be $1. (3) A *hand-operated* machine will add only $1,000 a year to his fixed costs but will cause variable costs per unit of $2.

Figure 2-9 shows that the hand-operated machine is most economical up to a volume of 3,000 units. In the 3,000 to 7,500 range, the semiautomatic machine is most economical. At volumes over 7,500 units, the automatic machine is more economical than either of the other two.

Figure 2-9 **Breakeven analysis: Which machine would be most economical?**

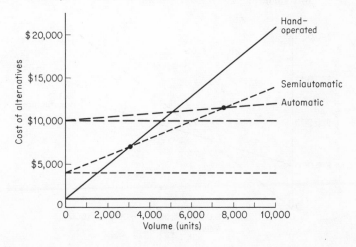

The make-or-buy decision

Many manufacturers have the option of *making* certain components, elements, or ingredients which are part of their finished products—or of *buying* from outside suppliers. A food manufacturer can make his containers, or he can buy them. An automobile manufacturer can make spark plugs, or he can buy them. Breakeven analysis can help the manufacturer decide whether he should make or buy.

Suppose a manufacturer of machinery puts specially machined gears into one of his lines. He now buys these gears from a foundry at $8 each. The manufacturer *could* make the gears. If he did make them, he believes the new machines he would have to buy would add $10,000 a year to his fixed costs; he thinks the total variable costs per gear would be $3.

A glance at Figure 2-10 suggests that if the manufacturer will be needing more than 2,000 gears per year, *to make* is more attractive than *to buy*.

Promotion mix

Every seller designs and uses whatever "promotion mix" he thinks will be most profitable. Personal selling, advertising, and sales promotion are the three broad promotional forces sellers use; within each of

Figure 2-10   **Breakeven analysis: Should the manufacturer make gears or buy them?**

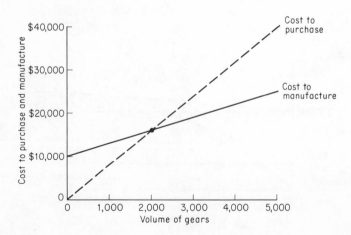

the three, there are many, many variations. Moreover, the proportion of personal selling, advertising, or sales promotion in the promotional mixes of sellers varies from seller to seller. Suppose a manufacturer is thinking of adding five salaried salesmen to his sales force. Or suppose another manufacturer is wondering if he should spend an additional $200,000 in advertising. What these new fixed costs may do to the breakeven points can be shown by breakeven analysis.

For our illustration, picture a manufacturer who sells his products for $5 each. Variable costs are $2 per unit, and the fixed cost total is $60,000. Contribution is $3, and $60,000/$3 = a breakeven point of 20,000 units. Sale of 30,000 units produces a profit of $30,000.

What would happen if this manufacturer began to spend $3,000 for advertising? Fixed costs would rise to $63,000, and $63,000/$3 = a breakeven point of 21,000 units. To make a profit of $30,000 the manufacturer now must sell 31,000 units. This answer may be solved for algebraically. Let x = unknown output.

$$\text{Profit} = \text{revenue} - \text{expense}$$
$$\$30,000 = x(\$5) - \$63,000 - x(\$2)$$
$$= \$5x - \$63,000 - \$2x$$
$$\$93,000 = \$3x$$
$$x = 31,000 \text{ units}$$

Distribution channels

Every manufacturer, whether his merchandise is for the consumer market, the industrial market, or both, must decide how he will get that merchandise to its markets. For example, the manufacturer of a line of food products may be thinking of replacing food brokers with his own regional sales offices and sales staffs. Or a textile manufacturer may be wondering if he should quit using a sales agent, establish a sales department and force, and begin to have his own salesmen call on buyers. Or, somewhat differently, a manufacturer may be debating the profitability of *exclusive* distribution (having only *one* retailer in a city) versus *selective* distribution (having *several* retailers in a city). Breakeven charting is worth attempting in such cases.

Suppose a New York manufacturer has been marketing his line of merchandise in the states of California, Oregon, and Washington through a manufacturers' agent. Last year on a sales volume of $2 million and on a commission of 7 per cent, the agent cost the manufacturer $140,000. The channel change contemplated by the manufacturer is the replacement of the agent with the manufacturer's own regional sales organization, all members of which would be on straight salary.

One basic question is by what amount fixed costs *actually* will rise during the first year of the new channel. Will they be *more* than $140,000—or *less*? Another basic question is whether, during this first year, revenue will be *greater* or *less* than $2 million. Breakeven analysis is worthwhile in cases such as this.

Conclusions

This group of decisions is illustrative only and not complete. They are examples of decisions that top managers are paid to make. They are examples of decisions which have great effect on profit. Breakeven analysis can be most helpful in making such decisions.

CAUTIONS ABOUT BREAKEVEN ANALYSIS

Some warnings and limitations are properly recognized and respected regarding the use of breakeven analysis. Here are eight:

1. Breakeven analysis can be sound and useful only if the firm in question has a good cost accounting system. The firm must use proper managerial accounting techniques and procedures. In short, there must be adequate figures, and they must be valid.

2. A basic assumption in breakeven analysis is that the cost-revenue-volume relationship is a linear relationship. This is realistic only over narrow ranges of output. For example, this type of analysis is worthwhile in deciding whether (*a*) selling price should be 50 or 60 cents, (*b*) volume should be attempted at 80 per cent of capacity rather than 85 per cent, (*c*) advertising expenditures should total $100,000 or $115,000, or (*d*) the product should be put in a package costing 70 rather than 90 cents.

3. A straight-line total revenue curve presumes that *any* quantity might be sold *at that one price*. Computations are often needed at *several* price levels—*several* total revenue curves are needed instead of just one. Otherwise, demand and demand schedules are not given the respect and weight they must be accorded.

4. Breakeven analysis is not a tool for *long*-range use. Clearly, its use should be restricted to the *short* run only. This fact suggests that breakeven analysis should be limited to the budget period of the firm, which, as you know, is usually the calendar year.

5. The area included in the analysis should be limited. If too many products, too many departments, or too many plants are lumped together and pictured on a single breakeven chart, both good and bad performance can easily be buried in the total picture of the group.

6. While caution 5 is completely valid, the job of getting data *by product* or *by brand* (and this is often what management needs) can be quite difficult.

7. Breakeven analysis is more helpful in situations which are relatively stable and slow-moving than in highly volatile, erratic, widely changing cases. Remember, the breakeven chart is a *static* device.

8. The breakeven chart presents an extremely simplified picture of cost-revenue-volume relationships. Each of these three is subject to outside influences as well as to the influence of the other two. Above all, then, breakeven analysis should be viewed as a *guide* to decision making—not as a substitute for judgment, logical thinking, or common sense.

SUMMARY

Most manufacturers and most retailers are operating at levels from which an increased volume of sales leads to greater profit. Typically, a reduction in the fixed cost total lowers the breakeven point. Typically, a reduction in variable costs per unit of product lowers the breakeven point. Therefore, typically, a simultaneous reduction in both types of costs causes a quick and significant drop in the breakeven point. If an increase in selling price can be achieved with no change in the other variables, once again there is a lowering of the breakeven point.

As for the breakeven chart, it is a simple quantitative device which permits management to *estimate in advance* the effects of certain economic decisions on the profit showing of the firm. It is used in profit planning. Management does not want just to break even—management wants to make a profit.

PROBLEMS

2-1 The Smith Manufacturing Company produces chairs. An analysis of their accounting data reveals:

Fixed cost $50,000 per year
Variable cost $2 per chair ,
Capacity   20,000 chairs per year
Selling price $7 per chair

a. Compute the breakeven point in number of chairs.
b. Find the number of chairs Smith must sell to show a profit of $30,000.
c. What is the fixed cost per chair at 75 per cent of capacity?

2-2 The Taylor Feed Company produces feeds for chickens, hogs, cattle, and dogs. From available records we know the following:

Feed for	Selling price per ton	VC per ton	% of $ sales volume
Chickens	$30	$15	40%
Hogs	40	16	20
Cattle	36	16	25
Dogs	32	12	15

Annual fixed costs: $80,000

a. Find the total contribution per overall sales dollar with the present product mix.
b. Find the breakeven point in dollars.

2-3 The Holmes Shoe Store currently stocks three lines of ladies' shoes. Holmes is considering dropping one line of shoes and adding two more. From the data given, decide whether or not Holmes should make this change. Give your reasons.

Shoes now stocked:

Type	Selling price	VC/pair	Sales this year
Flats	$10	$ 6	$ 30,000
Golf	16	12	10,000
Dress	20	12	60,000
			$100,000

Fixed costs: $30,000

Shoes stocked if proposal is accepted:

Type	Selling price	VC/pair	Expected sales
Flats	$10	$ 6	$ 25,000
Dress	20	12	60,000
Evening	16	8	10,000
Bedroom	6	3	5,000
			$100,000

2-4 The Ace Publishing Company must set a price for a new book. The sales manager is considering 3 prices—$8, $6, and $4.50. Fixed costs allocated to this book are $8,000; variable costs per book total $3. Sales forecasts are:

4,000 books at $8 per book
6,000 books at $6 per book
10,000 books at $4.50 per book

What price should be put on the book?

2-5 A producer of electrical equipment is considering the installation of one of two types of machines. A long-run sales forecast indicates that sales will not fall below 8,200 units per year for the next 5 years, the expected life of each machine. Machine 1 will increase fixed costs by $20,000 per year, but will reduce variable costs by $6 per unit. Machine 2 will increase fixed costs by $4,000 per year, but will reduce variable costs by $4 per unit. Variable costs now amount to $20 per unit. At what point are you indifferent as to which machine to purchase? Which machine should be bought?

2-6 The Brown Motor Company currently buys exhaust valves for its motors at $2.50 each. An estimate of the cost to the company to manufacture these valves reveals that the fixed costs will be $4,800 per year and the variable costs per valve will be $1.25. Each motor requires one exhaust valve, and Brown's annual capacity is 6,000 motors per year. At what per cent of capacity does it pay the company to manufacture its own valves?

2-7 The King Company is considering an advertising program which will add $7,000 to fixed cost. Their product, now selling for $10, has a variable cost of $3. Current fixed costs are $35,000. How many additional units must be sold to justify the advertising? What is the new breakeven point in units?

2-8 Here are a firm's annual costs:

Depreciation	$40,000
Salaries	53,000
Materials used	30,000
Advertising	15,000
Direct labor	8,000
Commissions on sales	16,000
Taxes	18,000

This firm sells six products; their total contribution per overall sales dollar is 36 per cent. What is the total variable cost at the breakeven point?

2-9   The XYZ Railroad operates a train daily over an established route. The railroad accountants have gathered the following cost figures for different train lengths:

	Total cost	Avg. cost per car
Engine and 10 cars	$2,700	$270
Engine and 20 cars	3,200	160
Engine and 30 cars	3,700	123
Engine and 40 cars	4,200	105
Engine and 50 cars (maximum)	4,700	94

The operation is currently profitable at an average train length of 35 cars. The railroad competes with the Cannonball Truck Line over the same route. The truck line approaches the railroad and offers to pay it $86 per truck to haul trucks piggyback over the same route. Each railroad flatcar will carry one truck, and the railroad has a plentiful supply of flatcars. Extra costs would be $7.50 per truck to cover the cost of loading and unloading. The trucking company will not guarantee any minimum number of trucks to be hauled. Evaluate this offer in terms of the profit opportunities. The train makes 300 round trips annually.

2-10   The ABC Motel consists of 50 rooms as follows: 20 single rooms which rent for $8 per night, 15 double rooms which rent for $12 per night, and 15 triple rooms which rent for $16 per night. Fixed cost annually amounts to $85,000, which includes all labor. Supplementary variable charges are $3 per room per night, covering linen, power, soap, etc. The rooms are rented in roughly the same ratio as their numbers—as many double rooms are rented as triple rooms, and one-third more single rooms are rented than double rooms. Compute the breakeven point in percentage occupancy, assuming a year of 360 nights. What level of occupancy would promote a profit of $38,000 annually?

BIBLIOGRAPHY

H. W. Broom and J. G. Longnecker, *Small Business Management* (Cincinnati: South-Western Publishing Company, 1961).

H. G. Hodges and R. J. Ziegler, *Managing the Industrial Concern* (Boston: Houghton Mifflin Company, 1963).

B. C. Lemke and J. D. Edwards (eds.), *Administrative Control and Executive Action* (Columbus, Ohio: Charles E. Merrill Books, Inc., 1961).

F. G. Moore, *Manufacturing Management* (Homewood, Ill.: Richard D. Irwin, Inc., 1961).

R. N. Owens, *Management of Industrial Enterprises* (Homewood, Ill.: Richard D. Irwin, Inc., 1961).

G. R. Terry, *Principles of Management* (Homewood, Ill.: Richard D. Irwin, Inc., 1960).

chapter
three

INTRODUCTION TO PROBABILITY THEORY

If it were possible to predict the future with complete certainty, the structure of the business world would be radically different from what it is. A wrong decision would be simply the result of failure to consider all the relevant information. There would be no excess production, no special clearance sales, and no speculation in the stock market, and business failure would be a rarity.

Unfortunately we do not live in a world where we are able to forecast the future with complete certainty. Our desire to reduce uncertainty leads us to the study and use of probability theory. In many instances a businessman has some knowledge about the possible outcomes of a decision. By organizing this information and considering it in a systematic manner, he can usually reach a sounder decision than by using a shot-in-the-dark approach.

OBJECTIVE AND SUBJECTIVE PROBABILITIES

Probabilities fall into two basic categories: objective and subjective. *Objective* probability is a probability for which there is definitive historical evidence and common experience (i.e., objective evidence) to support the assignment of probabilities.

For example, it is commonly accepted that the probability of heads on the toss of a coin is .50 (or ½, or 50 per cent). This implicitly assumes that the coin is *fair* (or unweighted, or unbiased) and that it is tossed in such a way that both heads and tails are equally likely to come up. No reasonable person would argue with these probabilities, because they have been repeatedly demonstrated to be true. The probability of .50 that the coin will come up heads on any toss is thus called an objective probability because it is empirically evident.

Frequently, historical evidence is not available for decision making; here the businessman must rely on his own estimation of a situation and the likelihood of the various possible outcomes. Such an estimate is known as a *subjective* probability.

For an example of subjective probability, picture a salesman and a retailer facing a problem—the problem of whether the retailer should order 100 units of a gift item for the Christmas selling season. Assume that both individuals are quite competent and that each has twenty years of experience in his present capacity. Assume further that the salesman wants to do what will work out best for the retailer. Because the retailer knows his local situation in great detail and because the salesman has been through this type of experience many times, the two will assign about the same probability of success to the action contemplated. Salesman and retailer could easily be in *complete* agreement about the wisdom —about the probable profitability—of the proposed purchase.

In a sense, subjective probabilities are guesses, but they are "educated guesses" based on a person's experience and general knowledge of the situation. Thus one has to guess only in part, because much is known either from historical information or from educated intuition.

THE FAIR COIN

Consider the act of tossing a fair coin (i.e., an unbiased coin with a head on one side and a tail on the other). We know in advance of the toss that either a head or a tail will come up, assuming, of course, that the coin will not land on its edge. However, on any given toss we have no way of knowing in advance with certainty that the coin will land with heads up or tails up. That is, half the time (in an infinite number of tosses) the result will be heads, and half the time it will be tails. Translating this into terms of probability, we have a .50 (or 50 per cent) probability that heads will occur on any toss and a .50 (or 50 per cent) probability that tails will occur on any toss, or in accepted symbols,

$$P(H) = .5$$
$$P(T) = \underline{.5}$$
$$1.0$$

These probabilities are called *marginal* or *unconditional* probabilities because the outcome of any toss is in no way affected or conditioned by the toss or tosses preceding it. If we toss an unbiased coin 3 times and get a head on each toss, what is the probability of the occurrence of a head on the 4th toss? Since the coin is not biased or defective in any way and we know that no single toss is conditioned by any other toss, we assign a probability of .5 to heads and .5 to tails on the 4th toss and on every toss.

Note that the sum of the two marginal or unconditional probabilities is 1.0. This is an extremely important characteristic of probability theory; namely, the probabilities of all possible outcomes of a given action, no two of which may occur at the same time, must add up to 1.0. This is easy to show by considering the fair coin again. Assume, as usual, that the coin is unbiased, that it has one head and one tail, and that it will not land on its edge (or if it should do so, we disregard the event). Now we assign the probability of heads .3 and the probability of tails .3. Thus we have

$$P(H) = .3$$
$$P(T) = \underline{.3}$$
$$.6$$

From this we would expect to get heads 30 per cent of the time and tails 30 per cent of the time. Clearly this does not make sense, since 40 per cent of the time is unaccounted for. If we use the familiar example of cutting a pie into sections to explain fractions, we are saying that two wedges of the pie, each equal to 30 per cent of the total, are equal to the whole pie.

In other words, the probability of any given outcome of a given action must be between 0 and 1 inclusively, and the sum of all these probabilities must be 1. If we assign a probability of 0 to an occurrence, we are expressing complete certainty that the occurrence *will not* take place. At the other extreme, if we assign a probability of 1 to an occurrence, we are expressing complete certainty that the occurrence *will* take place. Any probability between 0 and 1 (for example, .20, .45, .60, .05, etc.) indicates some point between complete certainty that the occurrence will not take place and complete certainty that it will take place. This is written $0 \leqslant P \leqslant 1$ and is read, "The probability of an outcome must be greater than or equal to 0 and less than or equal to 1."

NORMALIZING DISTRIBUTIONS

Information is sometimes available with only the number of occurrences in the given categories. For example, in Spanish 1 courses at a certain university, the grades have fallen into the following distribution over the past 5 years:

Grade	Number of students
A	63
B	127
C	502
D	346
F	462
Total	1,500

Assume that the enrollment in Spanish 1 this year is 315 and that we want to estimate how many will fall in each grade range, based on the past distribution. To do this we must convert the raw scores into percentages of the total number of students. Thus we divide each score by 1,500 as follows:

A $\quad \dfrac{63}{1,500} \times 100\% = \quad 4.20\%$

B $\quad \dfrac{127}{1,500} \times 100\% = \quad 8.47\%$

C $\quad \dfrac{502}{1,500} \times 100\% = \quad 33.47\%$

D $\quad \dfrac{346}{1,500} \times 100\% = \quad 23.06\%$

F $\quad \dfrac{462}{1,500} \times 100\% = \quad \underline{30.80\%}$

$\qquad\qquad\qquad\qquad\qquad\qquad 100.00\%$

To determine the expected number of students who will receive an A this year, we simply multiply 315 by 4.20 per cent. The *expected* distribution, rounded to the nearest whole number, is as follows:

Grade	Number of students
A	13
B	27
C	105
D	73
F	97
Total	315

As another example, assume that we have a box containing 6 black marbles, 1 red marble, 8 yellow marbles, and 5 blue marbles. (All are identical in size and feel.) We then have the following distribution:

Color	Quantity
Black	6
Red	1
Yellow	8
Blue	5
Total	20

We are asked to assign the probability of drawing a black marble. To do so we must divide the number of black marbles by the total number of marbles; i.e., $6/20 = .30$, or 30 per cent. Thus we would say that the probability of drawing a black marble is .30, or 30 per cent. A similar procedure is followed to find the probabilities of the other colors. The new distribution is called the *normalized* distribution because the sum of the percentages is 100 per cent, or if decimals are used, the sum is 1.00. Note that this agrees with the earlier statement that the sum of the probabilities of all the possible outcomes of an event must be 1. In this case the possible outcomes are the different colors that may be drawn.

The normalized distribution is given below:

Color	Quantity	Expressed as percentage	Expressed as decimal
Black	6	30%	.30
Red	1	5	.05
Yellow	8	40	.40
Blue	5	25	.25
Total	20	100%	1.00

MUTUALLY EXCLUSIVE EVENTS

Events are said to be mutually exclusive if one and only one outcome can take place at a time. Consider again the example of the fair coin. There are two possible outcomes, heads and tails. On any one toss with one coin, either heads or tails may turn up, *but not both*. The events *heads* and *tails* are thus said to be mutually exclusive.

As another example, we might have an urn containing 4 balls, identical except that no two are the same color. Assume that the colors are red, blue, green, and yellow. We draw out 1 ball and see that it is blue. By drawing the blue ball, we preclude any possibility of drawing another color at that time. Consequently, since only 1 ball can be drawn at a time, the events (or draws) are mutually exclusive.

The crucial question in determining whether events are mutually exclusive is "Can two or more events occur at one time?" If the answer is yes the events *are not* mutually exclusive.

For example, we have an ordinary, unbiased (i.e., unweighted, fair, true, honest, etc.) die, and we want to know if the numbers on the surfaces are mutually exclusive. We can have one and only one surface facing up each roll. Obviously, the numbers must be mutually exclusive; otherwise we could have two or more surfaces facing up on any given roll.

Additivity of mutually exclusive events

The probabilities of events that are mutually exclusive can be added. That is, the individual probabilities of the events can be added, and if the list includes all possible outcomes, the total will be (and must be) 1.0.

In the case of the urn with 4 balls, each of a different color and equally likely to occur, we have a list of mutually exclusive events that can be added (or which are additive).

Event	Probability
Draw a red ball	.25
Draw a blue ball	.25
Draw a green ball	.25
Draw a yellow ball	.25
Total	1.00

These events necessarily add to 1.00, since there are only 4 possible results of drawing a ball and each of the results is equally likely.

Now consider a case in which an urn contains 6 balls of the following description:

Description	Quantity	Probability
Red and dotted	2	2/6
Green and dotted	2	2/6
Solid red	1	1/6
Solid green	1	1/6
Total	6	6/6 = 1

What is the probability of drawing a ball with green on it? There are 3 balls which fit this criterion, namely, 2 green and dotted and

1 solid green. The sum of the probabilities of these 3 balls is 3/6, or 1/2, or .50, or 50 per cent:

Probability of green and dotted	2/6
Probability of solid green	1/6
Total probability of a ball with green on it	3/6

COLLECTIVELY EXHAUSTIVE EVENTS

When a list of outcomes of a given action includes every possible outcome of that action, the list is said to be collectively exhaustive. That is, taken together, the outcomes include all the possible outcomes. No outcome other than the ones listed is possible.

In the fair coin example, there are two possible outcomes, *heads* and *tails*. Since the result of any toss must be either heads or tails, the list of these two outcomes is collectively exhaustive.

A list of outcomes (or events) can be both mutually exclusive and collectively exhaustive. In the preceding section it was shown that on any toss either heads or tails resulted, *but not both;* and thus we concluded that the events were mutually exclusive. Therefore, the list of outcomes for the fair coin (i.e., heads and tails) is both mutually exclusive and collectively exhaustive.

Consider again rolling an ordinary die. The outcomes and their individual probabilities are listed below.

Possible outcomes (or events)	Probability
1 shows	1/6
2 shows	1/6
3 shows	1/6
4 shows	1/6
5 shows	1/6
6 shows	1/6
Total	6/6 = 1

Since no other outcome is possible, the list is collectively exhaustive. It is also mutually exclusive, because only one outcome is possible at a time.

Notice that the sum of the probabilities is 1. This is an essential characteristic of every list of events or outcomes which are both mutually exclusive and collectively exhaustive.

STATISTICALLY INDEPENDENT EVENTS

When events are statistically independent, the occurrence of one event *has no effect* on the probability of the occurrence of any *other* event. There are three types of probabilities under statistical independence: (1) marginal, (2) joint, and (3) conditional.

1. Marginal probabilities under statistical independence

Marginal probability is the simple probability of the occurrence of an event. Here are two examples:

a. In the fair coin example, we have $P(H) = .5$ and $P(T) = .5$ (i.e., the probability of heads equals .5 and the probability of tails equals .5). This is true for every toss, no matter how many tosses may precede it or what their outcomes may be. Every event (toss) stands alone and is in no way connected with any other event (toss). Thus each toss of a fair coin is a statistically independent event.

b. Assume that we have a biased or unfair coin which has been altered in such a way that heads occurs .90 of the time and tails .10 of the time. On each individual toss, $P(H) = .90$ and $P(T) = .10$. The outcome of any particular toss is completely unrelated to the outcomes of the tosses which may precede it, as well as to the outcomes of any which may follow. The toss of *this* coin, too, is therefore statistically independent, even though the coin is biased.

2. Joint probabilities under statistical independence

The probability of two or more *independent* events occurring together or in succession is the product of their marginal probabilities. Mathematically, this is defined as

$$P(AB) = P(A) \times P(B)$$

where $P(AB)$ = probability of events A and B occurring together or in succession; this is known as a *joint probability*

           $P(A)$ = marginal probability of event A occurring

           $P(B)$ = marginal probability of event B occurring

In terms of the fair coin example, the probability of heads on 2 successive tosses is the probability of heads on the 1st toss (shown as H_1) times the probability of heads on the 2d toss (shown as H_2). That is, $P(H_1H_2) = P(H_1) \times P(H_2)$. We have shown previously that the events are statistically independent because the probability of any outcome is not affected by any preceding outcome. Therefore the probability of heads on any toss is .5. $P(H_1H_2) = .5 \times .5 = .25$; thus the probability of heads on 2 successive tosses is .25 (or ¼, or 25 per cent).

Likewise, the probability of getting 3 heads on 3 successive tosses is $P(H_1H_2H_3) = .5 \times .5 \times .5 = .125$ (or ⅛, or 12.5 per cent).

Assume that we are going to toss an unfair coin which has $P(H) = .9$ and $P(T) = .1$. The events (outcomes) are independent because the probabilities of all tosses are exactly the same. That is, the individual tosses are completely separate and in no way affected by any other toss or outcome.

What is the probability of getting 3 heads on 3 successive tosses? $P(H_1H_2H_3) = P(H_1) \times P(H_2) \times P(H_3) = .9 \times .9 \times .9 = .729$.

What is the probability of getting 3 tails on 3 successive tosses? $P(T_1T_2T_3) = P(T_1) \times P(T_2) \times P(T_3) = .1 \times .1 \times .1 = .001$.

Note that these two probabilities do not add up to 1 because $P(H_1H_2H_3)$ and $P(T_1T_2T_3)$ do not constitute a collectively exhaustive list. They are mutually exclusive because if one occurs, the other cannot.

As further illustration, construct a probability tree, showing the possible outcomes and their respective probabilities of 3 tosses of a fair coin.

For toss 1 we have two possible outcomes, heads and tails, each with probability of .5. This is shown in Figure 3-1.

Assume that the outcome of toss 1 is heads. We toss again. The 2d toss has two possible outcomes, heads and tails, each with probability of .5. In Figure 3-2 we add these two branches of the tree.

Next we consider the possibility that the outcome of toss 1 is tails. Then the 2d toss must stem from the second branch of toss 1. Thus in Figure 3-3 we add two more branches to the tree.

Notice that on 2 tosses we have 4 possible outcomes. They are:

1. H_1H_2
2. H_1T_2
3. T_1H_2
4. T_1T_2

(The subscripts indicate the toss number, e.g., T_2 means tails on toss 2.) Thus after 2 tosses we may arrive at any 1 of 4 possible points. Since we are going to toss 3 times, we must add more branches to the tree.

Assuming that we have had heads on the first 2 tosses, we are now ready to begin adding branches for the 3d toss. As before, the two pos-

Figure 3-1

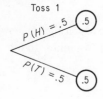

Figure 3-2

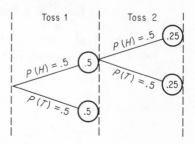

Figure 3-3

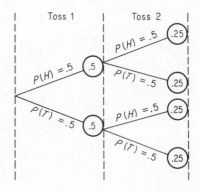

sible outcomes are heads and tails, each with a probability of .5. The first step is shown in Figure 3-4.

The additional branches are added in exactly the same manner. The completed probability tree is given in Figure 3-5.

Note that both heads and tails have a probability of .5 of occurring no matter how far from the origin (1st toss) the particular toss may be. This follows from our definition of independence; i.e., no event is affected by the events preceding or following it.

Suppose we are going to toss a fair coin and want to know the probability that all 3 tosses will result in heads. Expressing the problem symbolically, we want to know $P(H_1H_2H_3)$. From the mathematical definition of the joint probability of independent events, we know that $P(H_1H_2H_3) = P(H_1) \times P(H_2) \times P(H_3) = .5 \times .5 \times .5 = .125$. We could have read this answer from the probability tree by following the branches giving $H_1H_2H_3$.

Here are other brief examples using the probability tree:

a. What is the probability of getting tails, heads, tails *in that order* on 3 successive tosses of a fair coin? $P(T_1H_2T_3) = P(T_1) \times P(H_2) \times P(T_3) = .125$. Following the prescribed path on the probability tree will give us the same answer.

b. What is the probability of getting tails, tails, heads in that order on 3 successive tosses of a fair coin? If we follow the branches giving

Figure 3-4

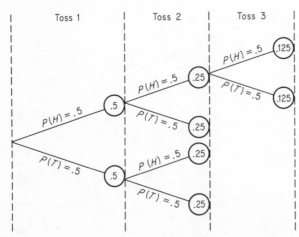

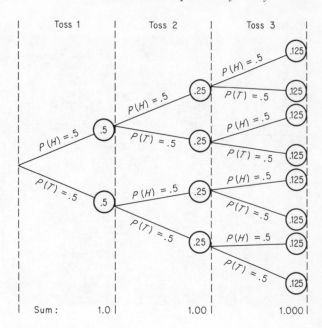

Figure 3-5 **Completed probability tree.**

tails on the 1st toss, tails on the 2d toss, and heads on the 3d toss, we arrive at the probability of .125. Thus $P(T_1 T_2 H_3) = .125$.

It is important to note that the probability of arriving at a given point by a given route is not the same as the probability of, say, heads on the 3d toss. $P(H_1 T_2 H_3) = .125$, but $P(H_3) = .5$. The first is a case of joint probability, i.e., the probability of getting heads on the 1st toss, tails on the 2d, and heads on the 3d. The latter, by contrast, is simply the probability of getting heads on a particular toss, in this instance toss 3.

Note that the sum of the probabilities of all the possible outcomes for each toss is 1. This results from the fact that we have mutually exclusive and collectively exhaustive lists of outcomes. These are given in Table 3-1.

Again referring to the probability tree, consider the following questions.

a. What is the probability of *at least* 2 heads on 3 tosses? Recalling that mutually exclusive independent events are additive, we can note the possible ways that at least 2 heads on 3 tosses can occur, and we can sum their individual probabilities. The outcomes which satisfy the re-

Table 3-1

Lists of outcomes					
Toss 1		Toss 2		Toss 3	
Possible outcomes	Probability	Possible outcomes	Probability	Possible outcomes	Probability
H_1	.5	$H_1 H_2$	.25	$H_1 H_2 H_3$	.125
T_1	.5	$H_1 T_2$	.25	$H_1 H_2 T_3$	.125
	$\overline{1.0}$	$T_1 H_2$	.25	$H_1 T_2 H_3$	.125
		$T_1 T_2$	.25	$H_1 T_2 T_3$	.125
			$\overline{1.00}$	$T_1 H_2 H_3$	.125
				$T_1 H_2 T_3$	.125
				$T_1 T_2 H_3$	.125
				$T_1 T_2 T_3$	.125
					$\overline{1.000}$

quirement are $H_1 H_2 H_3$, $H_1 H_2 T_3$, $H_1 T_2 H_3$, and $T_1 H_2 H_3$. Since each of these has an individual probability of .125, the sum is .5. Thus the probability of at least 2 heads on 3 tosses is .5.

b. What is the probability of *at least* 1 tail on 3 tosses? There is only one case in which no tails occur, namely, $H_1 H_2 H_3$. Therefore we can simply subtract for the answer: $1 - P(H_1 H_2 H_3) = 1 - .125 = .875$. The probability of at least 1 tail occurring in 3 successive tosses is .875.

c. What is the probability of at least 1 head on 2 tosses? The possible ways a head may occur are $H_1 H_2$, $H_1 T_2$, $T_1 H_2$. Each of these has a probability of .25. Therefore the probability of at least 1 head on 2 tosses is .75. Alternatively, we could consider the case in which no head occurs, namely, $T_1 T_2$, and subtract its probability from 1, i.e., $1 - P(T_1 T_2) = 1 - .25 = .75$.

Remember that these are *average* probabilities over a large number of tosses. We might toss a fair coin 10 times and get 10 heads. But over a long series of tosses, we expect heads to occur half the time and tails half the time.

3. Conditional probabilities under statistical independence

Thus far we have considered two types of probabilities: marginal (or unconditional) probability and joint probability. Symbolically, marginal probability is $P(A)$ and joint probability is $P(AB)$. There is only one other type of probability: it is known as conditional probability. Symbolically, conditional probability is written $P(A|B)$ and is read "The probability of event A, *given that event B has occurred.*"

For *statistically independent* events, the conditional probability of event A given that event B has occurred is simply the probability of event A. At first glance this may seem contradictory. However, by definition, independent events are those whose probabilities are in no way affected by the occurrence of any other events. In fact, statistical independence is symbolically defined as the condition in which $P(A|B) = P(A)$.

Example. What is the probability that the 2d toss of a fair coin will result in heads, given that heads resulted on the 1st toss? Symbolically this is written as $P(H_2|H_1)$. Remember that for two independent events, the results of the 1st toss have absolutely no effect on the results of the 2d toss. Since the probabilities of heads and tails are identical for every toss, the probability of heads on the 2d toss is .5; thus, we must say that $P(H_2|H_1) = P(H) = .5$.

For a summary of the three types of probabilities and their mathematical formulas under conditions of statistical independence, see Table 3-2.

Table 3-2

Probabilities under statistical independence

Type of probability	Symbol	Formula
1. Marginal (or unconditional)	$P(A)$	$P(A)$
2. Joint	$P(AB)$	$P(A) \times P(B)$
3. Conditional	$P(A|B)$	$P(A)$

STATISTICALLY DEPENDENT EVENTS

Statistical dependence exists when the probability of some event is dependent upon or affected by the occurrence of some other event. Just as with independent events, the types of probabilities under statistical dependence are (1) marginal, (2) conditional, and (3) joint.

1. Marginal probabilities under statistical dependence

The marginal probability of a statistically dependent event is exactly the same as that of a statistically independent event. This is not difficult to see if we note that a marginal probability is symbolized $P(A)$. *One* and only *one* probability is involved in the consideration. Therefore, even though two dependent events may be involved, a marginal probability refers to only one of them. Here are two examples:

a. We have a box containing 3 balls: 1 red, 1 green, and 1 blue. We have also 3 urns, each containing 6 marbles. They are as follows:

Urn 1 contains 3 white and 3 black marbles.
Urn 2 contains 2 white, 2 black, and 2 yellow marbles.
Urn 3 contains 6 black marbles.

If we draw a red ball from the box, we go to urn 1 and draw a marble; if we draw a green ball, we go to urn 2 and draw a marble; if we draw a blue ball, we go to urn 3 and draw a marble.

Is the probability of drawing a yellow marble affected by the color of ball we draw? It clearly is, because only urn 2 contains yellow marbles, and the only way we can draw from urn 2 is to draw the green ball from the box. Therefore, the two events (drawing from the box *and* drawing from the urn) are statistically dependent; *but* the marginal probability of drawing a yellow marble from urn 2 is still 2 yellow marbles/ 6 marbles = 1/3.

b. We are going to toss a fair coin. If it lands with heads up, we shall toss the same coin again. However, if it lands with tails up, we shall toss an unfair (or biased) coin which has a probability of .9 for heads and a probability of .1 for tails [or $P(H) = .9$ and $P(T) = .1$]. Is the probability of heads on the 2d toss affected by the outcome of the first toss? Yes; the probabilities of heads and tails are obviously conditioned by (or dependent upon) the results of the 1st toss.

If the 1st toss gives heads, we shall toss the fair coin again. The probabilities of heads and tails on the 2d toss are exactly the same as for the 1st toss, namely, $P(H) = .5$ and $P(T) = .5$. However, assume that the 1st toss gives tails. What is the marginal probability of a head on the 2d toss? It must be the probability of a head given the unfair coin, i.e., $P(H) = .9$. The events are statistically dependent, but the marginal probability for any *one* event is still computed as it was under statistical independence.

2. Conditional probabilities under statistical dependence

Conditional and joint probabilities under statistical dependence are somewhat more involved than marginal probabilities. Conditional probabilities will be treated first, because the concept of joint probabilities is best illustrated using conditional probabilities as a basis.

Assume that we have one urn containing 10 balls distributed as follows:

3 are red and dotted.
1 is red and striped.
2 are green and dotted.
4 are green and striped.

The probability of drawing any 1 ball from this urn is .1, since there are 10 balls each with equal probability of being drawn. The discussion of the following examples will be facilitated by reference to Table 3-3.

Example a. Suppose someone draws a ball from the urn and tells us it is *red*. What is the probability that it is dotted? The question then can be expressed symbolically as $P(D \mid R)$, or "What is the conditional probability that this ball is dotted, given that it is red?"

Our question can be expressed diagramatically as shown in Figure 3-6.

We have been told that the ball drawn is red. Therefore, to calculate the probability that the ball is dotted, we completely ignore all the green balls and concern ourselves with red only. Diagrammatically, we consider only what is shown in Figure 3-7.

Table 3-3

Color and pattern on 10 balls		
Event	*Probability of event*	
1	.1	
2	.1	Red and dotted
3	.1	
4	.1	Red and striped
5	.1	Green and dotted
6	.1	
7	.1	
8	.1	Green and striped
9	.1	
10	.1	

From the statement of the problem, we know that there are 4 red balls, 3 of which are dotted and 1 of which is striped. Our problem is now broken down to one of finding the simple probabilities of dotted and striped. To do so we divide the number of balls in each category by the total number of red balls:

$$P(D) = \frac{3}{4} = .75$$

$$P(S) = \frac{1}{4} = \frac{.25}{1.00}$$

Figure 3-6

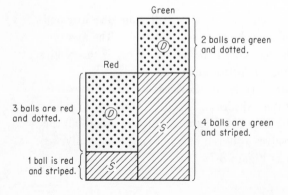

Figure 3-7 **Probability of dotted and of striped, given red.**

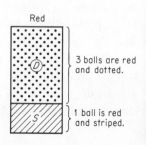

In other words, 3/4 of the red balls are dotted and 1/4 of the red balls are striped. Thus the probability of dotted, given that the ball is red, is .75. Likewise, the probability of striped, given that the ball is red, is .25.

Now that we have calculated the answer, let us observe how our reasoning will enable us to develop the formula for conditional probability under statistical dependence. We can first assure ourselves that these events *are* statistically dependent by observing that the color of the balls determines the probabilities that they are either striped or dotted, e.g., a green ball is more likely to be striped than a red ball. Since color affects the probability of striped or dotted, these two events can be said to be dependent.

To calculate the probability of dotted given red, $P(D|R)$, we divided the probability of *red and dotted* balls (3 out of 10, or .3) by the probability of red balls (4 out of 10, or .4). Thus

$$P(D|R) = \frac{P(DR)}{P(R)}$$

or expressed as a general formula using the letters A and B to represent the two events,

$$P(A|B) = \frac{P(AB)}{P(B)}$$

This is the formula for conditional probability under statistical dependence.

Example b. What is $P(D|G)$? $P(S|G)$?

$$P(D|G) = \frac{P(DG)}{P(G)} = \frac{.2}{.6} = \frac{1}{3}$$

$$P(S|G) = \frac{P(SG)}{P(G)} = \frac{.4}{.6} = \frac{2}{3}$$

The problem is shown diagrammatically in Figure 3-8.

Green

2 balls are green and dotted, each with probability of .1 .

4 balls are green and striped, each with probability of .1 .

Figure 3-8   Probability of dotted and of striped, given green.

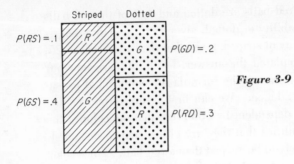

Figure 3-9

The total probability of green is .6 (6 out of 10 balls). To determine the probability that the ball (which we know is green) will be dotted, divide the probability of green and dotted (.2) by the probability of green (.6), or $.2/.6 = 1/3$. Similarly, to determine the probability that the ball will be striped, divide the probability of green and striped (.4) by the probability of green (.6), or $.4/.6 = 2/3$.

Example c.   Calculate $P(R|D)$ and $P(G|D)$.

See Figure 3-9. Having been told that the ball drawn is dotted, we disregard striped entirely and consider only dotted.

Now see Figure 3-10 showing the probabilities of red and green, given dotted. Notice that the relative proportions of the two are as .4 is to .6.

$$P(G|D) = \frac{P(GD)}{P(D)} = \frac{.2}{.5} = \quad .4$$

$$P(R|D) = \frac{P(RD)}{P(D)} = \frac{.3}{.5} = \frac{.6}{1.0}$$

Example d.   Calculate $P(R|S)$ and $P(G|S)$.

$$P(R|S) = \frac{P(RS)}{P(S)} = \frac{.1}{.5} = \quad .2$$

$$P(G|S) = \frac{P(GS)}{P(S)} = \frac{.4}{.5} = \frac{.8}{1.0}$$

3. Joint probabilities under
statistical dependence

We have shown that the formula for conditional probability under conditions of statistical dependence is $P(A|B) = P(AB)/P(B)$. If we solve this formula for $P(AB)$ (and this can be done simply by cross multiplication), we find that $P(AB) = P(A|B) \times P(B)$. This is the formula for joint probability under conditions of statistical dependence. It is read "The joint probability of events A and B equals the probability of event A, given that event B has occurred, times the probability of event B." Notice that this formula is *not* $P(AB) = P(A) \times P(B)$, as it would be under conditions of statistical independence.

Converting the general formula $P(AB) = P(A|B) \times P(B)$ to terms of red, green, dotted, and striped, we have $P(RD) = P(R|D) \times P(D)$ or $P(RD) = .6 \times .5 = .3$, where .6 is the probability of red given dotted (computed in example c above) and .5 is the probability of dotted (also computed in example c).

$P(RD) = .3$ may be verified in Table 3-3, where we originally arrived at the probability by inspection. (There are 3 balls out of 10 which are red and dotted.)

The following joint probabilities are computed in the same manner as the preceding. They may also be substantiated by reference to Table 3-3.

$P(RS) = P(R|S) \times P(S) = .2 \times .5 = .1$
$P(GD) = P(G|D) \times P(D) = .4 \times .5 = .2$
$P(GS) = P(G|S) \times P(S) = .8 \times .5 = .4$

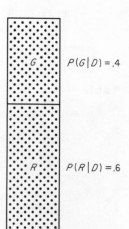

$P(G|D) = .4$

$P(R|D) = .6$

Figure 3-10 **Probability of red and of green, given dotted. (Probability of striped = 0.)**

Note that the marginal probability of the event *red* can be computed by summing the probabilities of the joint events in which red is contained:

$$P(R) = P(RD) + P(RS) = .3 + .1 = .4$$

Similarly, the marginal probability of the event *green* can be computed by summing the probabilities of the joint events in which green is contained:

$$P(G) = P(GD) + P(GS) = .2 + .4 = .6$$

Similarly, the marginal probability of *dotted* can be computed by summing the probabilities of the joint events in which dotted is contained:

$$P(D) = P(RD) + P(GD) = .3 + .2 = .5$$

And finally, the marginal probability of *striped* can be computed by summing the probabilities of the joint events in which striped is contained:

$$P(S) = P(RS) + P(GS) = .1 + .4 = .5$$

These four marginal probabilities—

$$P(R) = .4$$
$$P(G) = .6$$
$$P(D) = .5$$
$$P(S) = .5$$

—can be verified by inspection of Table 3-3.

We have now considered the three types of probability—marginal, conditional, and joint—under conditions of statistical dependence. Table 3-4 provides a résumé.

Table 3-4

Probabilities under statistical dependence		
Type of probability	Symbol	Formula
1. Marginal (or unconditional)	$P(A)$	$P(A)$
2. Joint	$P(AB)$	$P(A \mid B) \times P(B)$
3. Conditional	$P(A \mid B)$	$\dfrac{P(AB)}{P(B)}$

RELATIONSHIP BETWEEN INDEPENDENCE AND DEPENDENCE

Under conditions of statistical dependence, the formula for conditional probability is $P(A|B) = P(AB)/P(B)$. Under independence, the formula for joint probability is $P(AB) = P(A) \times P(B)$. Substituting $P(A) \times P(B)$ for $P(AB)$ in the formula for conditionality, we get

$$P(A|B) = \frac{P(A) \times P(B)}{P(B)}$$

Since $P(B)$ occurs in both the denominator and the numerator, we can cancel the two as follows:

$$P(A|B) = \frac{P(A) \times P(B)}{P(B)} = P(A)$$

The resulting formula $P(A|B) = P(A)$ is known as the *mathematical definition of statistical independence*. Some examples will show that this is true.

1. What is the probability of heads on the 2d toss of a fair coin, given that tails occurred on the 1st toss?

Converting the formula $P(A|B) = \dfrac{P(A) \times P(B)}{P(B)}$ to terms of heads and tails, we have $P(H_2|T_1) = \dfrac{P(H_2) \times P(T_1)}{P(T_1)} = \dfrac{.5 \times .5}{.5} = .5$. The probability of heads on the 2d toss is not affected by the result of the 1st toss. In other words, $P(H_2|T_1) = P(H_2)$. Notice that this has the same form as the general formula $P(A|B) = P(A)$.

2. What is the probability of heads on the 3d toss of a fair coin, given that tails has occurred on the first 2 tosses?

$$P(H_3|T_1T_2) = \frac{P(H_3) \times P(T_1) \times P(T_2)}{P(T_1) \times P(T_2)} = \frac{.5 \times .5 \times .5}{.5 \times .5} = \frac{.125}{.25} = .5$$

Notice that we have expanded the general formula for independence, but we have not altered the concept. Let us compare the two.

$P(H_3|T_1T_2)$ is identical in meaning to $P(A|B)$ because H_3 in the former is equivalent to A in the latter, and T_1T_2 is equivalent to B.

Also, $\dfrac{P(A) \times P(B)}{P(B)}$ is equivalent to $\dfrac{P(H_3) \times P(T_1) \times P(T_2)}{P(T_1) \times P(T_2)}$.

Thus by expanding the formula, we have shown that $P(H_3 \mid T_1 T_2) = P(H_3)$.

The mathematical proof that $P(AB) = P(A) \times P(B)$ under statistical independence is more complicated than the intuitive approach. Therefore, we shall use the latter.

Assume that an urn contains 2 balls, 1 red (R) and 1 blue (B). What is the probability of getting a red ball on each of 2 successive draws? (The balls are replaced in the urn after each drawing.) To determine the answer we may consider all the possible ways that 2 balls may be drawn. On 2 draws there are 4 possibilities: (1) RR, (2) RB, (3) BB, and (4) BR. This list is mutually exclusive and collectively exhaustive; therefore the probabilities must sum to 1. The 4 events are also equally likely. Consequently, the probability of each is $1/4$ or .25. We now have the following:

Event	Probability
RR	.25
RB	.25
BB	.25
BR	.25
	1.00

Since there are only 2 balls, the probability of drawing each is ½ or .5, i.e., $P(R) = P(B) = .5$. Thus we can see that each of the individual probabilities of the events is $.5 \times .5 = .25$. This agrees with the formula $P(AB) = P(A) \times P(B)$ for statistically independent events, e.g., $P(RR) = P(R) \times P(R)$.

Note that we could not have arrived at the same probabilities found above if the events had not been equally likely. For example, consider a case where there are 9 red balls and 1 blue ball in an urn. The possible outcomes remain the same: RR, RB, BB, BR. But the chance of drawing a red ball is 9 times as great as that of drawing a blue ball. This gives us the probabilities listed at the top of page 71.

Event	Probability
RR	.9 × .9 = .81
RB	.9 × .1 = .09
BB	.1 × .1 = .01
BR	.1 × .9 = .09
	1.00

This concludes our development of probabilities under both statistical independence and statistical dependence. Table 3-5 is given as a quick reference.

Table 3-5

Probabilities under statistical independence and dependence

Type of probability	Symbol	Formula under statistical independence	Formula under statistical dependence
1. Marginal	$P(A)$	$P(A)$	$P(A)$
2. Joint	$P(AB)$	$P(A) \times P(B)$	$P(A \mid B) \times P(B)$
3. Conditional	$P(A \mid B)$	$P(A)$	$\dfrac{P(AB)}{P(B)}$

REVISING PRIOR ESTIMATES OF PROBABILITIES

One can often alter probabilities after getting additional information. The new or altered probabilities are known as *revised probabilities*. The fact that probabilities can be revised as more information is gained makes probability theory of great value in decision making under uncertainty.

As a simple example, assume that we have two types of deformed (biased or weighted) dice in an urn. On half of them, ace (or one dot) comes up 30 per cent of the time; $P(\text{ace}) = .3$. On the other half, ace comes up 60 per cent of the time; $P(\text{ace}) = .6$. Let us call the former type 1 and the latter type 2. One is drawn, rolled once, and comes up ace. What is the probability that it is a type 1 die? Knowing there is the same number of both types, we might answer that the probability is one-half; but we can do better than this. To answer the question more intelligently, we set up Table 3-6.

Table 3-6

Elementary event	Probability of elementary event	P(ace | elementary event)	P(ace, event)
Type 1	.5	.3	.15
Type 2	.5	.6	.30
	1.0	.9	.45

The sum of the probabilities of the elementary events is 1.0 because there are only two types of dice; the probability of each type is .5. The two types constitute a mutually exclusive and collectively exhaustive list.

The sum of P(ace \| elementary event) does not equal 1.0. The figures .3 and .6 simply represent the conditional probabilities of getting an ace, given type 1 and type 2, respectively.

The fourth column is the joint probability of ace and type 1 occurring together .5 $\times$ .3 = .15, and the joint probability of ace and type 2 occurring together .5 $\times$ .6 = .30. The sum of these joint probabilities (.45) is the marginal probability of getting an ace. (This concept was developed on page 68.) Note that in each case the joint probability was obtained by using the formula $P(AB) = P(A|B) \times P(B)$.

To find the probability that the die we have drawn is type 1, we use the formula for conditional probability under statistical dependence:

$$P(A|B) = \frac{P(AB)}{P(B)}$$

Converting to our problem, we have

$$P(\text{type 1}|\text{ace}) = \frac{P(\text{type 1, ace})}{P(\text{ace})}$$

or $\qquad P(\text{type } 1 | \text{ace}) = \dfrac{.15}{.45} = \dfrac{1}{3}$

Thus the probability that we have drawn a type 1 die is one-third. Let us compute the probability that the die is type 2.

$$P(\text{type } 2 | \text{ace}) = \frac{P(\text{type } 2, \text{ace})}{P(\text{ace})} = \frac{.30}{.45} = \frac{2}{3}$$

Assume that the same die is rolled a second time and again comes up ace. What is the further revised probability that the die is type 1? See Table 3-7.

Table 3-7

Elementary event	Probability of elementary event	$P(\text{ace} | \text{elementary event})$	$P(2 \text{ aces} | \text{elementary event})$	$P(2 \text{ aces}, \text{elementary event})$
Type 1	.5	.3	.09	.045
Type 2	.5	.6	.36	.180
	1.0			.225

We have one new column for the table—$P(2 \text{ aces} | \text{elementary event})$. This gives the joint probability of 2 aces on two successive rolls if the die is type 1 and if it is type 2, i.e., $P(2 \text{ aces} | \text{type } 1) = .3 \times .3 = .09$ and $P(2 \text{ aces} | \text{type } 2) = .6 \times .6 = .36$. The joint probabilities of 2 aces on two successive rolls and the elementary events (type 1 and type 2) are given in the last column, i.e., $P(2 \text{ aces, type } 1)$ equals the probability of type 1 times $P(2 \text{ aces} | \text{type } 1)$, or $.5 \times .09 = .045$, and $P(2 \text{ aces}, \text{type } 2)$ equals the probability of type 2 times $P(2 \text{ aces} | \text{type } 2)$, or $.5 \times .36 = .180$. The sum of these (.225) is the marginal probability of 2 aces on two successive rolls.

We are now ready to compute the probability that the die we have drawn is type 1, given ace on each of two successive rolls. Using the same general formula as before, we convert to

$$P(\text{type } 1 | 2 \text{ aces}) = \frac{P(\text{type } 1, 2 \text{ aces})}{P(2 \text{ aces})} = \frac{.045}{.225} = .2$$

Similarly,

$$P(\text{type } 2 \,|\, 2 \text{ aces}) = \frac{P(\text{type } 2, 2 \text{ aces})}{P(2 \text{ aces})} = \frac{.180}{.225} = .8$$

What have we accomplished? When we first drew the die, all we knew was that there was a probability of .5 that it was type 1 and a probability of .5 that it was type 2. Stated alternatively, there was a 50:50 chance that it was either type 1 or type 2. After rolling the die once, we revised these original probabilities to the following:

Probability that it is type 1 = 1/3
Probability that it is type 2 = 2/3

After the second roll, we revised the probabilities again:

Probability that it is type 1 = .2
Probability that it is type 2 = .8

We have thus changed the original probabilities from .5 for each type to .2 for type 1 and .8 for type 2. This means that in view of the new information gained from rolling the die twice, we can be 80 per cent certain that the die is type 2. Alternatively, if we were to bet that a die which turns up ace on two successive rolls is of type 2, we would be right 80 per cent of the time over a long series of draws and rolls.

As a somewhat more practical problem, consider the case of a manufacturer who has an automatic machine which produces ball bearings. If the machine is correctly set up (i.e., properly adjusted), it will produce 90 per cent acceptable parts. If it is incorrectly set up, it will produce 40 per cent acceptable parts. Past experience indicates that 70 per cent of the setups are correctly done. After a certain setup, the machine produces 3 acceptable bearings as the first 3 pieces. What is the revised probability that the setup has been correctly done? See Table 3-8.

We are now ready to compute the revised probability that the machine is correctly set up. We convert the general formula $P(A \,|\, B) = P(AB)/P(B)$ to

$$P(\text{correct} \,|\, 3 \text{ good parts}) = \frac{P(\text{correct, 3 good parts})}{P(3 \text{ good parts})} = \frac{.5103}{.5295} = .9637$$

Table 3-8

Event	P(event)	P(1 good part|event)	P(3 good parts|event)	P(event, 3 good parts)
Correct	.70	.90	.729	.5103
Incorrect	.30	.40	.064	.0192
	1.00			.5295

The table headings are interpreted as follows:

P(event) means the individual probabilities of correct and incorrect; i.e., P(correct) = .70 (as given in the problem) and P(incorrect) = .30 = 1.00 − P(correct) = 1.00 − .70.

P(1 good part\|event) means the probability of a good part, given that the setup is correct or incorrect. These probabilities are given in the problem.

P(3 good parts\|event) is the probability of getting 3 good parts on 3 successive tries, given the event (i.e., given correct or incorrect). The probabilities are computed as follows:
P(3 good parts\|correct) = .9 × .9 × .9 = .729
P(3 good parts\|incorrect) = .4 × .4 × .4 = .064

P(event, 3 good parts) is the probability of the joint occurrence of the event (correct or incorrect) and 3 good parts. The probabilities are computed as follows:
P(correct, 3 good parts) = .729 × .70 = .5103
P(incorrect, 3 good parts) = .064 × .30 = .0192

Notice that the last 2 probabilities conform to the general mathematical formula for joint probabilities under conditions of dependence: $P(AB) = P(A|B) \times P(B)$.

The probability that the machine is correctly set up is .9637 or 96.37 per cent. We have thus revised our original probability of a correct set-up from 70 per cent to 96.37 per cent, based on 3 parts produced.

The origin of the concept of revised probabilities is attributed to the Reverend Thomas Bayes (eighteenth century), and the basic formula for conditional probability under dependence, $P(A|B) = P(AB)/P(B)$, is called Bayes' theorem.

Bayes' theorem offers a powerful statistical method of evaluating new information and revising our estimates (based upon limited information only) of the probability that matters are in one state or another. If correctly used, it obviates the gathering of masses of data over long periods of time in order to make decisions based upon probabilities. His discovery so alarmed the good Rev. Mr. Bayes that he refused to permit publication of his work during his lifetime.

PROBLEMS

3-1 Normalize the following distribution of classes I to VII.

Class	Number in class
I	35
II	24
III	41
IV	27
V	33
VI	19
VII	21

3-2 A box contains the following balls:

3 red
1 striped and red
1 dotted and red
1 dotted and green
4 striped and green

Assume each ball is replaced before another is drawn.

a. What is the probability of drawing a ball which is striped and red?
b. What is the probability of drawing a ball which is striped?
c. What is the probability of drawing a ball which is green?

3-3 Given a fair coin:

a. What is the probability of flipping 2 heads in a row?
b. What is the probability of flipping a head and a tail in that order?

3-4 Given a coin which is unfair: $P(H) = .7$; $P(T) = .3$.

a. What is the probability of tossing 2 heads and 1 tail in that order?
b. What is the probability of tossing 2 tails?

3-5 What is the probability of at least 1 head on 3 tosses of a fair coin?

3-6 An urn contains the following balls:

	Probability of occurrence
5 red and dotted	.25
3 red and striped	.15
4 red	.20
2 green and dotted	.10
3 green and striped	.15
3 green	.15
20 total	1.00

a. Given that the ball you draw is dotted, what is the probability that it is red?

b. Given that the ball you draw is green, what is the probability that it is striped?

3-7 An urn contains several weighted dice. The probability of an ace on one-half of them (type 1) is .4; the probability of an ace on the other half (type 2) is .7. One die is drawn and rolled 3 times; an ace comes up on 1 of these rolls.

What is the probability that the die is of type 2?

3-8 The probability that a machine is correctly set up is .9; if it *is* correctly set up, the probability of a good part is .95. If, however, the machine is not correctly set up, the probability of a good part is only .3.

The first part produced was tested and found to be unsatisfactory. At this point, what is the probability that the machine is set up correctly?

3-9 Using the information given in the previous problem, what is the probability of a correct setup given 2 good parts?

3-10 Thirty per cent of the past chemical blending setups by a fertilizer company have been unacceptable. If the process is correctly set up, it will produce 90 per cent acceptable batches of fertilizer. If errors have been made in the setup, only 20 per cent acceptable batches will be produced. The process is adjusted, and the first 5 batches run are tested (1) unacceptable, (2) acceptable, (3) acceptable, (4) unacceptable, (5) acceptable. Should we continue manufacturing?

BIBLIOGRAPHY

H. Bierman, L. E. Fouraker, and R. K. Jaedicke, *Quantitative Analysis for Business Decisions* (Homewood, Ill.: Richard D. Irwin, Inc., 1961).

B. Hanes, *Mathematics for Management Science* (Columbus, Ohio: Charles E. Merrill Books, Inc., 1962).

J. E. Howell and D. Teichroew, *Mathematical Analysis for Business Decisions* (Homewood, Ill.: Richard D. Irwin, Inc., 1963).

A. Kaufmann, *Methods and Models of Operations Research* (Englewood Cliffs, N.J.: Prentice-Hall, Inc., 1963).

R. C. Meier and S. H. Archer, *An Introduction to Mathematics for Business Analysis* (New York: McGraw-Hill Book Company, 1960).

R. Schlaifer, *Probability and Statistics for Business Decisions* (New York: McGraw-Hill Book Company, 1959).

A. Shuchman, *Scientific Decision Making in Business* (New York: Holt, Rinehart and Winston, Inc., 1963).

chapter
four

DECISION
MAKING
UNDER
UNCERTAINTY

$\mathbf{A}$lthough some business decisions can be made under conditions approaching certainty, elements of uncertainty underlie most of the decisions managers make. Businessmen cannot know in advance and with precision what their sales and costs (and thus profits) will be. Because of this fact, the businessman must develop the best estimates or forecasts he can for these two basic variables and make decisions in the light of the estimates.

Probabilities can be used in making these estimates. The probability approach to decision making can be used, for example, in the area of *sales*. This approach demands that the past behavior of sales be analyzed and that probabilities be assigned to possible sales volumes during the future period. The decision maker:

1. Considers the various sales volumes possible for the future period.
2. Assigns a probability to each of those possible values.
3. Settles on a sales forecast for the period.

RANDOM VARIABLE

A random variable is a value or magnitude that changes, occurrence after occurrence or event after event, in no predictable sequence. For example, tomorrow's sales of cases of milk by a dairy (that has no way of knowing *exactly* what tomorrow's sales will be) are a random variable.

The *values* of a random variable may be thought of as the numerical values corresponding to each possible outcome of an event. In the instance of the dairy, let us say that past sales records indicate that the values of the random variable may range from sales of 200 to 210 cases daily.

Assume that the dairy has kept a record of the number of cases sold during the past 100 days, as shown in Table 4-1. On the basis of this record, a probability can be assigned to each possible level of sales (the random variable) by normalizing the distribution as in Table 4-2.

The value of the random variable is not known until the event occurs, i.e., until total sales of cases of milk are determined at the end of each day. However, given the information in Table 4-2, the dairy can determine an *expected* or *average* volume by multiplying the values of the random variable by the individual probability of each. See Table 4-3.

The expected value of the random variable is 205.89 cases per day. Notice that the expected value of the random variable is a *weighted average* rather than a simple arithmetic average; the individual values of

Table 4-1

Cases sold during 100 days	
Quantity sold	No. days this quantity sold
200	2
201	3
202	4
203	7
204	9
205	13
206	15
207	21
208	16
209	9
210	1
	100

Table 4-2

Normalizing the distribution	
Value of random variable	Probability that random variable will take on the particular value
200 cases	.02
201 cases	.03
202 cases	.04
203 cases	.07
204 cases	.09
205 cases	.13
206 cases	.15
207 cases	.21
208 cases	.16
209 cases	.09
210 cases	.01
	1.00

Table 4-3

Finding the expected volume		
(1)	(2)	(3)
Value of random variable	Probability that random variable will take on the particular value	(1) × (2)
200 cases	.02	4.00
201 cases	.03	6.03
202 cases	.04	8.08
203 cases	.07	14.21
204 cases	.09	18.36
205 cases	.13	26.65
206 cases	.15	30.90
207 cases	.21	43.47
208 cases	.16	33.28
209 cases	.09	18.81
210 cases	.01	2.10
	1.00	205.89

the random variable are weighted by (or multiplied by) the corresponding probability of each. The weighted average is 205.89, while the arithmetic average is 205.

$$\frac{200 + 201 + 202 + 203 + 204 + 205 + 206 + 207 + 208 + 209 + 210}{11} = 205$$

It is important to note that the value 205.89 cases of milk (the mean or average value of the random variable) does not imply that tomorrow's sales of milk will be exactly 205.89 cases, but rather that the average sales over a period of time will turn out to be 205.89 cases.

The concept of a random variable and the concept of the mean of a random variable become quite useful to managers making decisions under conditions of uncertainty. When faced with a problem such as the dairy problem above, where tomorrow's sales are not known, the management of the dairy can make a decision based upon the mean of the random variable (205.89 cases) and be more nearly correct than they would if they tried each day to "second-guess" what sales would be that day.

They may be wrong tomorrow using this technique, but over time, their decisions will be more nearly optimal than if they guessed each day.

Of course, over time, if they have reason to believe that conditions are changing, the executives would recompute this weighted average or mean of a random variable and use the revised figure for decision-making purposes.

A PROBLEM INVOLVING UNCERTAINTY

Most buying decisions of merchants are good examples of business decisions that have to be made under conditions of uncertainty. Some firms buy and stock products which lose all or part of their utility if not sold on the day after receipt. Often a retailer handling such a product does not know how many calls he will get for it on a particular day—but he must order in advance some definite quantity for that day's business.

Picture a newspaper dealer who buys his newspapers for 6 cents each and sells them for 10 cents each. Assume that any papers not sold by the end of the day are completely worthless to him. The dealer's problem is to determine the optimum number he should order each day. On days when he stocks more than he sells, his profits are reduced by the cost of the unsold papers. If buyers request more copies than the number stocked, the result is lost sales and smaller profits than were possible.

Now suppose that the dealer has kept a record, shown in Table 4-4, of his sales for the past 100 days. This information is a *random* and

Table 4-4

Distribution of newspaper sales		
Daily sales	No. days sold	Probability of each number being sold
300	15	.15
400	20	.20
500	45	.45
600	15	.15
700	5	.05
	100	1.00

discrete distribution of the dealer's past sales. It is *random* in that there is no way of knowing which one quantity (300, 500, 600) buyers will buy on any certain day. It is a *discrete* distribution because sales volume can take on only a limited number of values. We assume, for example, that sales on any day will *not* be 550, 625, or 475. We assume further that the dealer has no reason to believe that sales volume will take on any value in the future other than those shown.

This information tells the dealer something about the historical pattern of his sales. Although it does *not* tell him what quantity buyers will request tomorrow, it *does* tell him that there are 45 chances in 100 that the quantity will be 500 papers. Therefore a probability of .45 is assigned to the sales figure of 500 papers. The probability column in Table 4-4 is the relationship between the total observations of sales (100 days) and the number of times each possible value of daily sales appeared in the 100 observations. The probability of each sales level occurring is thus derived by taking the total number of times each value has appeared in the 100 observations and dividing it by the total number of observations; i.e., 15/100, 20/100, 45/100, 15/100, and 5/100. We shall show how to make the final buying decision shortly.

Here is another example. A retailer buys a certain item for $2 a case and sells it for $5 a case. This high markup of 60 per cent reflects the perishability of the item and the great risk of stocking it; the product has no value after the first day it is offered for sale. The retailer faces the problem of how many to order today for tomorrow's business.

A 90-day observation of past sales gives the information shown in Table 4-5. The probabilities are obtained just as they were in Table 4-4. Sales were 10 cases on 9 of the 90 days—9/90 of the time = 1/10 of the time = .10 of the time.

Table 4-5

Cases sold during 90 days		
Daily sales	No. days sold	Probability of each number being sold
10	9	.10
11	18	.20
12	36	.40
13	27	.30
	90	1.00

This distribution, too, is discrete and random. There are only four possible values for sales volume, and there is no discernible pattern in the sequence in which these four values occur.

If we assume the retailer has no reason to believe sales volume will behave differently in the future, his problem is that of determining how many cases he should buy today for tomorrow's business. If buyers tomorrow call for more cases than the number in stock, the retailer's profits suffer by $3 (selling price minus cost) for each sale he cannot make. On the other hand, there are costs which result from the stocking of too many units on any day. Suppose that on a certain day the retailer has 13 cases in stock, but sells only 10. He makes a profit of $30, $3 per case on 10 cases. But this must be reduced by $6, the cost of the 3 cases not sold and of no value.

CONDITIONAL PROFITS

One way of illustrating this retailer's problem is to construct a table showing the results in dollars of all possible combinations of purchases and sales. The only values for purchases and for sales which have meaning to us are these: 10, 11, 12, or 13 cases. These were the sales magnitudes. There is no reason for the retailer to consider buying less than 10 cases or more than 13 cases.

Table 4-6 is called a conditional profit table and shows the profit resulting from any possible combination of supply and demand. The profits can be either positive or negative and are conditional in that a certain profit results from taking a specific stocking action (ordering 10, 11,

Table 4-6

Conditional profit table

Possible demand (sales)	Possible stock action			
	10 cases	11 cases	12 cases	13 cases
10 cases	$30	$28	$26	$24
11 cases	30	33	31	29
12 cases	30	33	36	34
13 cases	30	33	36	39

12, or 13 cases) and having sales of a specific number of cases (10, 11, 12, or 13 cases).

Table 4-6 reflects the losses which occur when stock remains unsold at the end of a day. It does not reflect profit denied the retailer because of inability to fill all buyers' requests—that is, because of an out-of-stock condition.

Notice that the stocking of 10 cases each day will always result in a profit of $30. Even when buyers want 13 cases on some days, the retailer can sell only 10.

When the retailer stocks 11 cases, his profit will be $33 on days when buyers request 11, 12, or 13 cases. But on days when he has 11 cases in stock and buyers buy only 10 cases, profit drops to $28. The $30 profit on the 10 cases sold must be reduced by $2, the cost of the unsold case.

A stock of 12 cases will increase daily profits to $36, but only on those days when buyers want 12 or 13 cases. Should buyers want only 10 cases, profit is reduced to $26; the $30 profit on the sale of 10 cases is reduced by $4, the cost of 2 unsold cases.

The stocking of 13 cases will result in a profit of $39 when there is a market for 13 cases. There will be a $3 profit on each case sold, with no unsold cases. When buyers buy fewer than 13 cases, such a stock action results in profits of less than $39. For example, with a stock of 13 cases and sale of only 11 cases, the profit is $29; the profit on 11 cases, $33, is reduced by the cost of 2 unsold cases, $4.

Such a conditional profit table does not tell the retailer which number of cases he should stock each day in order to maximize profits. It only shows him what the outcome will be *if* a specific number of cases is stocked and a specific number of cases is sold. Under uncertainty he does not know in advance the size of any day's market, but he must still decide which number of cases, stocked consistently, will maximize profits over a long period of time.

EXPECTED PROFITS

The next step in determining the best number of cases to stock is to assign probabilities to the possible outcomes or profits. We saw in Table 4-5 that the probabilities of the possible values for sales were as follows:

	Probability
10 cases	.10
11 cases	.20
12 cases	.40
13 cases	.30

Using these probabilities and the information contained in Table 4-6, we can now compute the expected monetary profit of each possible stock action.

It was stated earlier that we could compute the mean of a random variable by weighting each possible value the variable could take by the probability of its taking on each value. Using this procedure, we can compute the mean or expected daily profit from stocking 10 cases each day as in Table 4-7.

The figures in the last column of Table 4-7 are obtained by weighting the conditional profit of each possible sales volume (column 2) by the probability of each conditional profit occurring (column 3). The sum

Table 4-7

Expected monetary profit from stocking 10 cases

Market size	Conditional profit		Probability of market size		Expected profit
10 cases	$30	×	.10	=	$ 3.00
11 cases	30	×	.20	=	6.00
12 cases	30	×	.40	=	12.00
13 cases	30	×	.30	=	9.00
			1.00		$30.00

of the last column is the mean or expected daily profit resulting from stocking 10 cases each day. It is not surprising that this expected profit is $30, since we saw in Table 4-6 that stocking 10 cases each day would always result in a daily profit of $30, regardless of whether buyers wanted 10, 11, 12, or 13 cases.

The same computation for a daily stock of 11 units can be made, as we have done in Table 4-8. This tells us that if the retailer stocks 11

Table 4-8

Expected monetary profit from stocking 11 cases					
Market size	Conditional profit		Probability of market size		Expected profit
10 cases	$28	×	.10	=	$ 2.80
11 cases	33	×	.20	=	6.60
12 cases	33	×	.40	=	13.20
13 cases	33	×	.30	=	9.90
			1.00		$32.50

cases each day, his expected or average profit over time will be $32.50 per day. Ninety per cent of the time the daily profit will be $33; on these days, buyers ask for 11, 12, or 13 cases. However, column 3 tells us that 10 per cent of the time, the market will take only 10 cases, resulting in a profit of only $28. It is this fact that reduces the daily expected profit to $32.50.

For 12 and 13 units the expected daily profit is computed as shown in Tables 4-9 and 4-10, respectively.

We have now computed the expected profit of each of the four stock actions open to the retailer. To summarize, these expected values are as follows:

If 10 cases are stocked each day, expected daily profit is $30.
If 11 cases are stocked each day, expected daily profit is $32.50.
If 12 cases are stocked each day, expected daily profit is $34.
If 13 cases are stocked each day, expected daily profit is $33.50.

Table 4-9

Expected monetary profit from stocking 12 cases					
Market size	Conditional profit		Probability of market size		Expected profit
10 cases	$26	×	.10	=	$ 2.60
11 cases	31	×	.20	=	6.20
12 cases	36	×	.40	=	14.40
13 cases	36	×	.30	=	10.80
			1.00		$34.00

Table 4-10

Expected monetary profit from stocking 13 cases						
Market size	Conditional profit		Probability of market size			Expected profit
10 cases	$24	×	.10		=	$ 2.40
11 cases	29	×	.20		=	5.80
12 cases	34	×	.40		=	13.60
13 cases	39	×	.30		=	11.70
			1.00			$33.50

The optimum stock action is the one that results in the greatest expected profit. It is the action that will result in the largest daily profits and thus the maximum total profits over a period of time. In this illustration the proper number to stock each day is 12 cases, since this quantity will give the highest possible average daily profits under the conditions given.

We have not removed uncertainty from the problem facing the retailer. Rather, we have used his past experience to determine the best stock action open to him under uncertainty. He still does not know how many cases will be requested on any given day. There is no guarantee that he will make a profit of $34 tomorrow. However, if he stocks 12 units each day under the conditions given, he will have *average* profits of $34 per day. This is the best he can do under uncertainty, because the choice of any one of the other three possible stock actions will result in a lower average daily profit.

EXPECTED PROFITS WITH PERFECT INFORMATION

Now suppose that the retailer in our illustration could remove the uncertainty from his problem by obtaining additional information. Complete and accurate information about the future, referred to as *perfect* information, would remove all uncertainty from the problem. This does not mean that sales would not vary from 10 to 13 cases per day. Sales would still be 10 cases per day 10 per cent of the time, 11 cases 20 per cent of the time, 12 cases 40 per cent of the time, and 13 cases 30 per

Table 4-11

	Conditional profit table under certainty			
Possible sales	Possible stock actions			
	10 cases	11 cases	12 cases	13 cases
10 cases	$30	—	—	—
11 cases	—	$33	—	—
12 cases	—	—	$36	—
13 cases	—	—	—	$39

cent of the time.   However, with perfect information the retailer would know *in advance* how many cases were going to be called for each day.

Under these circumstances, the retailer would stock today the exact number of cases buyers will want tomorrow.   For sales of 10 cases the retailer would stock 10 cases and realize a profit of $30.   When sales were going to be 11 cases, he would stock exactly 11 cases, thus realizing a profit of $33.

Table 4-11 shows the conditional profit values that are applicable to the retailer's problem if he has perfect information.   Given the size of market in advance for a particular day, the retailer chooses the stock action that will maximize his profits.   This means he buys and stocks so as to avoid *all* losses from obsolete stock as well as all opportunity losses which reflect lost profits on unfilled requests for merchandise.

We can now proceed to the computation of the expected profit under certainty.   This is shown in Table 4-12.   The procedure is the same as when we computed the expected profit under uncertainty.   However, you

Table 4-12

	Expected profit under certainty				
Market size	Conditional profit under certainty		Probability of market size		Expected profit under certainty
10 cases	$30	×	.10	=	$ 3.00
11 cases	33	×	.20	=	6.60
12 cases	36	×	.40	=	14.40
13 cases	39	×	.30	=	11.70
			1.00		$35.70

will notice that the conditional profit figures in column 2 of Table 4-12 are the maximum profits possible for each sales volume. For example, when buyers buy 12 cases, the retailer will always make a profit of $36 under certainty because he will have stocked exactly 12 cases. With perfect information, then, our retailer could count on making an average profit of $35.70 a day. This is a significant figure because it is the maximum profit possible.

AN ALTERNATE APPROACH— MINIMIZING LOSSES

We have just solved the retailer's problem by maximizing his expected daily profit. There is another approach to this same problem. We can compute the amounts by which maximum profit possible ($35.70) will be reduced under various stocking actions; then we can choose that course of action which will minimize these reductions or "losses."

Two types of "losses" are involved. (1) *Obsolescence* losses are those caused by stocking too many units. (2) *Opportunity* losses are those caused by being out of stock when buyers want to buy.

Table 4-13 is a table of conditional losses for our retailer. Each value in the table is conditional on a specific number of cases being stocked and a specific number being requested. The values include not only those losses from obsolete inventory when the number of cases stocked exceeds the number buyers desire, but also those opportunity losses resulting from lost sales when the market would have taken more than the number stocked.

Neither of these losses is incurred when the number stocked on any

Table 4-13

| Possible | Conditional loss table | | | |
| sales | Possible stock actions | | | |
	10 cases	11 cases	12 cases	13 cases
10 cases	$0	$2	$4	$6
11 cases	3	0	2	4
12 cases	6	3	0	2
13 cases	9	6	3	0

day is the same as the number requested. This condition results in the diagonal row of zeros. Dollar figures above any zero represent losses arising from obsolete inventory; in each case the number stocked is greater than the number sold. For example, if 13 cases are stocked and only 10 cases are sold, there is a $6 loss resulting from the cost of the 3 cases unsold.

Values to the left and below the diagonal row of zeros represent opportunity losses resulting from requests that cannot be filled. For example, if only 10 cases are stocked but 13 cases are wanted, there is an opportunity loss of $9. This is represented by the lost profit of $3 per case on the 3 cases requested but not available.

The next step is to assign probabilities to the quantities buyers will be wanting. Table 4-5 gave these probabilities as:

	Probability
10 cases	.10
11 cases	.20
12 cases	.40
13 cases	.30

Applying these probabilities to the information in Table 4-13, we can compute the expected "loss" (reduction from maximum profit possible of $35.70) of each possible stock action. We do this by weighting each of the four possible loss figures in each column of Table 4-13 by the probabilities from Table 4-5. For a stock action of 10 cases, the expected loss is computed as in Table 4-14.

Table 4-14

Market size	Conditional loss		Probability of market size		Expected loss
10 cases	$0	×	.10	=	$0.00
11 cases	3	×	.20	=	0.60
12 cases	6	×	.40	=	2.40
13 cases	9	×	.30	=	2.70
			1.00		$5.70

Expected loss from stocking 10 cases

The conditional losses in Table 4-14 are taken from Table 4-13 for a stock action of 10 cases. The sum of the last column tells us that if 10 cases are stocked each day, over a long period of time the average or expected loss will be $5.70 a day. There is no guarantee that *tomorrow's* loss will be exactly $5.70.

Tables 4-15 to 4-17 show the computation of the expected loss resulting from decisions to stock 11, 12, and 13 cases, respectively. The optimum stock action is the one which will minimize expected losses; this action calls for the stocking of 12 cases each day. Note from Table 4-18 that the alternate approach (minimizing loss) *and* the original approach (maximizing profit) lead to the same conclusion.

Table 4-15

Expected loss from stocking 11 cases

Market size	Conditional loss		Probability of market size		Expected loss
10 cases	$2	×	.10	=	$0.20
11 cases	0	×	.20	=	0.00
12 cases	3	×	.40	=	1.20
13 cases	6	×	.30	=	1.80
			1.00		$3.20

Table 4-16

Expected loss from stocking 12 cases

Market size	Conditional loss		Probability of market size		Expected loss
10 cases	$4	×	.10	=	$0.40
11 cases	2	×	.20	=	0.40
12 cases	0	×	.40	=	0.00
13 cases	3	×	.30	=	0.90
			1.00		$1.70

Table 4-17

Expected loss from stocking 13 cases						
Market size	Conditional loss		Probability of market size		Expected loss	
10 cases	$6	×	.10	=	$0.60	
11 cases	4	×	.20	=	0.80	
12 cases	2	×	.40	=	0.80	
13 cases	0	×	.30	=	0.00	
			1.00		$2.20	

Table 4-18

Expected monetary profit and expected loss under uncertainty				
	Stock action			
	10 cases	11 cases	12 cases	13 cases
Expected profit	$30.00	$32.50	$34.00	$33.50
Expected loss	5.70	3.20	1.70	2.20

↑
Optimum

EXPECTED VALUE OF
PERFECT INFORMATION

Assuming a retailer could obtain a perfect predictor which would remove all uncertainty about the future, what would be the value of such a predictor to him? He must compare what such additional information costs him with the additional profit he would realize as a result of having the information.

The retailer in our illustration can earn average daily profits of $35.70 if he has perfect information about the future (see Table 4-12). His best expected daily profit without the predictor is only $34 (see Tables 4-7 to 4-10). The difference of $1.70 is the maximum amount the retailer would be willing to pay, per day, for a perfect predictor because that is the maximum amount by which he can increase his expected daily profit. This difference is the expected value of perfect information and is referred to as EVPI. There is no sense in paying more than $1.70 for the predictor—to do so would lower the expected daily profit.

AN INVENTORY PROBLEM
WITH SALVAGE VALUE

In all the previous illustrations we assumed that the products being sold were completely worthless if not sold on the day after delivery, the "selling" day. This assumption that they have no salvage value is, of course, not always realistic. If the product *does* have some salvage value, then this amount must be considered in computing conditional profits for each stock action.

Picture an item which must be ordered and received on the day before the selling day. It costs $5 per unit, it sells for $8 per unit, and any units remaining unsold at the end of the day can be disposed of at a salvage price of $2 per unit. Observation shows that past sales have ranged from 10 to 13 units per day; there is no reason to believe that sales volume will take on any other magnitudes in the future.

Using the same procedures as in Table 4-5, we establish these probabilities for the values sales will take:

	Probability
10 units	.10
11 units	.20
12 units	.40
13 units	.30
	1.00

The conditional profit table resulting from the above data is Table 4-19. A stock of 10 units each day will result in daily profits of $30 regardless of whether demand is for 10, 11, 12, or 13 units. The 10 units stocked will always be sold, but no more than this can be sold on any day.

A stock of 12 units each day will result in a profit of $36 on those days when demand is either 12 or 13 units. So far, the computation of

Table 4-19

Conditional profit table			
Possible demand (sales)	Possible stock actions		
	10 units	11 units	12 units	13 units
10 units	$30	$27	$24	$21
11 units	30	33	30	27
12 units	30	33	36	33
13 units	30	33	36	39

conditional profits is the same as in all our previous examples. However, any time the number stocked exceeds the demand on the selling day, the computation of conditional profit must take salvage value into consideration. This happens, for example, when 12 units are stocked but only 10 units are sold. Conditional profit in this event is computed as follows:

Profit on the 10 units sold	$30
Less cost of the 2 units unsold	−10
	$20
Plus salvage value of 2 units	+ 4
Conditional profit	$24

Salvage value can also be considered as a reduction in the cost of unsold units. In our example, the net cost of each *unsold* unit is $3, the original cost of $5 less the salvage value of $2. Thus, when 13 units are stocked but only 11 units are sold, the conditional profit is $27; this is $3 per unit on the 11 units sold less $6, the net cost of the two units not sold.

The presence of salvage value in an inventory problem does not alter the application of any of the principles discussed earlier in this chapter. It simply means that we must consider its effect on conditional profits and losses. We have just seen that salvage value increases conditional profits because it reduces the losses caused by overstocking.

Under conditions of certainty, salvage value is not involved because there will never be any items remaining unsold at the end of the sales period.

We proceed just as before in determining the optimum stock action to be taken. The next step is to determine the expected monetary profit of each of the four possible stock actions. This involves weighting the conditional profit figures for each stock action by the probabilities that each will occur, and then summing the results for each stock action.

Table 4-20 presents the resulting expected profit figures; the stocking of 12 units each day is the optimum stock action. Over time, we can realize greater average and total profits by stocking 12 units each day, even though on some days demand will be for 10, 11, or 13.

USE OF MARGINAL ANALYSIS IN INVENTORY PROBLEMS

In many inventory problems the use of conditional profit and expected profit tables would be difficult because of the number of computations required. Table 4-20 showed 4 possible stock actions and 4 possible sales levels—resulting in a conditional profit table containing 16 possibilities for conditional profits. Suppose there had been 200 possible values for sales volume and an equal number of possible stock actions. There would have been a tremendous number of calculations in determining the conditional and expected profit from each possible combination. The marginal approach avoids this problem of excessive computational work.

When an additional unit of an item is bought, two fates are possible: The unit will be sold—or it will not be sold. The sum of the probabilities of these two events must be 1. For example, if the probability of selling the additional unit is .4, then the probability of not selling it must be .6. The sum? 1.

If we let p represent the probability of selling one additional unit, then $1 - p$ must be the probability of *not* selling it. If the additional unit is sold, we will realize an increase in our conditional profits as a result of the profit from the additional unit. This is referred to as *marginal profit* and is designated MP. (You recall from economics that the *last unit added* is the *marginal* unit.) In our illustration the marginal profit resulting from the sale of an additional unit is $3, selling price less cost.

Reference to Table 4-20 will illustrate this point. If we stock 10 units each day and daily demand is for 10 or more units, our conditional profit is $30 per day. Now we decide to stock 11 units each day. If the 11th unit is sold (and this is the case when demand is for 11, 12, or 13 units), our conditional profit is increased to $33 per day. Notice that the increase in conditional profit does not follow merely from the *stocking* of the 11th unit. Under the conditions of uncertainty assumed in

Table 4-20

Expected monetary profit table

Possible stock actions

Market size	Probability of market size	10 units		11 units		12 units		13 units	
		Conditional profit	Expected profit	Conditional profit	Expected profit	Conditional profit	Expected profit	Conditional profit	Expected profit
10 units	.10	$30	$ 3.00	$27	$ 2.70	$24	$ 2.40	$21	$ 2.10
11 units	.20	30	6.00	33	6.60	30	6.00	27	5.40
12 units	.40	30	12.00	33	13.20	36	14.40	33	13.20
13 units	.30	30	9.00	33	9.90	36	10.80	39	10.80
	1.00		$30.00		$32.40		$33.60		$31.50

Optimum action ←

98

the problem, this increase in profit will result *only* when demand is for 11 or more units; this will be the case 90 per cent of the time.

We must also consider the effect on profits of stocking an additional unit and not selling it. This reduces our conditional profit. The amount of the reduction is referred to as the *marginal loss* (ML) resulting from the stocking of an item which is not sold.

Reference again to Table 4-20 will illustrate marginal loss. Assume once more that we decide to stock 11 units. Now assume that the 11th unit (the marginal unit) is not sold—that only 10 units are sold. The conditional profit is now $27; the $30 conditional profit when 10 units were stocked and 10 were sold is now reduced by $3. This $3 is the cost of the unsold unit ($5) less the salvage value ($2).

Additional units should be stocked so long as the *expected marginal profit* from stocking each of them is greater than the *expected marginal loss* from stocking each. The size of each order should be increased up to that point where the expected marginal profit from stocking one more unit *if it sells* is just equal to the expected marginal loss from stocking that unit *if it remains unsold*.

In our illustration, the probability of demand is:

Market size	Probability of market size
10	.10
11	.20
12	.40
13	.30
	1.00

This distribution tells us that as we increase our stock, the probability of selling 1 additional unit (this is p) decreases. For example, as we increase our stock from 10 to 11 units, the probability of selling all 11 is .90. This is the probability that demand will be for 11 units or more. Here is the computation:

Probability that demand will be for 11	.20
Probability that demand will be for 12	.40
Probability that demand will be for 13	.30
Probability that demand will be for 11 or more units	.90

With the addition of a 12th unit, the probability of selling all 12 units is reduced to .70, the sum of the probabilities of demand for 12 or 13 units. Finally, the addition of a 13th unit carries with it only a .30 probability of our selling all 13 units, because demand will be for 13 units only 30 per cent of the time.

The expected marginal profit from stocking and selling an additional unit is the marginal profit of the unit multiplied by the probability that the unit will be sold; this is $p(MP)$. The expected marginal loss from stocking an additional unsold unit is the marginal loss incurred if the unit is unsold multiplied by the probability that the unit will not be sold; this is $(1 - p)(ML)$. Quantity to order to maximize profit is where

$$p(MP) = (1 - p)(ML) \tag{4-1}$$

This equation describes the point at which the expected profit from stocking an additional unit, $p(MP)$, is equal to the expected loss from stocking the unit, $(1 - p)(ML)$. So long as $p(MP)$ is larger than $(1 - p)(ML)$, additional units should be stocked because the expected profit from such a decision is greater than the expected loss.

In any given inventory problem, there will be only one value of p for which the maximizing equation will be true. We must determine that value in order to know the optimum stock action to take. We can do this by taking our maximizing equation and solving it for p in the following manner:

$$p(MP) = (1 - p)(ML) \tag{4-1}$$

Multiplying the two terms on the right side of the equation, we get

$$p(MP) = ML - p(ML)$$

Collecting terms containing p, we have

$$p(MP) + p(ML) = ML$$
$$\text{or} \quad p(MP + ML) = ML$$

Dividing both sides of the equation by $(MP + ML)$ gives

$$p = \frac{ML}{MP + ML} \tag{4-2}$$

The letter p represents the minimum probability of selling at least an additional unit in order to justify the stocking of that additional unit. Additional units should be stocked so long as the probability of selling at least an additional unit is greater than p.

We can now compute p for our illustration. The marginal profit per unit is $3 (selling price less cost); the marginal loss per unit is also $3 (cost of each unit less salvage value); thus

$$p = \frac{\text{ML}}{\text{MP} + \text{ML}} = \frac{\$3}{\$3 + \$3} = \frac{\$3}{\$6} = .5$$

This value of .5 for p means that in order to make the stocking of an additional unit justifiable, we must have at least a .5 cumulative probability of selling that unit. In order to determine the probability of selling each additional unit we consider stocking, we must compute a series of cumulative probabilities as in Table 4-21.

Table 4-21

Cumulative probabilities of sales

Sales	Probability of this sales level	Cumulative probability that sales will be at this level or greater
10 units	.10	1.00
11 units	.20	.90
12 units	.40	.70
13 units	.30	.30

The cumulative probabilities in the right-hand column of Table 4-21 represent the probabilities that sales will reach or exceed each of the four sales levels. For example, the 1.00 which appears beside the 10-unit sales level means that we are 100 per cent certain of selling 10 or more units. This must be true because our problem assumed that one of the four sales levels would always occur.

The .90 probability value beside the 11-unit sales figure means that we are only .90 sure of selling 11 or more units. This can be calculated in two ways. First, we could add the chances of selling 11, 12, and 13 units:

11 units	.20
12 units	.40
13 units	+.30
	.90

.90   probability of selling 11 or more

Or we could reason that sales of 11 or more units include all possible outcomes except sales of 10 units—which has a probability of .10.

All possible outcomes	1.00
Probability of selling 10	−.10
	.90

.90   probability of selling 11 or more

The cumulative probability value of .70 assigned to sales of 12 units or more can be established in similar fashion. Sales of 12 or more must mean sales of 12 or of 13 units; so:

Probability of selling 12	.40
Probability of selling 13	+.30
	.70

.70   probability of selling 12 or more

And, of course, the cumulative probability of selling 13 units is still .30 because we have assumed that sales will never exceed 13.

As mentioned previously, the value of p decreases as the levels of sales increase. This increase causes the expected marginal profit to decrease and the expected marginal loss to increase until at some point our stocking of an additional unit would not be profitable.

We have said that additional units should be stocked so long as the probability of selling at least an additional unit is greater than p. We can now apply this rule to our probability distribution of sales and determine how many units should be stocked.

This procedure tells us that we should stock an 11th unit because the probability of selling 11 or more is .90, a figure clearly greater than our p of .50. This also means that the expected marginal profit from stocking this unit is greater than the expected marginal loss from stocking it. This can be verified as follows:

$p(\text{MP}) = .90(\$3) = \$2.70$ expected marginal profit
$(1 − p)(\text{ML}) = .10(\$3) = \$0.30$ expected marginal loss

A 12th unit should be stocked because the probability of selling 12 or more units (.70) is greater than the required p of .50. Such action will result in the following expected marginal profit and expected marginal loss:

p(MP) = .70($3) = $2.10 expected marginal profit
$(1 - p)$(ML) = .30($3) = $0.90 expected marginal loss

This is the optimum number of units to stock because the addition of a 13th unit carries with it only a .30 probability that it will be sold; this is less than our required p of .50. The following figures show why the 13th unit should not be stocked:

p(MP) = .30($3) = $0.90 expected marginal profit
$(1 - p)$(ML) = .70($3) = $2.10 expected marginal loss

This tells us that if we stock a 13th unit, we will add more to expected loss than we add to expected profit.

Notice that the use of marginal analysis leads us to the same conclusion reached with the use of conditional profit and expected profit tables. Both methods of analysis result in a decision to stock 12 units each period.

THE CONTINUOUS PROBABILITY DISTRIBUTION

In all the problems discussed so far, the distribution of past sales was *discrete,* that is, sales took on only a very few values. In actual practice this would seldom be the case. In most inventory problems the random variable, *sales,* can take on any value within a wide range of values. This type of distribution is known as a *continuous* distribution. The use of conditional profit and expected profit tables in these cases would certainly be impracticable.

Consider, for example, a case in which past sales for a certain product for a 30-day representative period are as listed in Table 4-22. We then take these 30 values for past sales and plot them on a graph as in Figure 4-1.

When we draw a rough line through the points, we find that this line takes the *approximate* shape of the often referred-to "bell-shaped" curve.

Table 4-22

Quantity sold	
26	20
13	19
33	5
10	18
13	17
5	13
7	19
10	18
3	10
13	17
18	13
9	22
9	9
10	7
17	17

We can, of course, calculate the average sales simply by dividing the total quantity sold during the 30-day period by 30 as follows:

$$\text{Average sales per day} = \frac{420}{30} = 14 \text{ per day}$$

Exactly what is the significance of the bell-shaped curve? Simply this: In most groups of historical data such as past daily sales of an item, there are a few values which are exceedingly small and a few values which are quite large; but most of the values tend to group or cluster around the average in much the same manner as our graph of past daily sales indicates. For instance, there are undoubtedly some individuals who are less than 3 feet tall and, of course, there are some who are over 8 feet in height, but most are between 5 and 6 feet tall. Important for our purposes is the fact that most groups of data such as these tend to take the shape of the bell-shaped curve when plotted. We shall assume that the actual values of past daily sales are normally distributed around their average of 14 units per day. We make this assumption because the

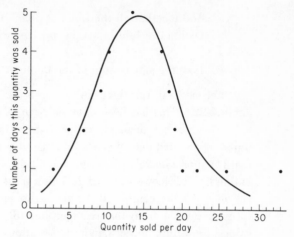

Figure 4-1   **Continuous distribution of past daily sales: the bell-shaped curve.**

bell-shaped distribution is in many cases a reasonable approximation of business phenomena.

In addition to this curve, there are curves where the values tend to be widely dispersed away from their average and other curves where the values tend to group themselves tightly around their average. These two curves are illustrated in Figure 4-2.

There is a statistical measure of the tendency for data to either group or disperse around their own average. This measure is called the "standard deviation." Because we can make important management inferences from our past sales data with this measure, we must learn how to calculate it and then learn what it means.

The standard deviation is calculated by following these five steps:

1. Subtract the average from each value in the data.
2. Square each of the differences obtained in step 1.

Figure 4-2   **Two variant curves.** (*a*) **The values are widely dispersed away from their average.** (*b*) **The values are tightly grouped about their average.**

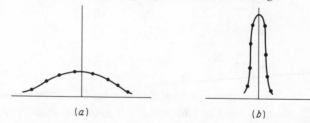

(*a*)   (*b*)

3. Add together all the squared differences.

4. Divide the sum of all the squared differences by the number of values.

5. Take the square root of the quotient obtained in step 4.

Let us perform these five operations on the original data from Table 4-22. This has been done on page 107.

The standard deviation of the distribution of past daily sales is 6.49 units. Now what does this mean? Just this: There is mathematical proof that (1) approximately 67 per cent of all the values in a bell-shaped distribution lie within one standard deviation (plus or minus) from the average; (2) about 95 per cent of all the values lie within two standard deviations (plus or minus) from the average; and (3) over 99 per cent of all the values lie within three standard deviations (plus or minus) from the average. Now apply these to our data.

If the average of our past daily sales is 14 and if our curve is perfectly bell-shaped, then approximately 67 per cent of all future sales will fall between 14 plus 6.49 units and 14 minus 6.49 units—between 20.49 units and 7.51 units. Similarly, about 95 per cent of all future sales will fall between 14 + (2 × 6.49) units and 14 − (2 × 6.49) units—between 26.98 and 1 case. There are statistical tables available which will indicate that portion of all the values in a distribution which is contained within any number of standard deviations from the average. Let us now make use of the standard deviation in solving an inventory stocking problem with a continuous distribution.

Using the original data from Table 4-22, we first add pricing and cost information to the problem. Assume our manager purchases this article for $4 per unit and sells it for $9 per unit. If the article is not sold on the selling day, it is worth nothing as salvage. Referring back to the marginal method of calculating optimum inventory purchase levels, we can calculate our required p in the same manner:

$$p = \frac{ML}{MP + ML} \tag{4-2}$$

$$= \frac{\$4}{\$5 + \$4}$$

$$= .44$$

Remember what this means: Our manager must be .44 sure of selling at least an additional unit before it would pay him to stock that unit.

Finding the standard deviation

Step 1	Step 2	Step 3
Subtract the average from each value	Square each of the differences	Add the squared differences
$26 - 14 = \quad 12$	$(12)^2 = 144$	144
$13 - 14 = \quad -1$	$(-1)^2 = \quad 1$	1
$33 - 14 = \quad 19$	$(19)^2 = 361$	361
$10 - 14 = \quad -4$	$(-4)^2 = \quad 16$	16
$13 - 14 = \quad -1$	$(-1)^2 = \quad 1$	1
$5 - 14 = \quad -9$	$(-9)^2 = \quad 81$	81
$7 - 14 = \quad -7$	$(-7)^2 = \quad 49$	49
$10 - 14 = \quad -4$	$(-4)^2 = \quad 16$	16
$3 - 14 = -11$	$(-11)^2 = 121$	121
$13 - 14 = \quad -1$	$(-1)^2 = \quad 1$	1
$18 - 14 = \quad 4$	$(4)^2 = \quad 16$	16
$9 - 14 = \quad -5$	$(-5)^2 = \quad 25$	25
$9 - 14 = \quad -5$	$(-5)^2 = \quad 25$	25
$10 - 14 = \quad -4$	$(-4)^2 = \quad 16$	16
$17 - 14 = \quad 3$	$(3)^2 = \quad 9$	9
$20 - 14 = \quad 6$	$(6)^2 = \quad 36$	36
$19 - 14 = \quad 5$	$(5)^2 = \quad 25$	25
$5 - 14 = \quad -9$	$(-9)^2 = \quad 81$	81
$18 - 14 = \quad 4$	$(4)^2 = \quad 16$	16
$17 - 14 = \quad 3$	$(3)^2 = \quad 9$	9
$13 - 14 = \quad -1$	$(-1)^2 = \quad 1$	1
$19 - 14 = \quad 5$	$(5)^2 = \quad 25$	25
$18 - 14 = \quad 4$	$(4)^2 = \quad 16$	16
$10 - 14 = \quad -4$	$(-4)^2 = \quad 16$	16
$17 - 14 = \quad 3$	$(3)^2 = \quad 9$	9
$13 - 14 = \quad -1$	$(-1)^2 = \quad 1$	1
$22 - 14 = \quad 8$	$(8)^2 = \quad 64$	64
$9 - 14 = \quad -5$	$(-5)^2 = \quad 25$	25
$7 - 14 = \quad -7$	$(-7)^2 = \quad 49$	49
$17 - 14 = \quad 3$	$(3)^2 = \quad 9$	9
		1,264

Step 4   Divide the sum of the squared differences by the number of values.

$$\frac{1,264}{30} = 42.13$$

Step 5   Take the square root of the quotient from step 4.

$$\sqrt{42.13} = 6.49$$

We now reproduce the curve of past sales and determine how to incorporate the marginal method into the continuous distribution of past daily sales.

One feature of the bell-shaped curve is that probabilities can be determined from it. The entire area under the curve represents a probability of 1.00; in other words, we are completely certain that sales will take on some value included in the distribution. Now refer to Figure 4-3. If we erect a vertical line *b* at 14 units, we can see that the area under the curve to the right of this line is about one-half the total area. This tells us that the probability of selling 14 or more units is about .5. *The area to the right of any such vertical line represents the probability of selling that quantity or more.* As the area to the right of any vertical line decreases, so does the probability that we will sell that quantity or more.

Suppose our manager considers stocking 4 units, line *a*. Most of the entire area under the curve lies to the right of the vertical line drawn at 4; thus the probability is great that the manager will sell 4 units or more. If he considers stocking 14 units (the average), about one-half the entire area under the curve lies to the right of vertical line *b*; thus he is about .5 sure of selling the 14 units or more. Suppose he considers stocking 20 units. Only a small portion of the entire area under the curve lies to the right of line *c*; thus the probability of selling the 20 units is quite small. To repeat, the area under the curve to the right of

Figure 4-3 **Continuous distribution of past daily sales.**

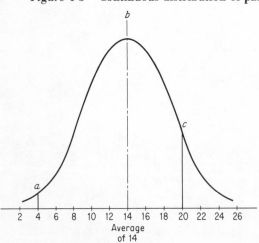

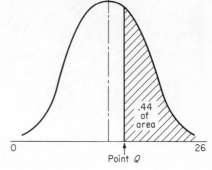

Figure 4-4 **Continuous probability distribution; .44 of the area under the curve
is shaded.**

a vertical line drawn at any stock level determines the probability of selling that quantity or more.

Figure 4-4 illustrates the .44 probability which must exist before it
pays our manager to stock another unit. He will stock additional units
until he reaches point Q. If he stocks a larger quantity, the shaded area
under the curve drops below .44 and the probability of selling another
unit or more falls below the required .44. How can we locate point Q?
There are, fortunately, statistical tables which help us. If we refer to
Appendix Table 1, we notice that it tells us how many standard deviations it takes to include any portion of the area under the curve measur-
ing to the right from the left-hand end of the curve. In this particular
case, since we know that the shaded area must be .44 of the area, then
the open area must be .56 of the total area under the curve. Looking in
the body of the table, we find that .56 of the area under the curve is
located between the left-hand end and a point .15 standard deviation to
the right of the average. Thus we know that point Q is .15 standard
deviation to the right of the average (14).

We had previously calculated one standard deviation for this distribution to be 6.49 units; so .15 times this would be

$.15 \times 6.49 = .9735$; treat this as 1 unit

Since point Q is 1 unit to the right of the average (14), it must be at 15
units. This is the optimum order for the manager to place: 15 units
per day.

Here is another problem utilizing the continuous probability distribution. This time, assume the following situation for a normally distributed daily sales record:

Average of past daily sales	30 cases
Standard deviation of past daily sales distribution	5 cases
Cost per case	$10
Selling price per case	$16
Value if not sold on selling day	$ 1

As we did in the initial problem, we first calculate the p which is required to justify the stocking of an additional case. In this instance,

$$p = \frac{ML}{MP + ML} \qquad\qquad (4\text{-}2)$$

$$= \frac{\$9}{\$6 + \$9} \qquad \text{(Notice that the salvage value of \$1 is deducted from the cost of \$10 to obtain the ML.)}$$

$$= \frac{\$9}{\$15}$$

$$= .6$$

We can now illustrate the probability on a bell-shaped curve by marking off .6 of the area under the curve, starting from the right-hand end of the curve, as in Figure 4-5.

Our manager will want to increase his order size this time until it reaches point Q. Notice that point Q lies to the *left* of the average, whereas in the preceding problem it lay to the right of the average. How can we locate point Q? Whenever the optimum stock level is smaller than the

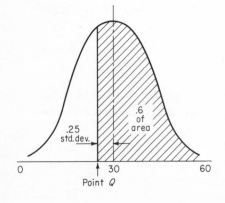

Figure 4-5 **Continuous probability distribution; .6 of the area under the curve is shaded.**

average sales figure, the distance between point Q and the average (this distance being measured in standard deviations) may be read *directly* from Appendix Table 1. We look for .6 in the body of the table. The nearest value to .6 is .5987; we notice that .5987 of the area under the curve is contained between the right-hand end of the curve and point Q; and the table indicates point Q to be .25 standard deviation from the average. We can now solve for point Q as follows:

$$.25 \times \text{standard deviation} = .25 \times 5 \text{ cases}$$
$$= 1.25 \text{ cases}$$
$$\text{Point } Q = \text{average less } 1.25 \text{ cases}$$
$$= 30 - 1.25 \text{ cases}$$
$$= 28.75, \text{ or } 29 \text{ cases}$$

The optimum stock for our manager to order each day is 29 cases.

The concept of the bell-shaped distribution is a powerful tool in managerial decision making when faced with uncertainty. It does not guarantee that the optimum decision will be made on each individual day. It does, however, represent the best possible long-run approach to maximizing profits when the sales pattern fluctuates randomly day after day. In such cases, methods similar to that described in this chapter will represent the best possible approach to decision making. You must remember, of course, that all business occurrences are not distributed in bell-shaped form.

PROBLEMS

4-1   Here is a discrete distribution of past sales:

Quantities buyers bought	Number of days occurred	p occurrence	p cumulative
20 units	10	.10	1.00
25 units	30	.30	.90
40 units	50	.50	.60
60 units	10	.10	.10

Selling price is $10 per unit and the cost is $6 per unit. If 25 units are stocked every day, what will be the expected profit per day over the long run?

4-2 Using the information given in problem 4-1, what will be the expected profits per day if 60 units are stocked daily?

4-3 Using the information given in problem 4-1, what quantity should be purchased every day to maximize long-run profits?

4-4 Using the information given in problem 4-1, what is the expected value of perfect information?

4-5 The Evans Company buys fruit which costs $9 per case and sells for $15 per case. If the fruit is not sold, it is salvaged for $3 per case. What is the minimum probability?

4-6 The item in this sales distribution costs $6 and sells for $8.

Quantities buyers bought	Number of days	p (occurrence)
100	9	.1
101	18	.2
102	45	.5
103	18	.2

What is the expected marginal profit and marginal loss from stocking the 103d unit? *Should* this unit be stocked?

4-7 Using the information given in problem 4-6, what level of stock should be carried daily?

4-8 The Alexander Company has average daily sales of 60 units with a standard deviation of 10 units. Units sell for $10 each and cost $5. There is no salvage value. What is the optimum daily stock for Alexander to carry?

4-9 The products the Mak-Mor Company sells for $10 each cost $3 each. From past sales data, it was found that sales per day average 50 units with a standard deviation of 20 units. What is the optimum level of stock which it should carry?

4-10 The Roberts Company has found that its average sales are 100 units per day with a standard deviation of 15 units. Each unit sells for $12 and costs $10. If the unit is not sold, it has a salvage value of $2. What is the optimum stock level?

BIBLIOGRAPHY

H. Bierman, L. E. Fouraker, and R. K. Jaedicke, *Quantitative Analysis for Business Decisions* (Homewood, Ill.: Richard D. Irwin, Inc., 1961).

H. Chernoff and L. E. Moses, *Elementary Decision Theory* (New York: John Wiley & Sons, Inc., 1959).

R. Schlaifer, *Probability and Statistics for Business Decisions* (New York: McGraw-Hill Book Company, 1959).

chapter
five
INVENTORY
MODELS

Inventory control certainly deserves the attention of top management. For many firms the inventory figure is the largest item in the current asset group. Inventory difficulties can and do contribute to business failures. When a firm does no more than unintentionally run out of an item, results are not pleasant. If the firm is a retail store, the merchant loses the gross margin on the item *and* he may lose some face in the eyes of the shopper. If the firm is a manufacturer, the stockout (inability to supply a requisitioned item from inventory) could, in extreme cases, bring production to a halt. Our conclusion must be that skillful inventory management can make a significant contribution to a firm's profit showing.

BASIC INVENTORY DECISIONS

There are two basic inventory decisions:

1. How much to order at one time
2. When to order this quantity

In approaching these two decisions, management feels somewhat ambivalent. One pressure is to order huge lots so as to minimize ordering costs. The other pressure is to order small lots so as to minimize carrying costs. If pushed too far, either of these courses will have an unfavorable effect on profits. The optimum course of action is a compromise between the two extremes. By using certain basic tools from operations research, we can arrive at a model for deriving the *economic order quantity*.

Inventory costs

A major objective of sound inventory management is that of minimizing total inventory costs. There are two types of these costs—*ordering* costs and *carrying* costs. Let us look at each.

1. *Ordering* costs are basically the costs of getting an item into the firm's inventory. They are incurred each time an order is placed. They are expressed as dollar cost per order. Ordering costs start with the requisition sent to the purchasing office, include all costs of issuing the purchase order and of following it up, continue with such steps as receiving the goods and placing them into inventory, and end with the buying

114

firm's paying the supplier. Salaries constitute the major ordering cost; stationery is another ordering cost.

Because we want the *incremental* cost per order, we need cost estimates from the purchasing department, from the receiving warehouse, and from the accounting office covering their operations at two different levels of operation, as shown in Table 5-1. From this table we see that the 2,000 additional orders are estimated to cost us $38,500; the incremental cost per order is $19.25.

Table 5-1

Ordering costs					
		At 3,000 orders/year		At 5,000 orders/year	
Expense category	Annual salary	Number required	Annual cost	Number required	Annual cost
Purchasing department chief	$12,000	1	$12,000	1	$12,000
Buyers	7,000	3	21,000	5	35,000
Assistant buyers	5,000	2	10,000	3	15,000
Follow-up men	4,000	1	4,000	2	8,000
Clerks	3,000	3	9,000	4	12,000
Typists	2,800	2	5,600	3	8,400
Supplies	—	—	1,500	—	2,500
Receiving clerks	4,000	2	8,000	3	12,000
Receiving supplies	—	—	300	—	500
Accounts payable clerks	4,200	3	12,600	4	16,800
Accounting supplies	—	—	450	—	750
Total expenses			$84,450		$122,950

2. *Carrying* costs, also referred to as holding costs, are basically the costs incurred because a firm owns or maintains inventories. Carrying costs include:

Interest on money invested in inventory. This is a major cost.
Obsolescence. This *can* be a major cost.
Storage space rent. This may include heat, lights, or refrigeration. This, too, *can* be a major cost.

Stores operation, including record keeping, the taking of physical inventory, and protection.

Taxes, insurance, and depreciation are usually minor costs; deterioration can be major *or* minor.

Carrying costs are an annual figure and are expressed as a percentage of average inventory value. This percentage can be obtained in much the same manner as that which we used to get incremental cost per order —by estimating total carrying costs at two different inventory levels. Carrying costs range from 10 to 50 per cent; many are in the 15 to 25 per cent bracket.

Figure 5-1 **Average inventory with constant usage.**

	Stock
Jan. 1	10,000
Feb. 1	9,167
Mar. 1	8,335
Apr. 1	7,499
May 1	6,667
June 1	5,833
July 1	4,999
Aug. 1	4,167
Sept. 1	3,333
Oct. 1	2,500
Nov. 1	1,667
Dec. 1	833
Dec. 31	0
	65,000

$$\text{Average inventory} = \frac{65,000}{13}$$

$$= 5,000$$

$$= \tfrac{1}{2} \text{ beginning inventory}$$

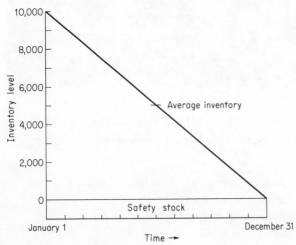

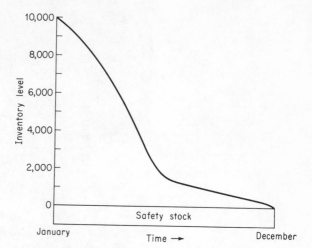

Figure 5-2   **Average inventory with seasonal usage.**

	Stock
Jan. 1	10,000
Feb. 1	9,000
Mar. 1	8,000
Apr. 1	6,600
May 1	5,000
June 1	3,000
July 1	1,600
Aug. 1	1,200
Sept. 1	1,000
Oct. 1	750
Nov. 1	500
Dec. 1	400
Dec. 31	0
	47,050

$$\text{Average inventory} = \frac{47,050}{13}$$

$$= 3,619$$

$$= 0.362 \text{ beginning inventory}$$

Concept of average inventory

If a firm buys an item only once for the coming year, if use of the item is constant, and if the last of the item is used on the last day of the year, then the firm's average inventory equals one-half the amount bought; this is the same as saying one-half the beginning inventory. Figure 5-1 shows average inventory under conditions of constant usage.

Where inventory usage is not constant, the average inventory for the year will be greater or less than one-half the beginning inventory. Figure 5-2 shows average inventory under conditions of seasonal (*not* constant) usage.

Table 5-2

Identifying the economic order quantity

(1)	Legend	No. orders/year	1	2	3	4	5	10	20
(2)	$10,000/(1)	$ per order	$10,000	$5,000	$3,333	$2,500	$2,000	$1,000	$500
(3)	(2)/2	Average inventory	5,000	2,500	1,666	1,250	1,000	500	250
(4)	(3) × 12½%	Carrying charges	625	313	208	156	125	63	31
(5)	(1) × $25	Ordering cost	25	50	75	100	125	250	500
(6)	(4) + (5)	Total cost/year	$ 650	$ 363	$ 283	$ 256	$ 250	$ 313	$531

↑
Optimum

118

The simplest (and least satisfactory) method of arriving at a figure for average inventory is to add opening inventory on January 1 to closing inventory on December 31 and divide by 2. A bit better is to add 3 inventory figures—January 1, July 1, and December 31—and divide by 3.

Probably the most common method is to add the beginning inventories of the 12 months *and* the closing inventory for December and divide by 13.

SOLVING FOR ECONOMIC ORDER QUANTITY

To minimize inventory costs, management tries to minimize *ordering* costs and *carrying* costs. Having seen how incremental ordering cost, carrying cost, and average inventory are determined, we are now ready to solve for economic order quantity. EOQ is that size order which minimizes total annual cost of ordering and carrying inventory. We are assuming conditions of certainty—annual requirements are known.

Tabular solution for EOQ

Assume that a manufacturer uses $10,000 worth of an item during the year. His accountants have determined that ordering costs amount to $25 per order and that carrying costs amount to 12½ per cent of average inventory. Construction of a table such as Table 5-2 is one approach to identifying the economic order quantity.

Note that as cost to carry declines, ordering costs increase. Note also that *total* costs, the figure we want to minimize, are lowest when carrying costs are equal to ordering costs. This is the point we always need to determine, because it is always the point of lowest total inventory costs for the year. Table 5-2 shows that the manufacturer should order 5 times during the year.

Graphic presentation of EOQ

Figure 5-3 makes *graphically* the same point presented in Table 5-2.

Derivation of three formulas

1. Optimum number of orders per year. To derive this formula,

Let $N =$ optimum number of orders per year to minimize total inventory costs

$A =$ total dollar value of the item used per year

$P =$ ordering cost per order placed

$C =$ carrying cost expressed as a percentage of average inventory

We have seen that the most economical point as regards total inventory costs is the point where ordering costs are the same in amount as carrying costs.   Thus, we can solve for N by letting

Total ordering cost per year $=$ carrying cost per year

Total ordering cost per year $= N \times P = NP$

Carrying cost per year $= \dfrac{A}{N} \times \dfrac{1}{2} \times C$

$$\left(\frac{\$ \text{ used per year}}{\text{no. orders per year}} \right) \quad \left(\begin{array}{c} \text{average} \\ \text{inventory} \\ \text{balance} \\ \text{with} \\ \text{constant} \\ \text{usage} \end{array} \right) \quad \left(\begin{array}{c} \text{carrying} \\ \text{cost \%} \end{array} \right)$$

$$= $$

$$\$ \text{ amount} \\ \text{per order}$$

Figure 5-3   **Identifying the economic order quantity.**

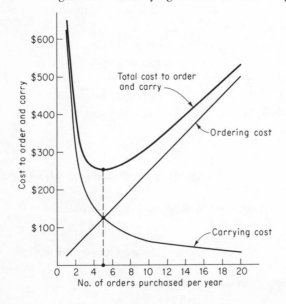

Equating, we get

$$NP = \frac{AC}{2N}$$

$$2N^2P = AC$$

$$N^2 = \frac{AC}{2P}$$

$$N = \sqrt{\frac{AC}{2P}} \tag{5-1}$$

Using the formula as derived, we can solve for N using the same data seen in Table 5-2 and Figure 5-3:

$$\sqrt{\frac{\$10,000 \times 0.125}{2 \times \$25}} = \sqrt{\frac{\$1,250}{\$50}} = \sqrt{25} = 5 \text{ orders per year}$$
$$\text{or}$$
$$\text{an order every 73 days}$$

2. Optimum number of units per order. Another formula can be derived, this one to give us the optimum number of units to order each time an order is placed.

Let R = price of each unit
        N = optimum number of units per order
        A = total number of units used per year
        P = ordering cost per order placed
        C = carrying cost expressed as a percentage of average inventory

Here we can solve for N by letting

Total ordering cost per year = carrying cost per year

$$\underbrace{\frac{A}{N}}_{\substack{\left(\frac{\text{no. units used per year}}{\text{no. units per order}}\right) \\ = \\ \text{no. orders per year}}} \times \underbrace{P}_{\left(\substack{\text{ordering cost} \\ \text{per order}}\right)} = \text{total ordering cost}$$

$$\frac{AR}{A/N} \quad \times \quad \frac{1}{2} \quad \times \quad C \quad = \quad \text{carrying cost per year}$$

$$\left(\begin{array}{c} \text{no. units used per year} \\ \underline{\times \text{ price per unit}} \\ \text{no. orders per year} \\ = \\ \text{\$ per order} \end{array} \right) \quad \left(\begin{array}{c} \text{average} \\ \text{inventory} \\ \text{balance} \\ \text{with} \\ \text{constant} \\ \text{usage} \end{array} \right) \quad \left(\begin{array}{c} \text{carrying} \\ \text{cost \%} \end{array} \right)$$

$$\frac{AP}{N} = \frac{ARC}{2A/N}$$

$$\frac{AP}{N} = \frac{RCN}{2}$$

$$N^2RC = 2AP$$

$$N^2 = \frac{2AP}{RC}$$

$$N = \sqrt{\frac{2AP}{RC}} \tag{5-2}$$

Assume that our company uses 10,000 units per year at a unit cost of \$1. You recall that ordering cost per order is \$25 and that carrying cost is 12½ per cent. Now, substituting our values into our formula, we get

$$\sqrt{\frac{2 \times 10,000 \times \$25}{\$1 \times 0.125}} = \sqrt{\frac{500,000}{0.125}} = \sqrt{4,000,000}$$

$$= 2,000 \text{ units per order}$$

Our first of the three formulas told us to place 5 orders a year. Now we are told to order 2,000 units per order. Multiplying these two figures gives us 10,000 units—the annual usage figure.

3. Optimum number of days' supply per order. Our third formula tells us how many days' usage we should cover or provide for each time we order.

Let N = optimum number of days' supply per order
         A = total number of units used per year

P = ordering cost per order placed
C = carrying cost expressed as a percentage of average inventory
R = price of each unit
365 = calendar days per year

Once again,

Total ordering cost per year = carrying cost per year

$$\frac{365}{N} \qquad \times \qquad P \qquad = \text{total ordering cost}$$

$$\left(\begin{array}{c} \text{no. days per year} \\ \hline \text{no. days per order} \\ = \\ \text{no. orders per year} \end{array} \right) \qquad \left(\begin{array}{c} \text{ordering cost} \\ \text{per order} \end{array} \right)$$

$$\frac{AR}{365/N} \qquad \times \qquad \frac{1}{2} \qquad \times \qquad C \qquad = \text{carrying cost per year}$$

$$\left(\begin{array}{c} \text{no. units used per year} \\ \underline{\times \text{ price per unit}} \\ \text{no. orders per year} \\ = \\ \text{\$ per order} \end{array} \right) \qquad \left(\begin{array}{c} \text{average} \\ \text{inventory} \\ \text{balance} \\ \text{with} \\ \text{constant} \\ \text{usage} \end{array} \right) \qquad \left(\begin{array}{c} \text{carrying} \\ \text{cost \%} \end{array} \right)$$

$$\frac{365P}{N} = \frac{ARC}{730/N}$$

$$\frac{365P}{N} = \frac{ARCN}{730}$$

$$N^2 ARC = 266{,}450P$$

$$N^2 = \frac{266{,}450P}{ARC}$$

$$N = \sqrt{\frac{266{,}450P}{ARC}} \tag{5-3}$$

Substituting, we get $\qquad N = \sqrt{\dfrac{266{,}450 \times \$25}{10{,}000 \times \$1 \times 0.125}}$

$$= \sqrt{5{,}321}$$
$$= \text{about 73 days' supply per optimum order}$$

Selective use of EOQ formulas

Keep in mind that the EOQ formulas are only tools for use in decision making and that the answers derived from them are only as good as the data fed into the formulas. No company, of course, will use the EOQ formulas for analyzing its purchasing of every item it buys and stocks. Some distinction must be made between items which account for a large part of the inventory value and those which are of minor importance. The pattern in Table 5-3 is quite common.

Table 5-3

Importance of inventory items			
Inventory classification	Degree of capital importance	% of inventory items	% of annual dollar usage
A	Major	10	80
B	Intermediate	20	15
C	Minor	70	5
		100	100

In the case shown in this table, formulas would be used as an aid in controlling the A group because it is here that management would want to concentrate its effort. Other tools, less technical, would be used for the B items and the C items; for example, management might set "rule of thumb" upper and lower inventory levels. B and C items would seldom be controlled closely because they total only 20 per cent of annual dollar usage.

QUANTITY DISCOUNTS

A discussion of quantity discounts offered by vendors has been postponed up to this point. To analyze a quantity discount properly, one must first understand the fundamentals of the economic order quantity formulas. Then and only then can one evaluate properly a vendor's offer of a quantity discount.

First let us look at the plus features and the minus features usually attributed to the policy of buying in large quantities. Then we shall examine two approaches to the analysis of quantity discounts: the *cost comparison* approach and the *price change* approach.

Advantages and disadvantages of quantity buying

Buyers who buy in large quantities may well enjoy some of these advantages claimed for the policy:

Lower unit prices   Lower ordering costs
Cheaper transportation   Fewer stockouts
Mass display by retailers Preferential treatment by sellers

But quantity buying can involve these disadvantages:

Higher carrying costs   Older stock
Lower stock turnover   More capital required
Less flexibility   Heavier deterioration and depreciation

Now look at the two methods of evaluating quantity discounts.

Cost comparison approach

One approach, probably the most used because of its simplicity, is that of comparing the total cost of ordering and carrying the inventory under EOQ with the total cost of ordering and carrying under conditions which qualify the buyer for the quantity discount. Here is an example.

The Sun Heat Company purchases thermostats and uses them on heating units Sun manufactures. Sun buys 2,000 of these thermostats annually. Unit cost is $20; ordering cost per order is $50; cost of carrying the inventory is 25 per cent of inventory value. The Thermo Company, seller of the thermostats, offers the Sun Heat Company a 3 per cent discount on purchases if Sun will buy in lots of 1,000 or more. To evaluate this proposal properly we must first calculate the total cost using EOQ but not taking the 3 per cent discount. Using Eq. (5-2) for optimum number of units per order, we get

$$N = \sqrt{\frac{2AP}{RC}} = \sqrt{\frac{2(2,000) \times \$50}{\$20 \times 0.25}} = \sqrt{\frac{\$200,000}{\$5}} = \sqrt{40,000}$$

$$= 200 \text{ units per order}$$

Because the optimum number of units to order in each lot is 200 and the unit price is $20, total cost per order is $4,000. Because use of the units is constant, average inventory is $4,000/2, or $2,000. Carrying cost, you remember, is 25 per cent, and 25 per cent of $2,000 is $500. Each year, 10 purchases (each for 200 units) must be made to provide the 2,000 units needed; thus ordering cost is 10 times $50, or $500.

The cost picture now looks like this:

Cost of thermostats	($20 × 2,000)	$40,000
Ordering cost	(10 × $50)	500
Carrying cost	(25% × $2,000)	500
Total annual cost of thermostats as now purchased		$41,000

This figure must be compared with total annual cost under the plan proposed by the Thermo Company.

If 1,000 units are bought in each lot as Thermo proposes, the cost of each lot would be

Cost of thermostats (1,000 × $20 × 0.97)	$19,400
(The 0.97 element reflects the 3% discount)	

Because each lot costs $19,400, average inventory would be one-half that figure, or $9,700. Total annual cost, assuming two orders a year, is

Cost of thermostats	(2 × $19,400)	$38,800
Ordering cost	(2 × $50)	100
Carrying cost	(25% × $9,700)	2,425
Total annual cost of thermostats taking quantity discounts		$41,325

Therefore the Sun Heat Company will not buy in lots which would entitle it to quantity discounts. Such buying would increase costs by $325.

Another approach for evaluating quantity discounts is to solve for the largest order quantity that is economical to order at the price offered by the discount. The optimum point under this approach is the point where the reduction in ordering cost and in unit price is equal to the additional carrying cost which results from buying in larger amounts.

Let X = largest order quantity economical to order at the lower unit price (expressed in dollars)

D = discount expressed as a percentage of A

A = old annual requirement in dollars

P = ordering cost per order

Q = EOQ in dollars previous to discount offer

C = carrying cost as a percentage of average inventory

Our first job in solving for X is to compute the amount by which carrying cost will rise once we start buying in larger quantities.

Carrying cost for the proposed plan is determined in this manner:

$$\frac{\substack{\text{Largest order quantity}\\\text{economical to order}\\\text{at reduced price}}}{2} \times \text{carrying cost} = \frac{X}{2}C$$

(new average inventory) $\left(\substack{\text{expressed as}\\\text{\% of average}\\\text{inventory}}\right)$

Next, we subtract from the carrying cost for the proposed plan the carrying cost of our present plan—the carrying cost under EOQ before the discount. *This* carrying cost is

$$\frac{\text{EOQ in dollars before discount}}{2} \times \text{carrying cost} = \frac{Q}{2}C$$

The *additional* carrying cost, then, amounts to

$$\frac{X}{2}C - \frac{Q}{2}C = \text{additional carrying cost}$$

The next step is to determine the reduction in the ordering cost. This reduction is found by subtracting the new ordering cost (when taking the quantity discount) from the ordering cost which prevailed before qualifying for and taking the quantity discount.

Old ordering cost $\;=\;$ no. orders per year $\times$ ordering cost per order

$$= \frac{\text{old annual usage in dollars}}{\text{dollar size of old orders}} \times P$$

$$= \frac{A}{Q} \times P$$

$$= \frac{A}{Q} P$$

New ordering cost $= $ no. orders per year $\times$ ordering cost per order

$$= \frac{\text{new annual usage in dollars}}{\text{dollar size of new orders}} \times P$$

$$= \frac{A(1 - D)}{X} \times P$$

$$= \frac{A(1 - D)}{X} P$$

Old ordering cost $-$ new ordering cost $=$ decrease in ordering cost; therefore

$$\frac{A}{Q} P - \left[\frac{A(1 - D)}{X} \right] P = \text{reduction in ordering cost}$$

and

Discount $\times$ annual requirement in dollars before discount
$$= D \times A$$
$$= DA$$
$$= \text{reduction in total cost of units because of lower unit price}$$

By equating the addition in carrying cost with the reduction in total buying price plus the savings in ordering cost, we obtain this equation for X:

$$\frac{XC}{2} - \frac{QC}{2} = DA + \frac{AP}{Q} - \frac{A(1 - D)P}{X}$$

To solve for X, we multiply both sides of the equation by X:

$$\frac{X^2C}{2} - \frac{XQC}{2} = XDA + \frac{XAP}{Q} - A(1 - D)P$$

We now convert to quadratic equation form $(ax^2 + bx + c = 0)$, the general algebraic form for a quadratic equation.

$$\frac{X^2C}{2} - \frac{XQC}{2} - XDA - \frac{XAP}{Q} + A(1 - D)P = 0$$

$$X^2\frac{C}{2} + X\left(-\frac{QC}{2} - DA - \frac{AP}{Q}\right) + A(1 - D)P = 0$$

Our legend becomes

$$a = \frac{C}{2} \qquad b = -\left(\frac{QC}{2} + DA + \frac{AP}{Q}\right) \qquad c = A(1 - D)P$$

We are now able to solve the quadratic formula:

$$X = \frac{-b \pm \sqrt{b^2 - 4AC}}{2A}$$

$$= \frac{\dfrac{QC}{2} + DA + \dfrac{AP}{Q} \pm \sqrt{\left[-\left(\dfrac{QC}{2} + DA + \dfrac{AP}{Q}\right)\right]^2 - 4\dfrac{C}{2}[A(1 - D)P]}}{2\dfrac{C}{2}}$$

$$= \frac{\dfrac{QC}{2} + DA + \dfrac{AP}{Q} + \sqrt{\left[-\left(\dfrac{QC}{2} + DA + \dfrac{AP}{Q}\right)\right]^2 - 2CAP(1 - D)}}{C}$$

(5-4)

This gives the largest order quantity economical to buy at the discount.

To illustrate, use the data from the Sun Heat Company problem on page 125. Earlier we noted that to take the discount offered by the supplier would cost Sun Heat an additional $325 a year. The question now is what quantity the Sun Heat Company should purchase at a time in view of the 3 per cent discount offered. To solve for this quantity, we can use the price change evaluation method formula.

Let D = discount offered (3%)

Q = optimum order quantity (10 orders/year @ $4,000)

A = annual requirement in dollars ($40,000)

P = ordering cost per order

C = carrying costs

X = largest quantity to buy at one time to get discount (3%)

$$X = \frac{\frac{QC}{2} + DA + \frac{AP}{Q} + \sqrt{\left[-\left(\frac{QC}{2} + DA + \frac{AP}{Q}\right)\right]^2 - 2CAP(1-}}{C}$$

$$= \frac{\frac{\$4,000 \times 25\%}{2} + (3\% \times \$40,000) + \frac{\$40,000 \times \$50}{\$4,000}}{}$$

$$+ \frac{\sqrt{\left[-\left(\frac{\$4,000 \times 25\%}{2} + (3\% \times \$40,000) + \frac{\$40,000 \times \$50}{\$4,000}\right)\right]}}{- 2(25\% \times \$40,000 \times \$50)(100\% - 3\%}}{25\%}$$

$$= \frac{\$500 + \$1,200 + \$500 + \sqrt{[-(\$500 + \$1,200 + \$500)]^2 - \$1,000,000\,(97\%)}}{25\%}$$

$$= \frac{\$2,200 + \sqrt{[-(\$2,200)]^2 - \$970,000}}{25\%}$$

$$= \frac{\$2,200 + \sqrt{\$4,840,000 - \$970,000}}{25\%}$$

$$= \frac{\$2,200 + \sqrt{\$3,870,000}}{25\%} = \$16,700$$

Thus $16,700 is the largest quantity of thermostats the Sun Heat Company should buy at one time in order to get the 3 per cent quantity discount offered. As $16,700 is less than the $20,000 purchase quantity necessary to get the discount, it will not pay Sun to take advantage of the offer.

The methods described above for analyzing discounts are believed to be good methods if properly used. It is essential, however, to realize that they, like other quantitative techniques, are only tools for management to employ in decision making. Judgment must be exercised in their use. Close watch must be maintained on all the factors involved in deriving the EOQ formulas, because these factors are all subject to changes which could affect results greatly.

THE REORDER PROBLEM

In dealing with economic order quantities, we have been operating under two assumptions: (1) that usage, consumption, demand, or sales are uniform, and (2) that the time interval between ordering goods and receiving those goods (known as "lead time") is constant. We have assumed that rate of use is known and will not change; we have assumed that lead time is known and will not vary. Figure 5-4 illustrates inventory level under those assumptions.

But these assumptions are not always true to life. Planned usage of a fabricating part, for example, can be thrown off schedule by a sales volume greater than expected, by a strike, by a power failure, or by weather change. The lead time between ordering a raw material and getting delivery often varies; the *supplier* may run into difficulties (fires, breakdowns), or the *transportation line* may run into delays (floods, accidents).

Figure 5-4 **Inventory level with constant usage and constant lead time (no safety stock).**

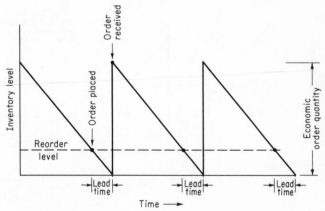

Stockouts

When a manufacturer's stores department cannot fill a requisition for an item which is normally on hand, a stockout occurs. Variations in rate of use and in lead time aggravate the stockout problem because they add to the uncertainty of a firm's operation. Figure 5-5 shows a stockout when demand (usage) was normal but receipt of goods ordered (delivery) was later than expected. Figure 5-6 shows a stockout when delivery was on schedule but usage was greater than expected.

Stockouts are undesirable because they cost the firm. Indeed, stockouts can be *quite* expensive. Lost sales and lost customers are examples of *external* costs. Idle machines and employee ill will are examples of *internal* costs. Management's desire to avoid stockouts leads to further consideration of *when* to order and reorder.

Reorder point

The reorder point is the condition which tells the purchasing agent that it is time to place a buying order to replenish the stock of some item. Reorder points, therefore, reflect the two variables already mentioned: rate of use and lead time. To determine the reorder point, multiply usage (number of units used per day) by lead time (in days).

Figure 5-5   **Inventory level with constant usage and excessively long lead time (no safety stock).**

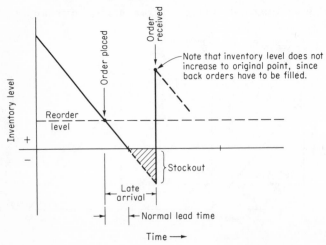

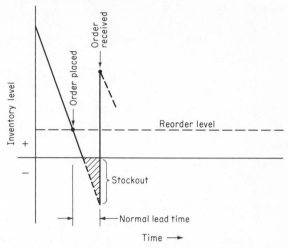

Figure 5-6   **Inventory level with excessive usage and constant lead time (no safety stock).**

Assume the Dasher Company makes washing machines and has an average daily output of 50 units. Dasher buys the electric motors it installs in its washing machines. Average lead time for normal purchase orders is 6 days; $50 \times 6 = 300$. Thus 300 is the reorder point for the electric motors; Dasher will order additional motors every time the inventory level falls to 300, a supply for 6 average days. But Figures 5-5 and 5-6 warn that the Dasher Company dare not risk such a close schedule—that a margin of safety is needed.

Safety stocks

The term safety stock refers to extra inventory held as a hedge or protection against the possibility of a stockout. It is obvious that a safety stock has two effects on a firm's costs. It will *decrease* the costs of stockouts, but it will *increase* carrying costs. The cost of a stockout multiplied by the number of stockouts prevented by the safety stock gives the cost reduction figure. The value of the safety stock multiplied by the carrying cost percentage gives the cost addition figure. Note that this cost addition is continuing—even permanent—in nature because the safety stock is always a part of total inventory. Note also that, because the safety stock does not often decline in quantity, we do not divide it by 2 as we did to get average inventory under conditions of linear usage.

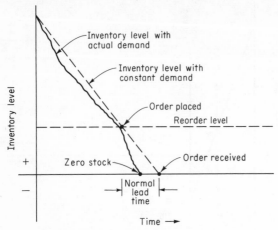

Figure 5-7 **Inventory level showing the effect of an increase in demand after the order has been placed.**

The optimum safety stock to carry is determined in the light of two goals, goals somewhat hostile to each other; these are (1) to minimize the costs of stockouts, but (2) at the same time, to minimize carrying costs on the safety stock. The decision of how much safety stock to carry is not an easy one. Every approach to this problem has its own limitations. In the next section we shall deal with the Dasher Company's decision about a safety stock. There we will use the *probability* approach, perhaps the most satisfactory approach developed to date. We will assume a constant lead time; we will also assume that each lot ordered is delivered all at one time. Under these assumptions, a stockout can be caused *only* by an increase in demand (usage) *after the reorder point has been reached.* Figure 5-7 illustrates this situation. Note that the stockout resulted from increased demand *after the order to replenish inventory had been placed.* If the increase had occurred *before* the reorder point was reached, a buying order would have been placed at the moment the inventory level fell to the reorder point level.

Optimum safety stock for Dasher Company

The Dasher Company has determined by EOQ formula that the optimum number of electric motors per order is 3,600 with an average usage of 50 per calendar day. Management has further determined that normal lead time is 6 days. It now wishes to determine how much safety stock to carry.

Dasher's first step is to analyze its inventory record card for these motors. By noting the usage during a number of past reorder periods, Dasher can assign a probability to various levels of usage, as shown in Table 5-4.

Table 5-4

Probabilities of usage during reorder period		
Use during reorder period	No. times this quantity was used	Use probability
150 units	3	3/100 or .03
200 units	4	4/100 or .04
250 units	6	6/100 or .06
300 units	68	68/100 or .68
350 units	9	9/100 or .09
400 units	7	7/100 or .07
450 units	3	3/100 or .03
	100 times	100%

If the Dasher Company reorders when the level of stock falls to 300 units, the company will be safe 81 per cent of the time (.68 + .06 + .04 + .03), but it will be out of stock of motors 19 per cent of the time (.09 + .07 + .03). Obviously, management is quite concerned over this figure of 19 per cent.

To reduce or to avoid this shortage, Dasher could carry some safety stock. Management might consider several levels of safety stock and pick the one which yields the lowest total for (1) cost of stockouts plus (2) carrying costs on the safety stock. Thus Dasher could consider carrying a safety stock of:

1. *50 units.* This would cover a usage of 350 during the reorder period; Dasher would be out of stock only when usage was 400 or 450 units; .07 + .03 = .1 of the time.

2. *100 units.* This would cover a usage of 350 or 400 during the reorder period; Dasher would be out of stock only when usage was 450 units; this would be .03 of the time.

3. *150 units.* This would cover usage of 350, 400, or 450 during the reorder period; Dasher should never run out of stock with this amount of safety stock.

Assume that the Dasher Company has determined that the cost of being out of stock of an item is $50 for each unit short. The danger of being out of stock will occur, of course, when stock is nearing the lowest point, the reorder point; thus we will have to take into consideration the number of times Dasher reorders during the year. Suppose one of the EOQ formulas told management that 5 orders per year is optimum. Dasher will, therefore, be in danger of running out of electric motors 5 times during the year. EOQ thus affects the reorder point.

The costs of being out of stock for the four courses of action (no safety stock, 50 units, 100 units, 150 units) are shown in Table 5-5.

Table 5-5

Costs of being out of stock

Safety stock	Probability of being out	Number short	Expected annual cost (no. short × probability of being short that many × cost of being out per unit × no. orders/year)		Total annual stockout costs
0	.09 when use is 350	50	50 × .09 × $50 × 5	$1,125	
	.07 when use is 400	100	100 × .07 × $50 × 5	1,750	
	.03 when use is 450	150	150 × .03 × $50 × 5	1,125	$4,000
50	.07 when use is 400	50	50 × .07 × $50 × 5	$ 875	
	.03 when use is 450	100	100 × .03 × $50 × 5	750	$1,625
100	.03 when use is 450	50	50 × .03 × $50 × 5	$ 375	$ 375
150	0	0	0		0

If the Dasher Company accountants calculated that the cost per year of carrying 1 motor in safety stock was $10, then the total annual costs of the four courses of action (stockout cost plus carrying costs on safety stock) would be as shown in Table 5-6.

Adoption of the safety stock policy would change the reorder point. If 100 motors are to be held as safety stock, then the reorder point is determined as follows:

Table 5-6

Costs of safety stock policies

Safety stock	Cost of being out of stock	Annual carrying costs (no. carried × cost/year)	Total cost/year (stockout cost + carrying costs)
0	$4,000	0	$4,000
50	$1,625	50 × $10 = $ 500	$2,125
100	$ 375	100 × $10 = $1,000	$1,375*
150	0	150 × $10 = $1,500	$1,500

*$1,375 is the lowest total cost per year; 100 units as safety stock is the optimum quantity.

Reorder point = average daily use × lead time in days + safety stock

or   50 × 6 + 100 = 400

EOQ CONCEPT AS APPLIED TO PRODUCTION RUNS

The concept that there is one best pattern of ordering to minimize annual inventory costs can be adapted to the production process. For instance, there are many companies which produce certain items among their product lines in lots or batches instead of manufacturing at a constant rate all year long. This method is generally followed because total annual sales of the finished item are not enough to warrant maintaining a production line for the exclusive manufacture of that item on a year-long continuous basis.

These firms incur a *setup cost* each time a batch is produced. Setup cost is roughly equivalent to the ordering cost per order already treated in this chapter; it consists of:

1. Engineering cost of setting up the production lines or machines
2. Paperwork cost of processing the work order and authorizing production
3. Ordering cost to provide raw materials for the batch or order

In addition to these setup costs, the company incurs carrying costs on the finished product from the time it is manufactured until it is sold.

The carrying charges on finished goods consist of the same items comprising the carrying costs on inventory, except that the value of finished goods is higher because of the cost of manufacturing—labor and overhead. We see, then, that the basic concept of an optimum number of batches or runs—the number to minimize total annual production costs for manufacturing of the intermittent type—is quite similar to the concept we have been using for raw material inventories.

Optimum production lot size: production for stock

One case where an optimum production lot size can be calculated involves finished goods which are to be placed in stock and then sold at a constant rate until some low level is reached; at that time another lot will be produced. Here the procedure for finding the optimum number of runs per year is the same as in the case of raw material inventory control. The symbols used correspond as shown in Table 5-7.

Table 5-7

Symbols for computing production for stock		
	Raw materials (optimum no. of orders)	Production runs (optimum no. per year)
A	Annual use of item in $	Annual sales of item (factory cost)
C	Carrying costs as a % of raw materials	Carrying costs as a % of finished goods
P	Ordering costs per order	Setup cost per run
N	Optimum no. of orders per year	Optimum no. of runs per year

If, for instance, (1) the XYZ Company sells $40,000 worth of special gears at the factory each year, (2) their carrying costs on finished stock are 20 per cent per year, and (3) setup cost per production run is $80, then the optimum number of production runs per year for this item would be

$$N = \sqrt{\frac{AC}{2P}} = \sqrt{\frac{\$40,000 \times 0.20}{2 \times \$80}} = \sqrt{\frac{\$8,000}{\$160}} = \sqrt{50}$$

$$= \text{about 7 runs per year}$$

In other words, to minimize their total annual cost of setting up to produce these gears and of storing them until the gears are sold, XYZ should manufacture their annual requirement for this item in 7 lots or batches per year. We could, of course, have used other EOQ formulas and derived the answer in terms of optimum number of units per run, or in terms of optimum number of months' sales in each run.

Optimum production lot size: simultaneous production and sales

Another case in which we can apply the concept of an optimum production lot size is one where the finished goods are being sold while each lot is being produced. In this case, the inventory of finished goods does not build up immediately to its maximum point, as it would in the case of receipt of a complete optimum order of raw materials. Instead, it builds up gradually as goods are produced faster than they are being sold; then it declines to its lowest point as production of a particular batch ceases although sales continue. This concept is illustrated in Figure 5-8.

Table 5-8 shows how symbols in this case correspond to those used in calculating raw material inventories.

We can express total setup cost and total carrying cost as follows:

If
N = optimum production in units

v = production rate in units produced per day

then
$\dfrac{N}{v}$ = number of days required to produce optimum run

Figure 5-8 **Finished goods inventory during simultaneous production and sales.**

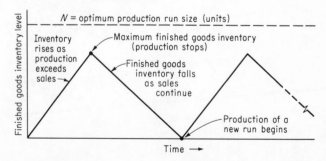

Table 5-8

Symbols for computing production for simultaneous sales	
Raw materials (optimum units per lot)	**Production runs** (optimum units per run)
A Annual need in units	Annual sales in units
P Ordering costs per order	Setup cost per run
R Price per unit	Factory cost per unit
C Carrying costs as a % of raw materials	Carrying costs as a % of finished goods
N Optimum no. of units per order	Optimum no. of units per run

If d = sales rate in units sold per day

then $\dfrac{N}{v}d$ = number of units sold during time optimum run is being produced

and $N - \dfrac{N}{v}d$ = largest finished goods inventory in units that can accumulate

Average inventory in units = ½ maximum inventory (constant sales)

$$= \frac{1}{2}\left(N - \frac{N}{v}d\right)$$

$$= \frac{1}{2}N\left(1 - \frac{d}{v}\right)$$

Average inventory in units $= \dfrac{N}{2}\left(1 - \dfrac{d}{v}\right)$

Carrying costs = average inventory in units × factory cost per unit × carrying costs (%)

$$= \frac{N}{2}\left(1 - \frac{d}{v}\right) \times R \times C$$

$$= \frac{RCN}{2}\left(1 - \frac{d}{v}\right)$$

No. runs per year $= \dfrac{A}{N}$

Setup cost $= \dfrac{A}{N} P$

From our previous derivation of EOQ formulas, we know that manufacturing is least expensive when total setup cost per year equals total carrying costs on the finished goods inventory. Using the symbols we have derived for setup cost and carrying costs, we equate the two as follows:

$$\frac{AP}{N} = \frac{RCN}{2}\left(1 - \frac{d}{v}\right)$$

We solve for N by cross multiplication:

$$RCN^2\left(1 - \frac{d}{v}\right) = 2AP$$

$$N^2 = \frac{2AP}{RC(1 - d/v)}$$

$$N = \sqrt{\frac{2AP}{RC(1 - d/v)}} \tag{5-5}$$

To apply this formula, use the following example. The ABC Company produces and sells 5,000 special bearings annually. The setup cost per run is \$90. Factory cost is \$5 each. Carrying costs on finished goods inventory is 20 per cent. Production rate is 100 per day, and sales amount to 14 per day. How many bearings should ABC produce per production run?

$$N = \sqrt{\frac{2 \times 5{,}000 \times \$90}{\$5 \times 0.20 \times (1 - 14/100)}}$$

$$= \sqrt{\frac{\$900{,}000}{\$1(1 - 0.14)}}$$

$$= \sqrt{\frac{\$900{,}000}{\$0.86}}$$

$$= \sqrt{1{,}046{,}000}$$

$$= 1{,}023 = \text{no. units per optimum production run}$$

PROBLEMS

5-1 Using the following symbols, derive a formula which will solve directly for the optimum number of week's supply to purchase at one time.

P = administrative cost per order
C = carrying charges as a per cent of average inventory
A = annual requirement in dollars
X = optimum number of weeks' supply to purchase at one time

5-2 Given the following, derive a formula which will solve directly for the optimum number of orders to place per month.

C = carrying charges as a per cent of average inventory
P = administrative cost per order
A = annual requirement in units
R = average price per unit
X = optimum number of orders per month

5-3 Using the following symbols, derive a formula which will solve directly for N.

A = annual requirement in dollars
R = price per unit
P = administrative cost per purchase
C = carrying charges in dollars per unit per year
N = units per economic lot

5-4 The Beyers Company has determined through an analysis of accounting data that the administrative cost per order of a raw material is $30. The company expects to use $60,000 of this material in the coming year; its carrying charge is 10 per cent of the average inventory. How many times should the raw material be ordered in the coming year?

5-5 The Sellers Company will need $81,000 of a certain material in the coming year. If the administrative cost per order is $25 and the carrying charge on the inventory is 20 per cent, how many months' supply should they purchase at one time?

5-6 The Ajax Barbell Company has found that its cost to purchase bars is $40 per order and the carrying charge on average inventory is 10 per cent. They currently purchase $20,000 of bars a year and make these purchases on an optimum basis. They have been offered a 3 per cent discount on the bars if they purchase quarterly. Should they accept?

5-7 A manufacturer of motors uses $50,000 of valves per year. The administrative cost per purchase is $50 and the carrying charge is 20 per cent of the average inventory. The company currently has an optimum purchasing policy but has been offered a 0.2 per cent discount if they purchase 5 times per year. Should the offer be accepted? If not, what counteroffer should be made?

5-8 Average reorder time for the Dobson Company is 5 days. Average use per day is 20 units. Below are facts about use during the reorder period.

Usage during past reorder period	Number of times this quantity was used
70	3
80	5
90	22
100	60
110	6
120	4

Optimum number of orders is 5 per year.

If the out-of-stock cost per unit per time is $50 and the carrying charge per unit per year of safety stock is $15, what level of safety stock should be carried?

5-9 Given the following data for the Miller Company, compute the reorder point:

EOQ = 10 per year
Average use per day = 4 units
Average reorder period = 25 days
Cost to store one unit per year = $5
Cost of being out of stock per unit per time = $20

Usage during reorder period	Probability of this usage
25	.05
50	.10
75	.15
100	.25
125	.20
150	.15
175	.10

5-10 What is the optimum number of units per production run given the following?

N = optimum number of units per production run	
V = production rate in units per day	20
D = sales rate per day	15
R = factory cost per unit	$1,000
C = carrying charge, per cent	10%
A = annual requirement in units	5,000
P = setup cost	$25

BIBLIOGRAPHY

R. H. Bock and W. K. Holstein, *Production Planning and Control* (Columbus, Ohio: Charles E. Merrill Books, Inc., 1963).

E. H. Bowman and R. B. Fetter, *Analysis for Production Management* (Homewood, Ill.: Richard D. Irwin, Inc., 1961).

H. N. Broom, *Production Management* (Homewood, Ill.: Richard D. Irwin, Inc., 1962).

E. S. Buffa, *Models for Production and Operations Management* (New York: John Wiley & Sons, Inc., 1963).

W. T. Morris, *Analysis for Materials Handling Management* (Homewood, Ill.: Richard D. Irwin, Inc., 1962).

A. Shuchman, *Scientific Decision Making in Business* (New York: Holt, Rinehart and Winston, Inc., 1963).

chapter **VECTORS AND**
six **DETERMINANTS**

U p to this point, students with a reasonable competence in ordinary algebra and elementary statistics should have had no difficulty with the text material. As for the topics which now follow, it *is* possible to treat them with no additional mathematical foundation. To do so, however, would involve using a mechanical or "rote" process in many instances. Because this is a dangerous practice, it will not be done.

Instead, some of the "newer" mathematical techniques will be introduced. These will allow students to proceed with a firm grasp and clear understanding of the material to follow. The word *newer* is in quotes because these techniques are not new by any means. In fact, determinants were used by Leibnitz in the seventeenth century. What *is* new is the application of these mathematical tools to the solution of problems which confront management.

Much but not all of the material in Chapters 6 and 7 is prerequisite to an understanding of Chapters 8 to 12. Many students, however, will probably want to go beyond the limitations of this particular text. Chapters 6 and 7 will provide an adequate foundation for more advanced work in the field of operations research.

Vectors, matrix algebra, and determinants will be introduced without the usual confusing mathematical symbols. The absence of such symbols does not reduce the rigor of the exposition in any sense. Indeed, by avoiding complex mathematical symbols we avoid one of the leading obstacles to the teaching and learning of quantitative methods.

The techniques explained in this chapter and in Chapter 7 find their application in linear programming (Chapters 8 and 9), games and strategies (Chapter 10), and Markov analysis (Chapter 11).

INTRODUCTION TO VECTORS

Vectors are useful tools in working out optimum solutions to business problems which involve many variables. For example, consider the business manager who can make several different products in the same plant. Each of these products returns a different per unit profit, each of them requires a different number of labor hours for its production, each has a different material requirement, and each uses different machines for its production. Finding the one best combination of these products to maximize profits is a difficult task if we use only the traditional mathematics we have studied for years. There are literally thousands of combinations of products which could be produced.

When we begin to represent the problem in vector form, however, its solution is highly simplified. For instance, suppose the business manager is looking at his problem of labor availability. Let the heavy vertical line at the right of Figure 6-1 represent the total number of man-hours of labor available to him for production (400). Let the arrow to the left (this arrow is a vector) represent the number of man-hours of labor required to produce, let us say, one chair; in this case, 50 man-hours are required. Obviously then, this manager can produce chairs until his labor availability is exhausted. This is the same as saying that production of chairs can continue until the arrow moves to the point where it touches the vertical line representing the total labor available. The manager could make eight chairs.

In such an example we could, of course, figure the answer with simple arithmetic, without talking about vectors. But now suppose that labor is *not* the only restraint on the production of chairs. Let us assume that capital is in short supply, plant space is limited, materials are not available in infinite supply, and certain machines are not always available for the production of chairs. Then each of these restrictions would be represented by a wall or line much as labor hours were in Figure 6-1. Now suppose that there are *many* products, not just chairs, which we can produce in the plant as long as we do not violate any of the restrictions (use more resources than are available). Then the problem is no longer simple; our traditional arithmetic fails us at this point.

We would have many arrows (or vectors) and many walls (or restrictions), and we would be required to move the arrows until they came in contact with one or more of the restrictions, one at a time, and then calculate which combinations of arrows (or vectors) would return the company the greatest profit. Thus the study of vectors becomes essential to the solution of business problems of this sort.

A vector is a *line with direction and length*. Vectors are generally described by a set of numbers, much the way a point on a map has a set of coordinates so that the map reader can locate the point. The vector illustrated in Figure 6-2 might represent a proposed march along a road x. This vector **(a)** is a line on road x 3 miles in length.

Figure 6-1 **Vector representation of labor availability.**

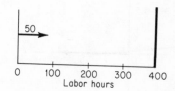

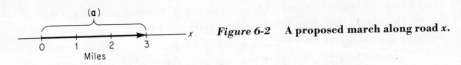

Figure 6-2   **A proposed march along road *x*.**

In vector language, our march would be represented as

$$(3)$$

thus indicating

1. That it is 3 units (miles) in length
2. That we are moving in the *x* direction
3. That we intend to remain on road *x*

Unfortunately, few maps contain just one road. To avoid confusion we must set up a system of vector description which will indicate exactly which direction among many possible directions we propose to take. For instance, in Figure 6-3 we have put another road (*y*) on our map. Assuming we intend to make the same march as before, the representation **(3)** would not clearly indicate which road we plan to use, since one of the marchers could assume that we meant 3 miles on the *y* road if he did not have a copy of Figure 6-3, which is our map.

To avoid such confusion, we would represent the proposed march on Figure 6-3 as follows:

$$\begin{pmatrix} 3 \\ 0 \end{pmatrix}$$

thus indicating that we wish to march 3 miles on road *x* and 0 miles on road *y*. In vector representation, the *x* coordinate is always read before the *y* coordinate. Thus the addition of another road or direction in

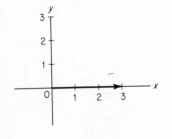

Figure 6-3   **A march along road *x* when there are two possible roads.**

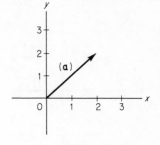

Figure 6-4   **A march through the woods.**

which we might conceivably march requires that the vector describing the march have two coordinates so that we can locate it accurately.

It is not reasonable to expect that all marches (vectors) will lie along one of the roads (*x*) only.   Figure 6-4 shows a vector **(a)** which represents a proposed march "through the woods," so to speak. The vector coordinates for vector **(a)** would be

$$\begin{pmatrix} 2 \\ 2 \end{pmatrix}$$

indicating that its ending point (the arrow at the end of the vector) is located by moving 2 units in a positive direction on the *x* axis and then 2 units in a positive direction on the *y* axis.

A vector may also have one or more negative coordinates, as in Figure 6-5.   Here the vector **(a)** would be described by the notation

$$\begin{pmatrix} 3 \\ -2 \end{pmatrix}$$

indicating that the end of the vector is found by moving 3 units in a positive direction on the *x* axis and then 2 units in a negative direction on the *y* axis.

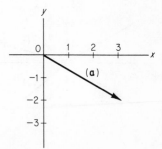

Figure 6-5   **A vector with one positive and one negative coordinate.**

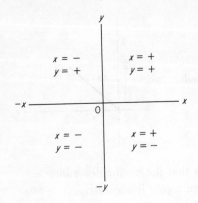

Figure 6-6 **Rules for positive and negative signs.**

You probably remember the simple rules for positive and negative signs shown in Figure 6-6.

The length of a vector which does not lie directly on one of the axes is not immediately known from looking at its vector representation, but it may be computed just like the hypotenuse of a right triangle in geometry. For example, in the case of Figure 6-5, the length of the vector **(a)** is computed as follows:

$$\begin{aligned}
\mathbf{(a)}^2 &= (3^2) + (-2^2) \\
&= 9 + 4 \\
&= 13 \\
\mathbf{(a)} &= \sqrt{13} \\
&= 3.6
\end{aligned} \tag{6-1}$$

Figure 6-7 shows several vectors on a two-dimensional map with the representation for each of them.

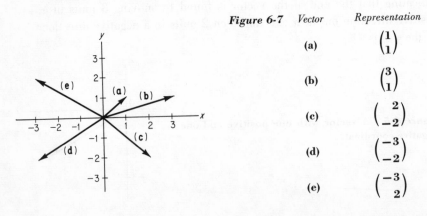

Figure 6-7

Vector	Representation
(a)	$\begin{pmatrix} 1 \\ 1 \end{pmatrix}$
(b)	$\begin{pmatrix} 3 \\ 1 \end{pmatrix}$
(c)	$\begin{pmatrix} 2 \\ -2 \end{pmatrix}$
(d)	$\begin{pmatrix} -3 \\ -2 \end{pmatrix}$
(e)	$\begin{pmatrix} -3 \\ 2 \end{pmatrix}$

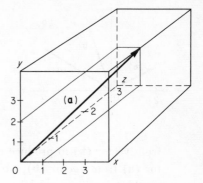

Figure 6-8 Addition of a third dimension *z*.

Three dimensions are represented in Figure 6-8 by the addition of a third dimension *z*. The head of vector **(a)** lies 1 positive unit in the *x* direction, 2 positive units in the *y* direction, and 3 positive units in the *z* direction. It is then expressed in vector notation as

$$\begin{pmatrix} 1 \\ 2 \\ 3 \end{pmatrix}$$

Note that the *x*, *y*, and *z* axes are all perpendicular to each other in Figure 6-8 and that *any* point in that three-dimensional area (often called three-dimensional space) can be represented by three coordinates, one in each dimension.

Addition and subtraction of vectors

Vectors with the same number of dimensions (vectors in the same space) may be added or subtracted by adding or subtracting the coordinates of each vector.

In Figure 6-9, the vectors **(a)** and **(b)** have been added to produce the resultant vector **(c)**. In Figure 6-10, vector **(a)** has been subtracted

Figure 6-9 **a + b = c**

$$\begin{pmatrix} 3 \\ 0 \end{pmatrix} + \begin{pmatrix} 0 \\ 3 \end{pmatrix} = \begin{pmatrix} 3 \\ 3 \end{pmatrix}$$

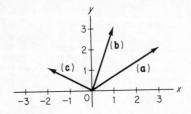

Figure 6-10 **b** − **a** = **c**

$$\begin{pmatrix} 1 \\ 3 \end{pmatrix} - \begin{pmatrix} 3 \\ 2 \end{pmatrix} = \begin{pmatrix} -2 \\ 1 \end{pmatrix}$$

from vector **(b)** to produce the resultant vector **(c)**. In subtracting vector **(a)** from vector **(b)**, we have performed the subtraction just as we would in ordinary algebra, i.e.,

$$1 - 3 = -2$$
$$3 - 2 = 1$$

Vector multiplication

A vector can be multiplied by any number to form a multiple of the original vector. The multiplier in each case is called a *scalar*. This multiplication is accomplished by multiplying *each* coordinate of the vector by the scalar. In Figure 6-11 the vector **(a)** has been multiplied by a scalar, in this case the number 2. The resultant vector **(b)**, $\begin{pmatrix} 4 \\ 4 \end{pmatrix}$, is called a scalar multiple of **(a)**.

If our scalar is a fraction, we may represent the multiplication as in Figure 6-12.

A scalar may be a negative number, in which case the multiplication is as given in Figure 6-13.

Returning to one dimension (one space) for a moment, we can see from Figure 6-14 that all vectors in that space are scalar multiples of

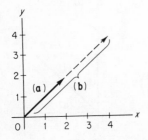

Figure 6-11 $\quad \dfrac{\overset{a}{\times 2}}{b} = \begin{pmatrix} 2 \\ 2 \end{pmatrix} \times 2 = \begin{pmatrix} 4 \\ 4 \end{pmatrix}$

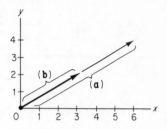

Figure 6-12 $\dfrac{\overset{a}{\times \frac{1}{2}}}{b} = \begin{pmatrix} 6 \\ 4 \end{pmatrix} \times \frac{1}{2} = \begin{pmatrix} 3 \\ 2 \end{pmatrix}$

Note that each coordinate of the vector is multiplied by the scalar in turn.

each other. The same concept is illustrated in Figure 6-15 for vectors lying on the y axis.

The same concept applies also to two space (two dimensions). In Figure 6-16 vectors **(a)** and **(b)** are drawn as reference vectors. Vector **(c)**, or for that matter, any vector in this space, can be described as a scalar multiple of the two reference vectors. These two reference vectors are called a "basis" for the space and are known as basis vectors. In two space, a basis may be thought of as a pair of vectors from which any vector in the space may be derived, through the use of scalars. Obviously three dimensions (three space) would require three reference vectors, one for each of the dimensions. In Figure 6-16, the two basis vectors are perpendicular to each other, and both of them lie on an axis. It is not necessary that basis vectors be perpendicular or that they lie directly on the axes—it is only necessary that they not be scalar multiples of each other. Examples of nonperpendicular basis vectors which do not lie on the axes of the space will be treated later.

In Figure 6-16, vector **(c)** can be formed from the basis vectors **(a)** and **(b)** by finding the appropriate scalars by which to multiply the basis vectors, as follows:

Vector **(c)** $=$ (some scalar)(vector **a**) $+$ (some scalar)(vector **b**)   (6-2)

Let A equal the appropriate scalar for vector **(a)** and B equal the appropriate scalar for vector **(b)**. Then

Figure 6-13 $\dfrac{\overset{a}{\times -1}}{b} = \begin{pmatrix} 3 \\ 2 \end{pmatrix} \times -1 = \begin{pmatrix} -3 \\ -2 \end{pmatrix}$

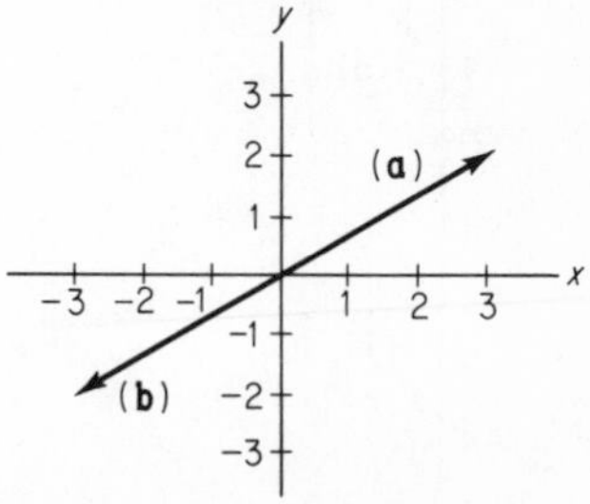

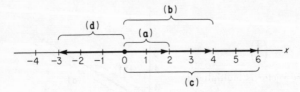

Figure 6-14 **All the vectors are scalar multiples of each other.**

Vector		Scalar					
b = a	×	2	= **(2)** × 2	=	**(4)**
c = a	×	3	= **(2)** × 3	=	**(6)**
a = c	×	⅓	= **(6)** × ⅓	=	**(2)**
b = c	×	⅔	= **(6)** × ⅔	=	**(4)**
d = b	×	−¾	= **(4)** × −¾	=	**(−3)**
d = c	×	−½	= **(6)** × −½	=	**(−3)**

$$(\mathbf{c}) = A(\mathbf{a}) + B(\mathbf{b})$$

$$= A\begin{pmatrix}2\\0\end{pmatrix} + B\begin{pmatrix}0\\3\end{pmatrix}$$

Since we know by looking at Figure 6-16 that vector $(\mathbf{c}) = \begin{pmatrix}3\\4\end{pmatrix}$, we may write it as such:

$$\begin{pmatrix}3\\4\end{pmatrix} = A\begin{pmatrix}2\\0\end{pmatrix} + B\begin{pmatrix}0\\3\end{pmatrix}$$

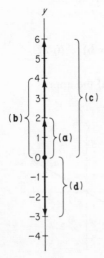

Figure 6-15 **All the vectors are scalar multiples of each other.**

Vector		Scalar					
b = a	×	2	= **(2)** × 2	=	**(4)**
c = a	×	3	= **(2)** × 3	=	**(6)**
a = c	×	⅓	= **(6)** × ⅓	=	**(2)**
b = c	×	⅔	= **(6)** × ⅔	=	**(4)**
d = b	×	−¾	= **(4)** × −¾	=	**(−3)**
d = c	×	−½	= **(6)** × −½	=	**(−3)**

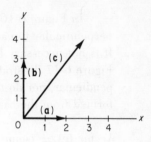

Figure 6-16 (a) and (b) are reference or basis vectors; (c) is a scalar multiple of them.

Clearing yields

$$\begin{pmatrix} 3 \\ 4 \end{pmatrix} = \begin{pmatrix} 2A \\ 0A \end{pmatrix} + \begin{pmatrix} 0B \\ 3B \end{pmatrix}$$

which reduces to two equations,

$$3 = 2A + 0B$$
$$4 = 0A + 3B$$

Solving the top equation yields

$$3 = 2A + 0$$
$$A = 3/2$$

Solving the bottom equation yields

$$4 = 0 + 3B$$
$$B = 4/3$$

thus, $3/2$ and $4/3$ are the correct scalars A and B to form vector **(c)** from the basis vectors **(a)** and **(b)**. This may be checked by substituting the scalars back into the original equation as follows:

$$(c) = A(a) + B(b)$$
$$\begin{pmatrix} 3 \\ 4 \end{pmatrix} = 3/2 \begin{pmatrix} 2 \\ 0 \end{pmatrix} + 4/3 \begin{pmatrix} 0 \\ 3 \end{pmatrix}$$
$$= \begin{pmatrix} 6/2 \\ 0 \end{pmatrix} + \begin{pmatrix} 0 \\ 12/3 \end{pmatrix}$$
$$= \begin{pmatrix} 3 \\ 0 \end{pmatrix} + \begin{pmatrix} 0 \\ 4 \end{pmatrix}$$
$$= \begin{pmatrix} 3 \\ 4 \end{pmatrix}$$

In Figure 6-16, it was seen that the basis vectors **(a)** and **(b)** were perpendicular to each other and lay on the x and y axes, respectively. It is not necessary for basis vectors to be perpendicular to each other. Figure 6-17 illustrates two basis vectors **(a)** and **(b)** which are not perpendicular, nor do they lie on the x and y axes. Vector **(c)** can still be formed from the basis vectors exactly as before.

Vector **(c)** = (some scalar)(vector **a**) + (some scalar)(vector **b**)

Again let A equal the appropriate scalar for vector **(a)** and B equal the appropriate scalar for vector **(b)**. Then

$$\mathbf{(c)} = A\mathbf{(a)} + B\mathbf{(b)}$$

$$= A\begin{pmatrix}5\\2\end{pmatrix} + B\begin{pmatrix}2\\5\end{pmatrix}$$

Because we know by looking at Figure 6-17 that vector **(c)** $= \begin{pmatrix}5\\5\end{pmatrix}$, we may write

$$\begin{pmatrix}5\\5\end{pmatrix} = A\begin{pmatrix}5\\2\end{pmatrix} + B\begin{pmatrix}2\\5\end{pmatrix}$$

Clearing this yields

$$\begin{pmatrix}5\\5\end{pmatrix} = \begin{pmatrix}5A\\2A\end{pmatrix} + \begin{pmatrix}2B\\5B\end{pmatrix}$$

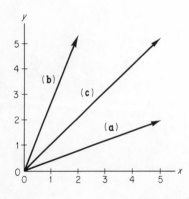

Figure 6-17   **Basis vectors (a) and (b) are not perpendicular and do not lie on the x and y axes.**

$$a = \begin{pmatrix}5\\2\end{pmatrix}$$

$$b = \begin{pmatrix}2\\5\end{pmatrix}$$

$$c = \begin{pmatrix}5\\5\end{pmatrix}$$

which reduces to two equations:

$$5 = 5A + 2B$$
$$5 = 2A + 5B$$

These two equations may be solved simultaneously by multiplying the top one by 2 and the bottom one by 5 and subtracting them:

$$
\begin{array}{rl}
10 = & 10A + \quad 4B \\
(-)\ 25 = & 10A + \quad 25B \\
\hline
-15 = & 0 \quad\ -21B \\
B = & 15/21 \text{ or } 5/7
\end{array}
$$

Substituting $5/7$ back into the top equation in place of B yields

$$
\begin{aligned}
10 &= 10A + 4(5/7) \\
10 &= 10A + 20/7 \\
70/7 &= 10A + 20/7 \\
10A &= 50/7 \\
A &= 5/7
\end{aligned}
$$

Thus, $5/7$ and $5/7$ are the appropriate scalars A and B necessary to form vector **(c)** from the basis vectors **(a)** and **(b)**. This may be checked by substituting the scalars back into the original equation as follows:

$$\textbf{(c)} = A\textbf{(a)} + B\textbf{(b)}$$

$$
\binom{5}{5} = 5/7 \binom{5}{2} + 5/7 \binom{2}{5}
$$

$$
= \binom{25/7}{10/7} + \binom{10/7}{25/7}
$$

$$
= \binom{35/7}{35/7}
$$

$$
= \binom{5}{5}
$$

One additional concept must be discussed in our treatment of vectors and scalars, i.e., the idea of independence. We have already shown how any vector in a space can be a scalar multiple of the basis vectors of that space.

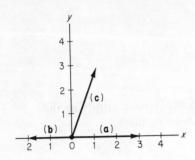

Figure 6-18 Vectors **(a)** and **(b)** are dependent. That is, they are not basis vectors; they are scalar multiples of each other.

$$a = \begin{pmatrix} 3 \\ 0 \end{pmatrix}$$

$$b = \begin{pmatrix} -2 \\ 0 \end{pmatrix}$$

In Figure 6-18 a two-dimensional space is illustrated; it contains two vectors **(a)** and **(b)** and another vector **(c)**. It is impossible to find any scalars which will form vector **(c)** from vectors **(a)** and **(b)**. This fact can be verified by reasoning as follows:

1. Vector **(c)** has a coordinate in the y direction of 3.
2. Vectors **(a)** and **(b)** both have y coordinates of 0.
3. There is no scalar which, when multiplied by 0, will produce 3 as an answer.
4. Therefore vector **(c)** cannot be formed from vectors **(a)** and **(b)**.

The reason for this impossibility is that vectors **(a)** and **(b)** are scalar multiples of each other and thus cannot be a basis; this is shown below:

(Vector **a**)(some scalar) = (vector **b**)

$$\begin{pmatrix} 3 \\ 0 \end{pmatrix}(-2/3) = \begin{pmatrix} -2 \\ 0 \end{pmatrix}$$
$$\begin{pmatrix} -6/3 \\ 0 \end{pmatrix} = \begin{pmatrix} -2 \\ 0 \end{pmatrix} \qquad (6\text{-}3)$$
$$\begin{pmatrix} -2 \\ 0 \end{pmatrix} = \begin{pmatrix} -2 \\ 0 \end{pmatrix}$$

In mathematical language, two vectors that are scalar multiples of each other are said to be *dependent*, and dependent vectors cannot be basis vectors.

To ensure that a proper independent basis exists, it is necessary only to show that the basis vectors are not scalar multiples of each other, i.e., one cannot be formed from the other.

Here are several sets of basis vectors; for the dependent ones, the appropriate scalar which will produce one vector from the other is shown.

Basis vectors

$$\binom{3}{0}; \binom{2}{0} \qquad \binom{3}{0} \times \frac{2}{3} = \binom{2}{0} \qquad \textit{dependent}$$

$$\binom{3}{2}; \binom{1}{4} \qquad \text{There is } \textit{no} \text{ scalar which will form}$$
$$\binom{1}{4} \text{ from } \binom{3}{2} \qquad \textit{independent}$$

$$\binom{2}{1}; \binom{4}{2} \qquad \binom{2}{1} \times 2 = \binom{4}{2} \qquad \textit{dependent}$$

This concludes our brief introduction to vectors and scalars. In subsequent chapters we shall see how the ability to define vectors in a space as scalar multiples of basis vectors, and the ability to move vectors about in a space through multiplication, will have great bearing on the solution of problems which could not otherwise be handled by management.

DETERMINANTS

You may remember from college algebra the lengthy chore involved in solving large sets of simultaneous equations which may have looked something like those below:

$$3x + 2y + 4z = 19$$
$$x - 3y - 6z = -23$$
$$5x + y - 7z = -11$$

The general process you were taught involved solving for one variable in terms of the others (two in this case) and then substituting it back into one of the equations several times in order to find a solution. There is a more efficient method of solving these and other types of problems. Since it will become a valuable tool for us in further analysis, we will now devote some time to the study of determinants.

A determinant is an array of numbers arranged into rows and columns; this array has a numerical value which may be solved for. Determinants will be of particular value to us in solving simultaneous equations.   Here is an example of a determinant with two rows and two columns:

$$\begin{vmatrix} 2 & 3 \\ 1 & 6 \end{vmatrix} \qquad \underset{\xrightarrow{}}{\text{Rows}} \qquad \text{Columns} \downarrow \qquad\qquad (6\text{-}4)$$

This determinant would be referred to as a 2×2 determinant; the number of rows always precedes the number of columns when describing a determinant.

Equation (6-5) illustrates several different determinants with size indicated beside each.   As we shall make use only of square determinants (number of rows = number of columns), we shall limit our illustrations to this type.

$$\begin{vmatrix} 3 & 1 \\ 4 & 2 \end{vmatrix} \qquad 2 \times 2$$

$$\begin{vmatrix} 4 & 1 & 0 \\ 1 & 2 & -4 \\ 3 & 1 & 6 \end{vmatrix} \qquad 3 \times 3 \qquad\qquad (6\text{-}5)$$

$$\begin{vmatrix} 7 & 6 & 1 & 2 \\ 1 & 6 & -3 & 4 \\ 3 & 5 & 2 & 1 \\ 0 & 1 & 2 & 3 \end{vmatrix} \qquad 4 \times 4$$

The location of individual elements within a determinant can be described by indicating the row and column (in that order) in which the elements appear.   In Eq. (6-6) the location of each element in the determinant is described by its row and column coordinates.

$$\begin{vmatrix} 1 & 3 & -2 \\ 4 & 6 & 9 \\ 7 & 5 & 0 \end{vmatrix} \qquad \begin{aligned} 1 &= \text{element} & 1, 1 \\ 4 &= \text{element} & 2, 1 \\ 7 &= \text{element} & 3, 1 \\ 3 &= \text{element} & 1, 2 \\ 6 &= \text{element} & 2, 2 \\ 5 &= \text{element} & 3, 2 \\ -2 &= \text{element} & 1, 3 \\ 9 &= \text{element} & 2, 3 \\ 0 &= \text{element} & 3, 3 \end{aligned} \qquad (6\text{-}6)$$

The diagonals of a determinant

A 2×2 determinant has one primary diagonal and one secondary diagonal, as illustrated in Eq. (6-7).

$$p = \text{primary diagonal} \qquad (6\text{-}7)$$
$$s = \text{secondary diagonal}$$

Determinants larger than 2×2 have multiple primary diagonals and multiple secondary diagonals. Equation (6-8) illustrates the diagonals in a 3×3 determinant.

$$(6\text{-}8)$$

Use of diagonals to find the numerical value of a determinant

The numerical value of a 2×2 determinant may be found by multiplying together the elements lying on the primary diagonal and subtracting from them the product of the elements lying on the secondary diagonal. Equation (6-9) illustrates this operation on several different 2×2 determinants.

Value $= (2)(3) - (1)(2)$
$\quad\quad\; = 6 \quad\;\; - \;\; 2$
$\quad\quad\; = 4$

$$\begin{vmatrix} 2 & -4 \\ -6 & 3 \end{vmatrix}$$

Value $= (3)(2) - (-6)(-4)$ $\qquad\qquad (6\text{-}9)$
$\quad\quad\; = 6 \quad\;\; - \quad\; 24$
$\quad\quad\; = -18$

$$\begin{vmatrix} -6 & -1 \\ 7 & -3 \end{vmatrix}$$

Value $= (-3)(-6) - (7)(-1)$

$\quad\;\; = 18 \qquad\quad\; -(-7)$

$\quad\;\; = 25$

The numerical value of a 3×3 determinant is calculated by a slight modification of the procedure used on a 2×2 determinant. A glance at Eq. (6-8) shows that neither the second nor the third primary and secondary diagonals pass through three elements. This can be rectified by repeating the first two columns of the determinant. This procedure and the resulting calculations are illustrated in Eq. (6-10).

Value $= (p_1 + p_2 + p_3) - (s_1 + s_2 + s_3)$

$$= \overbrace{[(-1)(7)(2)}^{p_1} + \overbrace{(5)(6)(3)}^{p_2} + \overbrace{(-4)(1)(4)]}^{p_3}$$

$$- \overbrace{[(5)(7)(4)}^{s_1} + \overbrace{(-4)(6)(2)}^{s_2} + \overbrace{(-1)(1)(3)]}^{s_3}$$

$= (-14 + 90 - 16) - (140 - 48 - 3)$

$= 60 - 89$

$= -29 =$ value of the determinant $\qquad\qquad$ (6-10)

This method of finding the numerical value of a determinant, although it works for 3×3 determinants, is quite cumbersome for determinants of 3×3 size. It should properly be limited to determinants of size 2×2. Fortunately, there *is* a satisfactory method of finding the numerical value of determinants of *any* size, one which should be used for determinants of size 3×3 and larger. This procedure is called expanding a determinant.

Expanding a determinant to find its numerical value

Any square determinant may be solved for its numerical value by *expanding* it by any one of its rows *or* any one of its columns. Expanding

a determinant by a row simply means choosing any row and then eliminating, in turn, each column which intersects that row.   Expanding by a
column, on the other hand, simply means choosing any column and
eliminating, in turn, each row which intersects that column.

The algebraic sign of each step in the expansion depends upon
which row and which column are eliminated.   If the sum of the numbers of the row and column which are eliminated is an even number
(i.e., row 1 + column 1 = 2), the algebraic sign of that step *is not*
changed; if the sum of the row and column which are eliminated is an
odd number (i.e., row 1 + column 2 = 3), the algebraic sign of that
step *is* changed.

The steps listed below in Eq. (6-11) illustrate the expansion of a
2 × 2 determinant to find its numerical value.   Although the method of
expansion is more useful on determinants of size 3 × 3 and larger, we
begin with a smaller one for the sake of simplicity.   In Eq. (6-11) we
have circled the point at which the row and column to be eliminated in
each step intersect.   Let us expand this determinant by its first row.

Original		2 1	row 1
determinant		3 4	row 2

Step 1

$$\begin{vmatrix} 2 & 1 \\ 3 & 4 \end{vmatrix}$$

Since this determinant is to be expanded by its
first row, we have drawn a line through the first
row.

Step 2

$$\begin{vmatrix} ② & 1 \\ 3 & 4 \end{vmatrix}$$

The first column to intersect the first row is column 1; we have drawn a line through this
column.

Step 3 $4 \times ② = 8$

We then multiply the one element which is not
lined out, 4, by the circled element, 2.

Step 4 $1 + 1 = 2$

We then determine the algebraic sign of step 3
by adding together the number of the row and
the number of the column which were eliminated (row 1 and column 1).

Step 5 $+8$

This is an even number; therefore the sign is
unchanged.   The value of the first part of our
expansion is $+8$.

Step 6 $\begin{vmatrix} 2 & \textcircled{1} \\ 3 & 4 \end{vmatrix}$

The second column to intersect the first row is column 2; we have drawn a line through this column.

Step 7 $3 \times \textcircled{1} = 3$

We then multiply the one element which is not lined out, 3, by the circled element, 1.

Step 8 $1 + 2 = 3$

We then determine the algebraic sign of step 7 by adding together the number of the row and column which were eliminated (row 1 and column 2).

Step 9 -3

This is an odd number; therefore the sign of step 7 is changed. The value of the second part of our expansion is then -3.

Step 10 $8 - 3 = 5$

Adding together the value of the first part of our expansion and the value of the second part of our expansion gives us the value of the determinant, $+5$.

(6-11)

This value can be verified by the diagonal method explained earlier:

Primary diagonal — secondary diagonal = answer
   (4×2) — (3×1) = answer
      8   —   3   = 5

Expansion of a determinant is illustrated for a 3×3 determinant in Eq. (6-12). We have arbitrarily chosen to expand this determinant by its third column. Note that in a 3×3 determinant, when a row and a column are deleted, a 2×2 determinant remains in each case. The value of this 2×2 determinant is then multiplied by the circled element. The procedure for determining the sign remains the same.

	col. 1	col. 2	col. 3	
Original	3	4	1	row 1
determinant	2	0	3	row 2
	-1	5	6	row 3

Step *a*
$$\begin{vmatrix} 3 & 4 & 1 \\ 2 & 0 & 3 \\ -1 & 5 & 6 \end{vmatrix} = \begin{vmatrix} 2 & 0 \\ -1 & 5 \end{vmatrix} \times 1 = 10 \times 1$$
$$= 10$$

Row 1 + col. 3 = even.
Sign is *unchanged*.

Step *b*
$$\begin{vmatrix} 3 & 4 & 1 \\ 2 & 0 & 3 \\ -1 & 5 & 6 \end{vmatrix} = \begin{vmatrix} 3 & 4 \\ -1 & 5 \end{vmatrix} \times 3 = 19 \times 3$$
$$= -57$$

Row 2 + col. 3 = odd.
Sign is *changed*.

Step *c*
$$\begin{vmatrix} 3 & 4 & 1 \\ 2 & 0 & 3 \\ -1 & 5 & 6 \end{vmatrix} = \begin{vmatrix} 3 & 4 \\ 2 & 0 \end{vmatrix} \times 6 = -8 \times 6$$
$$= -48$$

Row 3 + col. 3 = even.
Sign is *unchanged*.

$$\begin{aligned} \text{The sum of steps } a, b, c &= 10 - 57 - 48 \\ &= -95 = \text{value of the} \\ &\qquad\qquad\text{determinant} \end{aligned}$$

(6-12)

In the expansion of a 4 × 4 determinant, the deletion of a row and a column would leave a 3 × 3 determinant to be multiplied by the circled element in each step. Since the value of a 3 × 3 determinant involves a considerable number of calculations itself, one can easily see how the calculation of the value of 4 × 4 and larger determinants becomes quite complex.

Use of determinants to solve simultaneous equations

A set of simultaneous equations such as the following:

$$7X + 6Y + 3Z = 19$$
$$3X + 2Y - 1Z = 7$$
$$1X + 4Y + 2Z = -2$$

(6-13)

may be solved quite easily by using determinants. The value of each of the unknown variables X, Y, and Z is found by solving a particular set of two determinants which form a fraction. In each case (X, Y, and Z), the determinant which forms the denominator of the fraction remains the same, while the determinant which forms the numerator of the fraction changes with each variable.

The determinants which will solve for the unknown X, for example, are represented in Eq. (6-14):

$$X = \frac{\begin{vmatrix} 19 & 6 & 3 \\ 7 & 2 & -1 \\ -2 & 4 & 2 \end{vmatrix}}{\begin{vmatrix} 7 & 6 & 3 \\ 3 & 2 & -1 \\ 1 & 4 & 2 \end{vmatrix}} \quad \begin{matrix} \text{numerator} \\[20pt] \text{denominator} \end{matrix} \tag{6-14}$$

Looking first at the determinant which forms the denominator of this fraction (and the denominator of the fractions for *all* the variables, since it remains unchanged), we can see that it is nothing more than the coefficients of the three unknowns arranged in the same form as they appeared in the original equations. This concept is illustrated in Eq. (6-15):

$$\begin{vmatrix} 7 & 6 & 3 \\ 3 & 2 & -1 \\ 1 & 4 & 2 \end{vmatrix} = \begin{vmatrix} 7 & X \\ 3 & X \\ 1 & X \end{vmatrix} \begin{vmatrix} 6 & Y \\ 2 & Y \\ 4 & Y \end{vmatrix} \begin{vmatrix} 3 & Z \\ -1 & Z \\ 2 & Z \end{vmatrix} \tag{6-15}$$

Now turning our attention to the determinant which forms the numerator of the fraction for the unknown X, we can see from Eq. (6-16) that it is identical to the determinant in Eq. (6-15) except that the column of coefficients for the unknown X has been replaced by the values to the right of the equality signs in the original equations:

$$\begin{vmatrix} 19 & 6 & 3 \\ 7 & 2 & -1 \\ -2 & 4 & 2 \end{vmatrix} \quad \begin{matrix} \text{numerator of the fraction:} \\ \text{for unknown } X \end{matrix} \tag{6-16}$$

In similar fashion, the determinant for the numerator of the fraction for the variable Y is formed by taking the determinant from Eq. (6-15), eliminating the column of coefficients for the unknown Y, and replacing it with the values to the right of the equality signs in the original equations. Equation (6-17) illustrates this process:

$$\begin{vmatrix} 7 & 19 & 3 \\ 3 & 7 & -1 \\ 1 & -2 & 2 \end{vmatrix} \qquad \text{for unknown } Y \qquad (6\text{-}17)$$

In the same manner, the determinant for the numerator of the fraction for the unknown Z is formed in Eq. (6-18):

$$\begin{vmatrix} 7 & 6 & 19 \\ 3 & 2 & 7 \\ 1 & 4 & -2 \end{vmatrix} \qquad \text{for unknown } Z \qquad (6\text{-}18)$$

Equations (6-19) illustrate the solution of the original set of equations by using determinants:

$$7X + 6Y + 3Z = 19$$
$$3X + 2Y - 1Z = 7 \qquad \text{original equations repeated}$$
$$1X + 4Y + 2Z = -2$$

$$X = \frac{\begin{vmatrix} 19 & 6 & 3 \\ 7 & 2 & -1 \\ -2 & 4 & 2 \end{vmatrix}}{\begin{vmatrix} 7 & 6 & 3 \\ 3 & 2 & -1 \\ 1 & 4 & 2 \end{vmatrix}} = \frac{176}{44} = 4$$

$$Y = \frac{\begin{vmatrix} 7 & 19 & 3 \\ 3 & 7 & -1 \\ 1 & -2 & 2 \end{vmatrix}}{\begin{vmatrix} 7 & 6 & 3 \\ 3 & 2 & -1 \\ 1 & 4 & 2 \end{vmatrix}} = \frac{-88}{44} = -2$$

The value obtained for the numerators and denominators may be obtained by the method illustrated in Eq. (6-10), or by expanding each determinant.

$$Z = \frac{\begin{vmatrix} 7 & 6 & 19 \\ 3 & 2 & 7 \\ 1 & 4 & -2 \end{vmatrix}}{\begin{vmatrix} 7 & 6 & 3 \\ 3 & 2 & -1 \\ 1 & 4 & 2 \end{vmatrix}} = \frac{44}{44} = 1$$

$$(6\text{-}19)$$

The accuracy of the process can be verified by testing the values of X, Y, and Z in the original equations.

Mathematical logic of determinants

Now that we have used determinants to solve sets of simultaneous equations, let us take a few paragraphs to explain the logic behind these useful tools. We can begin by using two simultaneous equations as follows:

$$2X_1 + 4X_2 = 6$$
$$8X_1 + 7X_2 = 15 \qquad\qquad (6\text{-}20)$$

These two equations can be rewritten to eliminate the numbers; in their place we put alphabetical letters to represent the values 2, 4, 6, 8, 7, and 15.

$$
\begin{aligned}
a &= 2 \\
b &= 4 \qquad aX_1 + bX_2 = K \qquad\qquad (6\text{-}21)\\
K &= 6 \\
c &= 8 \\
d &= 7 \qquad cX_1 + dX_2 = L \qquad\qquad (6\text{-}22)\\
L &= 15
\end{aligned}
$$

From Eq. (6-21) we can say

$$aX_1 = K - bX_2$$

or $\qquad X_1 = \dfrac{K - bX_2}{a} \qquad\qquad (6\text{-}23)$

and from Eq. (6-22) we can say

$$dX_2 = L - cX_1$$

or $\qquad X_2 = \dfrac{L - cX_1}{d} \qquad\qquad (6\text{-}24)$

Now, if $X_1 = \dfrac{K - bX_2}{a}$

then $\qquad X_1 = \dfrac{K - b[(L - cX_1)/d]}{a}$

Multiplying both sides of this equation by a yields

$$aX_1 = K - b\left(\frac{L - cX_1}{d}\right)$$

When we multiply both sides by d, we get

$$adX_1 = dK - b(L - cX_1)$$

or

$$adX_1 = dK - bL + bcX_1$$

Now, collect X_1 terms on the left-hand side:

$$adX_1 - bcX_1 = dK - bL$$

or

$$X_1(ad - bc) = dK - bL$$

or

$$X_1 = \frac{dK - bL}{ad - bc} \tag{6-25}$$

This is really the expression of the determinants required to solve for X_1:

$$X_1 = \frac{\begin{vmatrix} K & b \\ L & d \end{vmatrix}}{\begin{vmatrix} a & b \\ c & d \end{vmatrix}} \qquad \begin{array}{c} (dK - bL) \\[2mm] (ad - bc) \end{array} \tag{6-26}$$

Now for X_2. In Eq. (6-24) we saw that

$$X_2 = \frac{L - cX_1}{d} \tag{6-24}$$

or

$$X_2 = \frac{L - c[(K - bX_2)/a]}{d}$$

Multiply both sides by d:

$$dX_2 = L - c\left(\frac{K - bX_2}{a}\right)$$

Multiply both sides now by a:

$$adX_2 = aL - c(K - bX_2)$$

Clearing terms, we get

$$adX_2 = aL - cK + cbX_2$$

Now collect X_2 terms on the left-hand side:

$$adX_2 - cbX_2 = aL - cK$$

or

$$X_2(ad - cb) = aL - cK$$

or

$$X_2 = \frac{aL - cK}{ad - cb} \tag{6-27}$$

This is really the expression of the determinants required to solve for X_2:

$$X_2 = \frac{\begin{vmatrix} a & K \\ c & L \end{vmatrix}}{\begin{vmatrix} a & b \\ c & d \end{vmatrix}} \quad \begin{matrix} (aL - cK) \\ \\ (ad - cb) \end{matrix} \tag{6-28}$$

We could, with much tedious algebra, show how the determinants for simultaneous equations in three unknowns [such as those in Eqs. (6-19)] were derived. But as the logic there is identical to the logic in what we have just illustrated, we will omit such unnecessary detail.

PROBLEMS

6-1 Add the following vectors to find the resultant vector:

    a. $\begin{pmatrix} 1 \\ 3 \end{pmatrix} + \begin{pmatrix} 0 \\ 1 \end{pmatrix} =$ *b.* $\begin{pmatrix} 4 \\ 2 \end{pmatrix} + \begin{pmatrix} 1 \\ 3 \end{pmatrix} =$

6-2 Subtract the following vectors:

    a. $\begin{pmatrix} A \\ B \end{pmatrix} - \begin{pmatrix} A \\ -B \end{pmatrix} =$ *b.* $\begin{pmatrix} 3 \\ 2 \end{pmatrix} - \begin{pmatrix} 4 \\ 1 \end{pmatrix} =$

6-3 Multiply the following:

a. $\begin{pmatrix} 1 \\ 3 \end{pmatrix} \times 2 =$

b. $\begin{pmatrix} 2 \\ 4 \end{pmatrix} \times \frac{1}{2} =$

6-4 Find the appropriate scalars, X and Y:

$$\begin{pmatrix} 2 \\ 0 \end{pmatrix} X + \begin{pmatrix} 0 \\ 3 \end{pmatrix} Y = \begin{pmatrix} 4 \\ 3 \end{pmatrix}$$

6-5 Solve for the appropriate scalars, W and Z:

$$\begin{pmatrix} 3 \\ 2 \end{pmatrix} W + \begin{pmatrix} 3 \\ 3 \end{pmatrix} Z = \begin{pmatrix} 5 \\ 4 \end{pmatrix}$$

6-6 Solve for the value of the following determinants:

a. $\begin{vmatrix} p & q \\ r & s \end{vmatrix} =$

b. $\begin{vmatrix} 3 & 6 \\ 8 & 5 \end{vmatrix} =$

6-7 Using determinants, solve for Y_2:

$+ay_1 + by_2 + cy_3 = S$
$-dy_1 - ey_2 + fy_3 = T$
$+gy_1 + hy_2 - iy_3 = Q$

6-8 State the elements which are left in the following determinant (1) when you delete row 1 and column 1, and (2) when you delete row 2 and column 3.

$$\begin{vmatrix} a & b & c \\ d & e & f \\ g & -h & i \end{vmatrix}$$

6-9 Expand the following determinant by the second row and solve for its value.

$$\begin{vmatrix} 3 & 4 & 8 \\ 2 & 4 & -3 \\ 1 & -5 & 6 \end{vmatrix}$$

6-10 Solve for A, B, and C, using determinants.

$2A + B - C = 10$
$A - 2B + 3C = -4$
$A + B + 2C = 10$

BIBLIOGRAPHY

B. Hanes, *Mathematics for Management Science* (Columbus, Ohio: Charles E. Merrill Books, Inc., 1962).

J. E. Howell and D. Teichroew, *Mathematical Analysis for Business Decisions* (Homewood, Ill.: Richard D. Irwin, Inc., 1963).

S. Karlin, *Math Methods and Theory in Games, Programming, and Economics* (Reading, Mass.: Addison-Wesley Publishing Company, Inc., 1959).

R. C. Meier and S. H. Archer, *An Introduction to Mathematics for Business Analysis* (New York: McGraw-Hill Book Company, 1960).

P. Sanders, *Elementary Mathematics* (Scranton, Pa.: International Textbook Company, 1963).

chapter
seven

MATRIX ALGEBRA

$\mathbf{A}$ matrix can be defined as an array of numbers arranged into rows and columns. This array is generally enclosed by two parentheses to differentiate it from a determinant. Whereas a determinant can be solved for its numerical value, a matrix, taken as a whole, has no numerical value. The numbers in a matrix, however, may represent useful business data. When seen as an entire unit, such data may be of considerable help in the solution to certain problems. Equation (7-1) shows a matrix with two rows and three columns.

$$\begin{pmatrix} 1 & 2 & 4 \\ 3 & 5 & 6 \end{pmatrix} \qquad \xrightarrow{\text{Rows}} \qquad \text{Columns} \downarrow \qquad\qquad (7\text{-}1)$$

From our previous study of vectors, we can observe that this matrix is composed of two row vectors placed together, or three column vectors placed together. It would be referred to as a 2×3 matrix, using the same row and column designation that was used in determinants. (The number of rows always precedes the number of columns when describing the dimensions of a matrix.) Equation (7-2) shows the original matrix expressed as (a) three column vectors and (b) two row vectors.

$$(a) \qquad\qquad\qquad (b)$$

$$\begin{pmatrix} 1 \\ 3 \end{pmatrix} \quad \begin{pmatrix} 2 \\ 5 \end{pmatrix} \quad \begin{pmatrix} 4 \\ 6 \end{pmatrix} \qquad \begin{array}{ccc} (1 & 2 & 4) \\ (3 & 5 & 6) \end{array} \qquad (7\text{-}2)$$

To illustrate a business use of matrices, let us assume a simple condition in international trade, i.e., countries X and Y import steel from countries A, B, and C. Country X receives 100 tons annually from A, 200 tons annually from B, and 400 tons annually from C. Y receives 300 tons annually from A, 500 tons annually from B, and 700 tons annually from C. In this written form, it is difficult to visualize the flow of steel from suppliers to users, but if the conditions are expressed in matrix form as in Eq. (7-3), the flows of steel are easily indicated.

$$\begin{array}{cc} & \textit{Suppliers} \\ & \begin{array}{ccc} \text{Country A} & \text{Country B} & \text{Country C} \end{array} \\ \textit{Users} \begin{array}{c} \text{Country X} \\ \text{Country Y} \end{array} & \begin{pmatrix} 100 & 200 & 400 \\ 300 & 500 & 700 \end{pmatrix} \end{array} \qquad (7\text{-}3)$$

The first column in the matrix indicates the total shipments from country A to both users. The second column indicates the total shipments from country B, and the third column indicates the total shipments from

174

country C. The first row indicates the total sources of country X's requirements, and the second row indicates the total sources of country Y's requirements. In this matrix form, the conditions are more easily visualized; the entire situation can be represented briefly, and the relationships are quite evident. Although this is not the *only* use we can make of matrices, further uses will have to wait until we have had some practice in understanding and dealing with matrices.

Equation (7-4) shows several different matrices with size indicated beside each.

$$\begin{pmatrix} 2 & 1 \\ 4 & 6 \end{pmatrix} \qquad 2 \times 2$$

$$\begin{pmatrix} 1 \\ 6 \end{pmatrix} \qquad 2 \times 1$$

$$(1 \quad 2 \quad 6) \qquad 1 \times 3$$

$$(4) \qquad 1 \times 1 \qquad (7\text{-}4)$$

$$\begin{pmatrix} -1 & 4 & 6 & 2 \\ 7 & 0 & -3 & 8 \end{pmatrix} \qquad 2 \times 4$$

$$\begin{pmatrix} 1 \\ -4 \\ 8 \end{pmatrix} \qquad 3 \times 1$$

The location of an individual element within any matrix can be described by indicating the row and column (in that order) in which the element appears. In Eq. (7-5) the location of each element in the matrix is described by its row and column location.

			Row no.	Col. no.
	$1 =$ element no. 1, 1	1	1
	$-1 =$ element no. 2, 1	2	1
	$3 =$ element no. 3, 1	3	1
$\begin{pmatrix} 1 & 2 & 7 \\ -1 & 4 & 6 \\ 3 & 5 & 8 \end{pmatrix}$	$2 =$ element no. 1, 2	1	2
	$4 =$ element no. 2, 2	2	2
	$5 =$ element no. 3, 2	3	2
	$7 =$ element no. 1, 3	1	3
	$6 =$ element no. 2, 3	2	3
	$8 =$ element no. 3, 3	3	3

(7-5)

MATRIX ADDITION AND SUBTRACTION

Matrices with the same dimensions may be added or subtracted by simply adding or subtracting elements which appear in the same location in each matrix. In Eq. (7-6) two 2×2 matrices are added.

Matrix A + *Matrix B* = *Matrix C*

$$\begin{pmatrix} 2 & 6 \\ 3 & 4 \end{pmatrix} + \begin{pmatrix} 1 & 7 \\ 8 & 5 \end{pmatrix} = \begin{pmatrix} 3 & 13 \\ 11 & 9 \end{pmatrix}$$

Matrix A		*Matrix B*		*Matrix C*	
2 (element 1, 1)	+	1 (element 1, 1)	=	3 (element 1, 1)	
6 (element 1, 2)	+	7 (element 1, 2)	=	13 (element 1, 2)	(7-6)
3 (element 2, 1)	+	8 (element 2, 1)	=	11 (element 2, 1)	
4 (element 2, 2)	+	5 (element 2, 2)	=	9 (element 2, 2)	

In like manner matrices may be subtracted from each other. In Eq. (7-7) matrix B is subtracted from matrix A.

Matrix A − *Matrix B* = *Matrix C*

$$\begin{pmatrix} 7 & 6 \\ 8 & 9 \end{pmatrix} - \begin{pmatrix} 1 & 2 \\ 6 & 4 \end{pmatrix} = \begin{pmatrix} 6 & 4 \\ 2 & 5 \end{pmatrix} \tag{7-7}$$

If negative numbers are involved, the addition or subtraction is carried out by observing the algebraic signs, as in Eq. (7-8).

$$\textit{a.} \quad \overset{\textstyle \textit{Matrix A}}{\begin{pmatrix} 1 & 7 & 2 \\ -1 & 4 & 6 \end{pmatrix}} + \overset{\textstyle \textit{Matrix B}}{\begin{pmatrix} -6 & 1 & 3 \\ 0 & 1 & -4 \end{pmatrix}} = \overset{\textstyle \textit{Matrix C}}{\begin{pmatrix} -5 & 8 & 5 \\ -1 & 5 & 2 \end{pmatrix}}$$

$$\tag{7-8}$$

$$\textit{b.} \quad \overset{\textstyle \textit{Matrix A}}{\begin{pmatrix} 1 & 7 & 2 \\ -1 & 4 & 6 \end{pmatrix}} - \overset{\textstyle \textit{Matrix B}}{\begin{pmatrix} -6 & 1 & 3 \\ 0 & 1 & -4 \end{pmatrix}} = \overset{\textstyle \textit{Matrix C}}{\begin{pmatrix} 7 & 6 & -1 \\ -1 & 3 & 10 \end{pmatrix}}$$

MATRIX MULTIPLICATION

Two matrices may be multiplied together if the *number of columns* in the first matrix equals the *number of rows* in the second matrix. If this condition is not met, then the multiplication is impossible. In Eq. (7-9), two matrices, A and B, are shown with their dimensions (the number of rows and columns) indicated directly beneath each of them.

Matrix A   *Matrix **B***

$$\begin{pmatrix} 2 & 1 \\ 4 & 3 \end{pmatrix} \times \begin{pmatrix} 3 & 1 \\ 2 & 1 \end{pmatrix}$$

$$2 \times ② \leftarrow = \rightarrow ② \times 2 \qquad\qquad (7\text{-}9)$$

If the two circled numbers (the number of columns in matrix A and the number of rows in matrix B) are equal, multiplication is possible. This rule is a basic definition in matrix algebra. Its logic will become obvious later in the exposition when you attempt to multiply matrices which do not conform to the rule.

This rule will *always* be satisfied when the two matrices to be multiplied are square and both of the same size, as in Eq. (7-9).

If two matrices placed side by side [as matrices A and B are in Eq. (7-10)] do not satisfy the rule and thus cannot be multiplied, a "swap" of positions may qualify them for multiplication.

Matrix A   *Matrix **B***

$$\begin{pmatrix} 2 \\ 4 \\ 9 \end{pmatrix} \times \begin{pmatrix} 1 & 3 & 7 \\ 4 & 2 & 2 \end{pmatrix} \qquad \textit{cannot} \text{ be multiplied}$$

$$3 \times ① \leftarrow \neq \rightarrow ② \times 3$$

$$\qquad\qquad (7\text{-}10)$$

*Matrix **B***   *Matrix A*

$$\begin{pmatrix} 1 & 3 & 7 \\ 4 & 2 & 2 \end{pmatrix} \times \begin{pmatrix} 2 \\ 4 \\ 9 \end{pmatrix} \qquad \textit{can} \text{ be multiplied}$$

$$2 \times ③ \leftarrow = \rightarrow ③ \times 1$$

In Eq. (7-11) several groups of matrices are shown; the number of columns in the first matrix in each case is compared with the number of rows in the second matrix, and a decision is made as to whether they can be multiplied.

$$\begin{pmatrix} 1 & 2 & 6 \\ 3 & 1 & 4 \end{pmatrix} \times \begin{pmatrix} 1 \\ 2 \\ 6 \end{pmatrix} \qquad can \text{ be multiplied}$$

$$2 \times ③ \leftarrow = \rightarrow ③ \times 1$$

$$(1 \quad 3 \quad 6) \times \begin{pmatrix} 1 \\ 7 \\ -2 \end{pmatrix} \qquad can \text{ be multiplied}$$

$$1 \times ③ \leftarrow = \rightarrow ③ \times 1$$

(7-11)

$$\begin{pmatrix} 1 & 2 & 3 \\ 1 & 2 & 6 \end{pmatrix} \times \begin{pmatrix} 1 & 2 \\ 3 & 1 \end{pmatrix} \qquad cannot \text{ be multiplied}$$

$$2 \times ③ \leftarrow \neq \rightarrow ② \times 2$$

$$\begin{pmatrix} 2 & 1 & 3 \\ 3 & 4 & 4 \\ 2 & 1 & 6 \end{pmatrix} \times \begin{pmatrix} 1 \\ 2 \\ 6 \\ 3 \end{pmatrix} \qquad cannot \text{ be multiplied}$$

$$3 \times ③ \leftarrow \neq \rightarrow ④ \times 1$$

In Eq. (7-12) two matrices A and B are shown. The number of *columns* in matrix A equals the number of *rows* in matrix B; thus they can be multiplied.

Matrix A   *Matrix B*

$$\begin{pmatrix} 5 \\ 6 \end{pmatrix} \quad \times \quad (4 \quad 3)$$

$$2 \times ① \leftarrow = \rightarrow ① \times 2$$

(7-12)

If we compare the outer two numbers of their dimensions as in Eq. (7-13), we obtain some useful information. The *outer two* numbers in the dimensions indicate the size of the matrix which we shall get as an answer; in this case the answer will be a 2×2 matrix. This is another basic help in matrix multiplication.

Matrix A   *Matrix B*

$$\binom{5}{6} \qquad (4 \quad 3)$$

Rows   Cols.

②× 1   1 ×②

The outer dimension of matrix A indicates the number of rows in the answer. The outer dimension of matrix B indicates the number of columns in the answer. (7-13)

The actual multiplication is quite simple now that we know the size of the answer. It is seen that if a 2 × 2 matrix will result, it must contain four elements. Equation (7-14) shows—first in symbolic form, then by numbers—how the multiplication is carried out. To obtain any element in the answer, first determine the *row* and *column* location of that element in the answer. For example, in Eq. (7-14), assume we desired to show how the element *24* was computed in the answer. This element is in the *second row* and the *first column*. To compute it, we simply multiplied the *second row of matrix A* by the *first column of matrix B;* e.g., 6 × 4 = 24.

Matrix A   *Matrix B*   *Matrix C*

$$\binom{a}{b} \times (c \quad d) = \binom{a \times c \quad a \times d}{b \times c \quad b \times d}$$

$$\binom{5}{6} \times (4 \quad 3) = \binom{20 \quad 15}{24 \quad 18}$$

Matrix A	*Matrix B*	*Calculations*	*Location of figure in answer*	
1st row **(5)** ×	1st col. **(4)**	**5 × 4 = 20**	1st row, 1st col.	
1st row **(5)** ×	2d col. **(3)**	**5 × 3 = 15**	1st row, 2d col.	(7-14)
2d row **(6)** ×	1st col. **(4)**	**6 × 4 = 24**	2d row, 1st col.	
2d row **(6)** ×	2d col. **(3)**	**6 × 3 = 18**	2d row, 2d col.	

Equation (7-15) shows the multiplication of two matrices A and B where the product contains only one element. Its location is 1, 1 (first row and first column). The multiplication process involves the multiplication of the first (and only) row of matrix A by the first (and only) column of matrix B. In this and all successive multiplications of matrices together, observe that in each step we are always multiplying some *row* of the first matrix by some *column* of the second matrix.

$$\begin{matrix} Matrix & & Matrix & & Matrix \\ A & \times & B & = & C \end{matrix}$$

$$(3 \quad 2 \quad 1) \times \begin{pmatrix} 4 \\ 5 \\ 6 \end{pmatrix} = \text{answer}$$

$$1 \times 3 \qquad 3 \times 1 \tag{7-15}$$

In Eq. (7-16), the row and column involved both contain three elements. The multiplication is illustrated first by symbols, then by numbers.

$$(a \quad b \quad c) \times \begin{pmatrix} d \\ e \\ f \end{pmatrix}$$

$$ad + be + cf = \text{answer}$$

$$(3 \quad 2 \quad 1) \times \begin{pmatrix} 4 \\ 5 \\ 6 \end{pmatrix}$$

$$\begin{array}{ccccccc} (3 \times 4) & + & (2 \times 5) & + & (1 \times 6) & = & \text{answer} \\ 12 & + & 10 & + & 6 & = & 28 \end{array} \tag{7-16}$$

Several examples of matrix multiplication are illustrated in the following examples.

$$\begin{matrix} Matrix & & Matrix & & Matrix \\ A & & B & & C \end{matrix}$$

$$\textbf{\textit{Example a.}} \quad \begin{pmatrix} 2 & 3 \\ -1 & 4 \end{pmatrix} \times \begin{pmatrix} 5 & 6 \\ 7 & -2 \end{pmatrix} = \begin{pmatrix} 31 & 6 \\ 23 & -14 \end{pmatrix}$$

Matrix *A*	Matrix *B*	Calculations	Location of figure in answer
1st row (2 3) × 1st col. $\begin{pmatrix} 5 \\ 7 \end{pmatrix}$		$(2)(5) + (3)(7) = 31$	1st row, 1st col.
1st row (2 3) × 2d col. $\begin{pmatrix} 6 \\ -2 \end{pmatrix}$		$(2)(6) + (3)(-2) = 6$	1st row, 2d col.
2d row (−1 4) × 1st col. $\begin{pmatrix} 5 \\ 7 \end{pmatrix}$		$(-1)(5) + (4)(7) = 23$	2d row, 1 col.
2d row (−1 4) × 2d col. $\begin{pmatrix} 6 \\ -2 \end{pmatrix}$		$(-1)(6) + (4)(-2)$ $= -14$	2d row, 2d col.

$$\text{Example b.} \quad \underset{\substack{Matrix \\ A}}{\begin{pmatrix} 2 & 1 & -6 \\ -1 & 4 & 3 \\ 6 & 1 & -5 \end{pmatrix}} \times \underset{\substack{Matrix \\ B}}{\begin{pmatrix} 3 \\ -5 \\ 7 \end{pmatrix}} = \underset{\substack{Matrix \\ C}}{\begin{pmatrix} -41 \\ -2 \\ -22 \end{pmatrix}}$$

Matrix A	Matrix B	Calculations	Location of figure in answer
1st row $(2 \quad 1 \quad -6)$ × 1st col.	$\begin{pmatrix} 3 \\ -5 \\ 7 \end{pmatrix}$	$(2)(3) + (1)(-5)$ $+ (-6)(7) = -41$	1st row, 1st col.
2d row $(-1 \quad 4 \quad 3)$ × 1st col.	$\begin{pmatrix} 3 \\ -5 \\ 7 \end{pmatrix}$	$(-1)(3) + (4)(-5)$ $+ (3)(7) = -2$	2d row, 1st col.
3d row $(6 \quad 1 \quad -5)$ × 1st col.	$\begin{pmatrix} 3 \\ -5 \\ 7 \end{pmatrix}$	$(6)(3) + (1)(-5)$ $+ (-5)(7) = -22$	3d row, 1st col.

$$\text{Example c.} \quad \underset{\substack{Matrix \\ A}}{\begin{pmatrix} 1 & 4 & -2 \\ 3 & 2 & 0 \\ 6 & 5 & 7 \end{pmatrix}} \times \underset{\substack{Matrix \\ B}}{\begin{pmatrix} -3 & 8 & -5 \\ 0 & 9 & -4 \\ -1 & 10 & 11 \end{pmatrix}} = \underset{\substack{Matrix \\ C}}{\begin{pmatrix} -1 & 24 & -43 \\ -9 & 42 & -23 \\ -25 & 163 & 27 \end{pmatrix}}$$

Matrix A	Matrix B	Calculations	Location of figure in answer
1st row $(1 \quad 4 \quad -2)$ × 1st col.	$\begin{pmatrix} -3 \\ 0 \\ -1 \end{pmatrix}$	$(1)(-3) + (4)(0)$ $+ (-2)(-1) = -1$	1st row, 1st col.
1st row $(1 \quad 4 \quad -2)$ × 2d col.	$\begin{pmatrix} 8 \\ 9 \\ 10 \end{pmatrix}$	$(1)(8) + (4)(9)$ $+ (-2)(10) = 24$	1st row, 2d col.
1st row $(1 \quad 4 \quad -2)$ × 3d col.	$\begin{pmatrix} -5 \\ -4 \\ 11 \end{pmatrix}$	$(1)(-5) + (4)(-4)$ $+ (-2)(11) = -43$	1st row, 3d col.
2d row $(3 \quad 2 \quad 0)$ × 1st col.	$\begin{pmatrix} -3 \\ 0 \\ -1 \end{pmatrix}$	$(3)(-3) + (2)(0)$ $+ (0)(-1) = -9$	2d row, 1st col.

2d row **(3 2 0)** × 2d col. $\begin{pmatrix} 8 \\ 9 \\ 10 \end{pmatrix}$ $\begin{matrix} (3)(8) + (2)(9) \\ + (0)(10) = 42 \end{matrix}$ 2d row, 2d col.

2d row **(3 2 0)** × 3d col. $\begin{pmatrix} -5 \\ -4 \\ 11 \end{pmatrix}$ $\begin{matrix} (3)(-5) + (2)(-4) \\ + (0)(11) = -23 \end{matrix}$ 2d row, 3d col.

3d row **(6 5 7)** × 1st col. $\begin{pmatrix} -3 \\ 0 \\ -1 \end{pmatrix}$ $\begin{matrix} (6)(-3) + (5)(0) \\ + (7)(-1) = -25 \end{matrix}$ 3d row, 1st col.

3d row **(6 5 7)** × 2d col. $\begin{pmatrix} 8 \\ 9 \\ 10 \end{pmatrix}$ $\begin{matrix} (6)(8) + (5)(9) \\ + (7)(10) = 163 \end{matrix}$ 3d row, 2d col.

3d row **(6 5 7)** × 3d col. $\begin{pmatrix} -5 \\ -4 \\ 11 \end{pmatrix}$ $\begin{matrix} (6)(-5) + (5)(-4) \\ + (7)(11) = 27 \end{matrix}$ 3d row, 3d col.

Example d. A contractor calculates the material requirements of several types of homes as follows:

Material (tons)	Ranch	Colonial	Modern	Cape Cod	
Brick	7	4	10	2	
Lumber	2	12	1	6	Material
Steel	1	0	4	0	matrix
Concrete	6	5	3	2	

Type home

His building schedule for the next three-month period is:

Ranch	4	houses	
Colonial	2	houses	Sales or building
Modern	3	houses	matrix
Cape Cod	5	houses	

Multiplying the material matrix by the building schedule matrix will yield the total number of tons of each material required to build all the homes.

Tons

$$\begin{pmatrix} 7 & 4 & 10 & 2 \\ 2 & 12 & 1 & 6 \\ 1 & 0 & 4 & 0 \\ 6 & 5 & 3 & 2 \end{pmatrix} \times \begin{pmatrix} 4 \\ 2 \\ 3 \\ 5 \end{pmatrix} = \begin{pmatrix} 76 \\ 65 \\ 16 \\ 53 \end{pmatrix} \begin{matrix} \text{brick} \\ \text{lumber} \\ \text{steel} \\ \text{concrete} \end{matrix}$$

If the contractor knows that the cost of materials is as follows, another matrix multiplication will yield the total cost of the materials for all homes.

Brick $150/ton
Lumber $300/ton
Steel $600/ton
Concrete $ 40/ton

$$
\begin{array}{cccc}
B & L & S & C \\
(\$150 & \$300 & \$600 & \$40)
\end{array}
\times
\begin{pmatrix} 76 \\ 65 \\ 16 \\ 53 \end{pmatrix}
= (\$42{,}620)
\quad
\begin{array}{l}
\text{Total cost of} \\
\text{direct materials} \\
\text{for all homes}
\end{array}
$$

$$
1 \times ④ \leftarrow = \rightarrow ④ \times 1
$$

It is obvious that this particular problem can be solved easily by using ordinary arithmetic; in fact, ordinary arithmetic may yield the correct solution much faster than matrix algebra. This example, however, is presented to show that matrix algebra, instead of being some abstract mathematical concept, is a useful tool for doing various calculations.

THE TRANSPOSE OF A MATRIX

The transpose of a matrix is formed by interchanging the rows with the columns. In Eq. (7-17), the transpose of a 2×3 matrix has been formed. Note that the *first row* of the original matrix is now the *first column* of the transpose and that the *second row* of the original matrix is now the *second column* of the transpose.

Original matrix   Transpose

$$
\begin{pmatrix} 3 & -2 & 1 \\ 4 & 6 & 9 \end{pmatrix}
\qquad
\begin{pmatrix} 3 & 4 \\ -2 & 6 \\ 1 & 9 \end{pmatrix}
\tag{7-17}
$$

Forming this transpose alters the dimensions of the original matrix: Whereas the original matrix was of dimension 2×3, the transpose is of dimension 3×2. If the original matrix had been square, i.e., 2×2,

3 × 3, etc., then forming the transpose would not, of course, have altered the dimensions of the original matrix; there would have been as many columns as there were rows.

The significance of the transpose may be illustrated by the following example. The original matrix below illustrates the shipments of steel from suppliers A, B, and C to users X and Y. All quantities are in tons.

Original matrix

Suppliers

$$\text{Users} \quad \begin{array}{c} X \\ Y \end{array} \begin{pmatrix} \overset{A}{100} & \overset{B}{200} & \overset{C}{400} \\ 300 & 500 & 700 \end{pmatrix}$$

Transpose

Users

$$\text{Suppliers} \quad \begin{array}{c} A \\ B \\ C \end{array} \begin{pmatrix} \overset{X}{100} & \overset{Y}{300} \\ 200 & 500 \\ 400 & 700 \end{pmatrix}$$

In the original matrix, the rows represent use. In the transpose, the rows represent shipments. In the original matrix, the columns represent shipments; in the transpose, the columns represent use. In other words, the transpose is a method often used to show data in a different form.

COFACTORS

Any square matrix of size 2 × 2 or larger may be separated into its cofactors. A cofactor is that element or group of elements which remains when a row and column have been removed from the matrix. In Eq. (7-18) the cofactor of the circled element ② has been formed.

$$\begin{array}{c} \text{Original} \\ \text{matrix} \end{array} - \begin{array}{c} \text{Row and column} \\ \text{removed} \end{array} = \text{Cofactor}$$

$$\begin{pmatrix} ② & 1 \\ 4 & 3 \end{pmatrix} \qquad \begin{pmatrix} 2 & 1 \\ 4 & \end{pmatrix} \qquad \begin{pmatrix} & \\ & 3 \end{pmatrix} \qquad (7\text{-}18)$$

The 2×2 matrix in Eq. (7-18) would have four cofactors as follows:

Element	Row and column removed	Cofactor
$\begin{pmatrix} 2 & 1 \\ 4 & 3 \end{pmatrix}$	$\begin{pmatrix} 2 & 1 \\ 4 & \end{pmatrix}$	$\begin{pmatrix} & \\ & 3 \end{pmatrix}$
$\begin{pmatrix} 2 & 1 \\ 4 & 3 \end{pmatrix}$	$\begin{pmatrix} 2 & 1 \\ & 3 \end{pmatrix}$	$\begin{pmatrix} & \\ -4 & \end{pmatrix}$
$\begin{pmatrix} 2 & 1 \\ 4 & 3 \end{pmatrix}$	$\begin{pmatrix} 2 & \\ 4 & 3 \end{pmatrix}$	$\begin{pmatrix} & -1 \\ & \end{pmatrix}$
$\begin{pmatrix} 2 & 1 \\ 4 & 3 \end{pmatrix}$	$\begin{pmatrix} & 1 \\ 4 & 3 \end{pmatrix}$	$\begin{pmatrix} 2 & \\ & \end{pmatrix}$

Observe that the sign of two of the cofactors was changed in the process of forming them. The sign of the cofactor is determined by adding together the location numbers of the row and column which have been removed. If the sum is an *even* number, the sign of the cofactor is *unchanged;* if the sum is an *odd* number, the sign of the cofactor is *changed.* Equation (7-19) illustrates this procedure.

$\begin{pmatrix} 3 & -1 \\ 4 & 7 \end{pmatrix}$ Original matrix

$\begin{pmatrix} & \\ & 7 \end{pmatrix}$ Cofactor formed by deleting 1st row and 1st column. $1 + 1 =$ even. The sign is *unchanged.*

$\begin{pmatrix} & \\ -4 & \end{pmatrix}$ Cofactor formed by deleting 1st row and 2d column. $1 + 2 =$ odd. The sign is *changed.*

$\begin{pmatrix} & 1 \\ & \end{pmatrix}$ Cofactor formed by deleting 2d row and 1st column. $2 + 1 =$ odd. The sign is *changed.*

$\begin{pmatrix} 3 & \\ & \end{pmatrix}$ Cofactor formed by deleting 2d row and 2d column. $2 + 2 =$ even. The sign is *unchanged.*

(7-19)

THE MATRIX OF COFACTORS

The matrix of cofactors must be computed in order to form the adjoint of a matrix. Both of these concepts will be useful in our study of games and strategies. If each of the numbers in the matrix originally shown in Eq. (7-18) were replaced by its cofactor, the matrix of cofactors would be formed. This is done in Eq. (7-20).

Original matrix $\begin{pmatrix} 2 & 1 \\ 4 & 3 \end{pmatrix}$ $\qquad$ $\begin{pmatrix} a & b \\ c & d \end{pmatrix}$

Rows and columns removed are shown

$$\overset{a}{} \quad \overset{b}{} \quad \overset{c}{} \quad \overset{d}{}$$
$$\begin{pmatrix} 2 & 1 \\ 4 & \end{pmatrix} \begin{pmatrix} 2 & 1 \\ & 3 \end{pmatrix} \begin{pmatrix} 2 & \\ 4 & 3 \end{pmatrix} \begin{pmatrix} & 1 \\ 4 & 3 \end{pmatrix}$$

Cofactors

$$\overset{a}{} \quad \overset{b}{} \quad \overset{c}{} \quad \overset{d}{}$$
$$\begin{pmatrix} & \\ & 3 \end{pmatrix} \begin{pmatrix} & \\ -4 & \end{pmatrix} \begin{pmatrix} & -1 \end{pmatrix} \begin{pmatrix} 2 & \end{pmatrix}$$

Original numbers a, b, c, d have been replaced by their cofactors $\begin{pmatrix} 3 & -4 \\ -1 & 2 \end{pmatrix} = \begin{matrix} \text{matrix of} \\ \text{cofactors} \end{matrix}$ $\qquad$ (7-20)

In square matrices larger than 2×2, the deletion of a row and a column which intersect each other forms a cofactor of size 2×2 or larger, as illustrated in Eq. (7-21).

Original matrix

Cofactor formed by deleting
1st row and 1st column

$$\begin{pmatrix} ① & 3 & 6 \\ 2 & 4 & 8 \\ 7 & 5 & 9 \end{pmatrix} \qquad \begin{pmatrix} & & \\ & 4 & 8 \\ & 5 & 9 \end{pmatrix} \qquad (7\text{-}21)$$

Because the single circled element ① in Eq. (7-21) cannot be replaced in the matrix of cofactors by its entire cofactor, which is

4 8
5 9

it is replaced by the value of the determinant of its cofactor:

$\begin{vmatrix} 4 & 8 \\ 5 & 9 \end{vmatrix} = -4$ (The sign of the cofactor will reflect the location of the row and column removed.)

Equations (7-22) and (7-23) illustrate the method used to form the matrix of cofactors for 3×3 and larger square matrices.

Original matrix $\begin{pmatrix} 2 & 3 & 6 \\ 1 & 4 & 3 \\ 0 & 5 & 7 \end{pmatrix}$

Row and column removed	Cofactors	Numerical value of cofactors

$\begin{pmatrix} ② & 3 & 6 \\ 1 & & \\ 0 & & \end{pmatrix}$ $\begin{pmatrix} & & \\ & 4 & 3 \\ & 5 & 7 \end{pmatrix}$ $\begin{vmatrix} 4 & 3 \\ 5 & 7 \end{vmatrix} = 13$ $\quad 1 + 1 = $ even; sign unchanged

$\begin{pmatrix} 2 & & \\ ① & 4 & 3 \\ 0 & & \end{pmatrix}$ $\begin{pmatrix} & 3 & 6 \\ & & \\ & 5 & 7 \end{pmatrix}$ $\begin{vmatrix} 3 & 6 \\ 5 & 7 \end{vmatrix} = 9$ $\quad 2 + 1 = $ odd; sign changed

$\begin{pmatrix} 2 & & \\ 1 & & \\ ⓪ & 5 & 7 \end{pmatrix}$ $\begin{pmatrix} & 3 & 6 \\ & 4 & 3 \\ & & \end{pmatrix}$ $\begin{vmatrix} 3 & 6 \\ 4 & 3 \end{vmatrix} = -15$ $\quad 3 + 1 = $ even; sign unchanged

$\begin{pmatrix} 2 & ③ & 6 \\ & 4 & \\ & 5 & \end{pmatrix}$ $\begin{pmatrix} & & \\ 1 & & 3 \\ 0 & & 7 \end{pmatrix}$ $\begin{vmatrix} 1 & 3 \\ 0 & 7 \end{vmatrix} = -7$ $\quad 1 + 2 = $ odd; sign changed

$\begin{pmatrix} & 3 & \\ 1 & ④ & 3 \\ & 5 & \end{pmatrix}$ $\begin{pmatrix} 2 & & 6 \\ & & \\ 0 & & 7 \end{pmatrix}$ $\begin{vmatrix} 2 & 6 \\ 0 & 7 \end{vmatrix} = 14$ $\quad 2 + 2 = $ even; sign unchanged

$\begin{pmatrix} & 3 & \\ & 4 & \\ 0 & ⑤ & 7 \end{pmatrix}$ $\begin{pmatrix} 2 & & 6 \\ 1 & & 3 \\ & & \end{pmatrix}$ $\begin{vmatrix} 2 & 6 \\ 1 & 3 \end{vmatrix} = 0$ $\quad 3 + 2 = $ odd; sign changed

$$\begin{pmatrix} 2 & 3 & ⑥ \\ & 3 & \\ & 7 \end{pmatrix} \begin{pmatrix} & & \\ 1 & 4 \\ 0 & 5 \end{pmatrix} \qquad \begin{vmatrix} 1 & 4 \\ 0 & 5 \end{vmatrix} = 5 \qquad \begin{array}{l} 1 + 3 = \text{even;} \\ \text{sign unchanged} \end{array}$$

$$\begin{pmatrix} & 6 \\ 1 & 4 & ③ \\ & 7 \end{pmatrix} \begin{pmatrix} 2 & 3 \\ & \\ 0 & 5 \end{pmatrix} \qquad \begin{vmatrix} 2 & 3 \\ 0 & 5 \end{vmatrix} = -10 \qquad \begin{array}{l} 2 + 3 = \text{odd;} \\ \text{sign changed} \end{array}$$

$$\begin{pmatrix} & 6 \\ & 3 \\ 0 & 5 & ⑦ \end{pmatrix} \begin{pmatrix} 2 & 3 \\ 1 & 4 \\ & \end{pmatrix} \qquad \begin{vmatrix} 2 & 3 \\ 1 & 4 \end{vmatrix} = 5 \qquad \begin{array}{l} 3 + 3 = \text{even;} \\ \text{sign unchanged} \end{array}$$

$$(7\text{-}22)$$

Replacing the 9 circled elements with the numerical value of their co-factors forms the matrix of cofactors.

$$\begin{pmatrix} 13 & -7 & 5 \\ 9 & 14 & -10 \\ -15 & 0 & 5 \end{pmatrix} = \text{matrix of cofactors} \qquad (7\text{-}23)$$

The matrix of cofactors of any square matrix larger than 3×3 is formed in the same way except that more calculations are involved. For instance, in the case of a 4×4 matrix, 16 steps would be involved; deleting each row and column would leave 16 cofactors of size 3×3 to be reckoned with.

THE ADJOINT OF A MATRIX

In our study of competitive games and optimum strategies, we shall have occasion to use the adjoint of a matrix. This is nothing more than the *transpose* of the *matrix of cofactors*. Since we already know how to form (1) the transpose of any matrix and (2) the matrix of cofactors, a simple juxtaposition of rows and columns will form the adjoint. In Eq. (7-24) we have taken the two matrices used in Eqs. (7-20) and (7-22), followed them with their matrices of cofactors, and then interchanged their rows and columns to form their adjoints.

Original matrix	Matrix of cofactors	Adjoint

$$a. \quad \begin{pmatrix} 2 & 1 \\ 4 & 3 \end{pmatrix} \qquad \begin{pmatrix} 3 & -4 \\ -1 & 2 \end{pmatrix} \qquad \begin{pmatrix} 3 & -1 \\ -4 & 2 \end{pmatrix}$$

$$b. \quad \begin{pmatrix} 2 & 3 & 6 \\ 1 & 4 & 3 \\ 0 & 5 & 7 \end{pmatrix} \begin{pmatrix} 13 & -7 & 5 \\ 9 & 14 & -10 \\ -15 & 0 & 5 \end{pmatrix} \begin{pmatrix} 13 & 9 & -15 \\ -7 & 14 & 0 \\ 5 & -10 & 5 \end{pmatrix} \quad (7\text{-}24)$$

THE IDENTITY OR UNIT MATRIX

A square matrix whose primary diagonal is formed entirely of ones and in which the remainder of the terms are zeros is called a unit matrix or an identity matrix. Equation (7-25) illustrates three identity matrices.

$$a. \quad \begin{pmatrix} 1 & 0 \\ 0 & 1 \end{pmatrix} \qquad b. \quad \begin{pmatrix} 1 & 0 & 0 \\ 0 & 1 & 0 \\ 0 & 0 & 1 \end{pmatrix} \qquad c. \quad \begin{pmatrix} 1 & 0 & 0 & 0 \\ 0 & 1 & 0 & 0 \\ 0 & 0 & 1 & 0 \\ 0 & 0 & 0 & 1 \end{pmatrix} \quad (7\text{-}25)$$

$$2 \times 2 \qquad\qquad 3 \times 3 \qquad\qquad\qquad 4 \times 4$$

Observe that an identity matrix is nothing more than a combination of vectors (each of *one unit* in length) which form a convenient basis for a space. Since each axis of the space is one unit in length, finding scalar multiples of these bases is greatly facilitated.

$$2 \text{ space} \quad \begin{pmatrix} 1 & 0 \\ 0 & 1 \end{pmatrix} \qquad \mathbf{a} = \begin{pmatrix} 1 \\ 0 \end{pmatrix} \qquad \mathbf{b} = \begin{pmatrix} 0 \\ 1 \end{pmatrix}$$

$$(7\text{-}26)$$

$$3 \text{ space} \quad \begin{pmatrix} 1 & 0 & 0 \\ 0 & 1 & 0 \\ 0 & 0 & 1 \end{pmatrix} \qquad \mathbf{a} = \begin{pmatrix} 1 \\ 0 \\ 0 \end{pmatrix} \qquad \mathbf{b} = \begin{pmatrix} 0 \\ 1 \\ 0 \end{pmatrix} \qquad \mathbf{c} = \begin{pmatrix} 0 \\ 0 \\ 1 \end{pmatrix}$$

(a)

(b)

As has been demonstrated previously, any vector in the space formed by the basis vectors can be shown to be a scalar multiple of the basis vectors. Using identity matrices as convenient bases is an integral part of the material to follow on matrix inversion, which is itself the basic idea in linear programming.

INVERSION OF A MATRIX

Multiplying the vector $(1 \quad 2)$ by the matrix $\begin{pmatrix} 2 & 3 \\ 4 & 5 \end{pmatrix}$ will change the vector $(1 \quad 2)$ to a new vector in two space, since the matrix acts as a combination of scalars. This multiplication has been accomplished in Eq. (7-27), using the same multiplication methods illustrated earlier in the chapter.

$$(1 \quad 2) \times \begin{pmatrix} 2 & 3 \\ 4 & 5 \end{pmatrix} = (10 \quad 13)$$

$$1 \times ② \leftarrow = \rightarrow ② \times 2 \qquad (7\text{-}27)$$

Multiplying the *inverse* of the matrix (steps in computing the inverse follow in just a moment) by the new vector $(10 \quad 13)$ will return it to its original point, $(1 \quad 2)$. Thus, the inverse of a matrix is used to return a vector *from* a point in space *to* its original location.

An inverse is formed by performing certain procedures on the original matrix. There are eight of these procedures, four involving the rows and four involving the columns. When forming an inverse, one must limit himself to *row procedures or column procedures;* he must never combine the two.

Row and column procedures

1. One row can be interchanged with another row.
2. One column can be interchanged with another column.
3. A row can be multiplied by a constant.
4. A column can be multiplied by a constant.
5. One row can be added to or subtracted from another row.
6. One column can be added to or subtracted from another column.
7. A multiple of a row can be added to or subtracted from another row.

8. A multiple of a column can be added to or subtracted from another column.

To invert a matrix, we first place beside it an identity matrix of the same size. The row *or* column procedures are then performed on both matrices *simultaneously*. When the original matrix has been altered by these procedures so that it becomes an identity matrix, the identity matrix which was originally placed there will be the inverse. In short, then, the object is to convert the original matrix into an identity matrix by performing the row or column procedures upon it. Equation (7-28) illustrates the inversion of the 2×2 matrix from Eq. (7-27) using *row* operations.

Original matrix	Identity matrix	Steps performed
$\begin{pmatrix} 2 & 3 \\ 4 & 5 \end{pmatrix}$	$\begin{pmatrix} 1 & 0 \\ 0 & 1 \end{pmatrix}$	1. Identity matrix placed next to original matrix.
$\begin{pmatrix} 1 & \frac{3}{2} \\ 4 & 5 \end{pmatrix}$	$\begin{pmatrix} \frac{1}{2} & 0 \\ 0 & 1 \end{pmatrix}$	2. 1st row multiplied by $\frac{1}{2}$ (procedure 3).
$\begin{pmatrix} 1 & \frac{3}{2} \\ 0 & -1 \end{pmatrix}$	$\begin{pmatrix} \frac{1}{2} & 0 \\ -2 & 1 \end{pmatrix}$	3. Multiply 1st row by 4 and subtract it from 2d row (procedure 7).
$\begin{pmatrix} 1 & \frac{3}{2} \\ 0 & 1 \end{pmatrix}$	$\begin{pmatrix} \frac{1}{2} & 0 \\ 2 & -1 \end{pmatrix}$	4. Multiply row 2 by (-1) (procedure 3).
$\begin{pmatrix} 1 & 0 \\ 0 & 1 \end{pmatrix}$	$\begin{pmatrix} -\frac{5}{2} & \frac{3}{2} \\ 2 & -1 \end{pmatrix}$	5. Subtract $\frac{3}{2}$ row 2 from row 1 (procedure 7).

$$(7\text{-}28)$$

Since the original matrix is now an identity matrix, we know our process is complete. Thus the inverse of the original matrix is

$$\begin{pmatrix} -\frac{5}{2} & \frac{3}{2} \\ 2 & -1 \end{pmatrix}$$

We can check our calculations by multiplying the inverse by the vector **(10 13)** [from Eq. (7-27)] to see if the multiplication will drive the vector back to its original point, **(1 2)**.

$$\mathbf{(10 \quad 13)} \times \begin{pmatrix} -\frac{5}{2} & \frac{3}{2} \\ 2 & -1 \end{pmatrix} = \mathbf{(1 \quad 2)} \tag{7-29}$$

Thus, the inverse $\begin{pmatrix} -\frac{5}{2} & \frac{3}{2} \\ 2 & -1 \end{pmatrix}$ represents that group of scalars which will drive the vector $(10 \quad 13)$ back to its original point $(1 \quad 2)$.

Any square matrix the value of whose determinant is not zero has an inverse. Equation (7-30) shows the inversion of a 3×3 matrix using column procedures.

Original matrix	Identity matrix	Steps performed
$\begin{pmatrix} 1 & 2 & 1 \\ 1 & 1 & 2 \\ 2 & 3 & 4 \end{pmatrix}$	$\begin{pmatrix} 1 & 0 & 0 \\ 0 & 1 & 0 \\ 0 & 0 & 1 \end{pmatrix}$	1. Identity matrix added to original matrix.
$\begin{pmatrix} 1 & 0 & 1 \\ 1 & -1 & 2 \\ 2 & -1 & 4 \end{pmatrix}$	$\begin{pmatrix} 1 & -2 & 0 \\ 0 & 1 & 0 \\ 0 & 0 & 1 \end{pmatrix}$	2. Multiply column 1 by 2 and subtract it from column 2 (procedure 8).
$\begin{pmatrix} 1 & 0 & 1 \\ 0 & -1 & 2 \\ 1 & -1 & 4 \end{pmatrix}$	$\begin{pmatrix} -1 & -2 & 0 \\ 1 & 1 & 0 \\ 0 & 0 & 1 \end{pmatrix}$	3. Add column 2 to column 1 (procedure 6).
$\begin{pmatrix} 1 & 0 & 0 \\ 0 & -1 & 2 \\ 1 & -1 & 3 \end{pmatrix}$	$\begin{pmatrix} -1 & -2 & 1 \\ 1 & 1 & -1 \\ 0 & 0 & 1 \end{pmatrix}$	4. Subtract column 1 from column 3 (procedure 6).
$\begin{pmatrix} 1 & 0 & 0 \\ 0 & -1 & 0 \\ 1 & -1 & 1 \end{pmatrix}$	$\begin{pmatrix} -1 & -2 & -3 \\ 1 & 1 & 1 \\ 0 & 0 & 1 \end{pmatrix}$	5. Add 2 times column 2 to column 3 (procedure 8).
$\begin{pmatrix} 1 & 0 & 0 \\ 0 & -1 & 0 \\ 1 & 0 & 1 \end{pmatrix}$	$\begin{pmatrix} -1 & -5 & -3 \\ 1 & 2 & 1 \\ 0 & 1 & 1 \end{pmatrix}$	6. Add column 3 to column 2 (procedure 6).
$\begin{pmatrix} 1 & 0 & 0 \\ 0 & -1 & 0 \\ 0 & 0 & 1 \end{pmatrix}$	$\begin{pmatrix} 2 & -5 & -3 \\ 0 & 2 & 1 \\ -1 & 1 & 1 \end{pmatrix}$	7. Subtract column 3 from column 1 (procedure 6).
$\begin{pmatrix} 1 & 0 & 0 \\ 0 & 1 & 0 \\ 0 & 0 & 1 \end{pmatrix}$	$\begin{pmatrix} 2 & 5 & -3 \\ 0 & -2 & 1 \\ -1 & -1 & 1 \end{pmatrix}$	8. Multiply column 2 by -1 (procedure 4).

$$(7\text{-}30)$$

To check our calculations this time, we shall use a second method, i.e., multiplying the inverse times the original matrix to see if we obtain the identity matrix. This has been accomplished in Eq. (7-31).

Original matrix	Inverse matrix	Identity matrix

$$\begin{pmatrix} 1 & 2 & 1 \\ 1 & 1 & 2 \\ 2 & 3 & 4 \end{pmatrix} \times \begin{pmatrix} 2 & 5 & -3 \\ 0 & -2 & 1 \\ -1 & -1 & 1 \end{pmatrix} = \begin{pmatrix} 1 & 0 & 0 \\ 0 & 1 & 0 \\ 0 & 0 & 1 \end{pmatrix} \qquad (7\text{-}31)$$

Use of matrix inversion to solve equations

At this point, one might ask of what use is the inverse of a matrix? It is easy to illustrate very quickly how matrix inversion can be used (and in fact *is* used in linear programming) to solve a set of simultaneous equations. Let us take the following set of equations:

$$2X_1 + 3X_2 = 8$$
$$X_1 + 4X_2 = 9 \qquad (7\text{-}32)$$

These two equations can be represented using ordinary algebraic terminology by the general formula

$$(\mathbf{A})X = B$$

where $\quad (\mathbf{A}) =$ matrix of coefficients, $\begin{pmatrix} 2 & 3 \\ 1 & 4 \end{pmatrix}$

$X =$ column vector $\begin{pmatrix} X_1 \\ X_2 \end{pmatrix}$

$B =$ column vector of constants $\begin{pmatrix} 8 \\ 9 \end{pmatrix}$

Now if we want to solve for the values of X_1 and X_2, we would begin by solving for X in the ordinary algebraic equation as follows:

If $\quad (\mathbf{A})X = B$

multiply both sides of the equation by $1/(\mathbf{A})$:

$$\frac{1}{(\mathbf{A})} (\mathbf{A})X = \frac{1}{(\mathbf{A})} \cdot B$$

Now cancel: $X = \dfrac{1}{(A)} \cdot B$

This tells us that we can find the proper values of X_1 and X_2 by multiplying B by $1/(A)$. But *what is* $1/(A)$? Does 1 over a matrix have any significance? Let us start with any ordinary number, say 2.

Now, if $2 \times 3 = 6$ and $6 \times \frac{1}{2} = 3$, we see that 1 over a number (commonly called a reciprocal) has the property of producing the exact reverse of multiplication.

This concept was introduced at the beginning of this section on matrix inversion when we mentioned that a matrix is a particular group of scalars which will move a vector to a particular point in space, and that the inverse of that same matrix, when multiplied by the new vector, will return it to its original position. Thus the inverse of a matrix can easily be thought of as the reciprocal of a matrix.

The solution to Eq. (7-32) is therefore found by multiplying the column vector of constants **(B)** by the inverse of **(A)** as follows:

$$
X = (\text{inverse of } \mathbf{A}) \cdot (\mathbf{B})
$$

$$
= \begin{pmatrix} \frac{4}{5} & -\frac{3}{5} \\ -\frac{1}{5} & \frac{2}{5} \end{pmatrix} \cdot \begin{pmatrix} 8 \\ 9 \end{pmatrix}
$$

$$
= \begin{pmatrix} 1 \\ 2 \end{pmatrix}
$$

Thus
$$
\begin{aligned}
X_1 &= 1 \\
X_2 &= 2
\end{aligned}
$$

In this way we can solve a set of equations using matrix algebra.

In our example, solution by substitution would have been faster. This does not hold, however, for large sets of equations.

PROBLEMS

7-1 Add the following matrices:

a. $\begin{pmatrix} 3 & 1 \\ 2 & 4 \end{pmatrix} + \begin{pmatrix} 5 & 2 \\ 6 & 3 \end{pmatrix} =$

b. $\begin{pmatrix} 8 & 1 \\ 2 & 4 \end{pmatrix} + \begin{pmatrix} 6 & 1 \\ 2 & 3 \end{pmatrix} =$

7-2 Subtract the following matrices:

    a. $\begin{pmatrix} 4 & 3 \\ 2 & -4 \end{pmatrix} - \begin{pmatrix} 5 & 2 \\ 1 & 3 \end{pmatrix} =$

    b. $\begin{pmatrix} 5 & 3 \\ 3 & 2 \end{pmatrix} - \begin{pmatrix} -5 & 4 \\ -3 & 6 \end{pmatrix} =$

7-3 Multiply the following matrices:

    a. $(1 \quad 3) \times \begin{pmatrix} 2 \\ 1 \end{pmatrix} =$

    b. $\begin{pmatrix} 3 & 2 \\ 4 & 1 \end{pmatrix} \times \begin{pmatrix} 3 & 3 \\ 3 & 3 \end{pmatrix} =$

7-4 Multiply the following matrices:

$$\begin{pmatrix} 2 & 1 & 3 \\ 3 & 4 & 1 \\ 4 & 2 & 1 \end{pmatrix} \times \begin{pmatrix} 3 & 2 & 2 \\ 4 & 3 & 5 \\ 1 & 2 & 1 \end{pmatrix} =$$

7-5 Form the transpose of each of the following matrices:

    a. $\begin{pmatrix} a & b \\ c & d \end{pmatrix}$
    b. $\begin{pmatrix} 3 & 2 & 1 \\ 5 & -6 & -3 \\ 4 & -1 & -2 \end{pmatrix}$

7-6 Find the matrix of cofactors for each of the following matrices:

    a. $\begin{pmatrix} 2 & -3 \\ 1 & -5 \end{pmatrix}$
    b. $\begin{pmatrix} 3 & -2 & 1 \\ -4 & 2 & 5 \\ 1 & 2 & -1 \end{pmatrix}$

7-7 Find the adjoint of the following matrices:

    a. $\begin{pmatrix} -3 & 2 \\ 5 & 4 \end{pmatrix}$
    b. $\begin{pmatrix} 3 & -2 & 1 \\ -4 & 2 & 5 \\ 1 & 2 & 1 \end{pmatrix}$

7-8 Invert the following matrix using column relationships:

$$\begin{pmatrix} 1 & 2 & 1 \\ 1 & 1 & 1 \\ 2 & 1 & 1 \end{pmatrix}$$

7-9 The King Roofing Company builds two types of standardized roofs (shingle and built-up) for a housing project. Each shingle roof requires 25 rolls of shingles at $6 per roll and 10 rolls of tar paper at $4 per roll. Each built-up roof requires 16 rolls of asphalt at $11 per roll and 25 rolls of tar paper at $4 per roll. In the next four months it is estimated that 30 shingle roofs and 14 built-up roofs will be built. Use matrix algebra to determine the total expected materials cost.

7-10 Use matrix algebra to determine the solution to the following set of equations:

$$2X_1 + 3X_2 - X_3 = 9$$
$$X_1 + X_2 + X_3 = 9$$
$$3X_1 - X_2 - X_3 = -1$$

BIBLIOGRAPHY

R. A. Frazer, W. J. Duncan, and A. R. Collar, *Elementary Matrices* (New York: Cambridge University Press, 1960).

F. R. Gantmacher, *The Theory of Matrices* (New York: Chelsea Publishing Company, vols. 1 and 2, 1960).

B. Hanes, *Mathematics for Management Science* (Columbus, Ohio: Charles E. Merrill Books, Inc., 1962).

J. E. Howell and D. Teichroew, *Mathematical Analysis for Business Decisions* (Homewood, Ill.: Richard D. Irwin, Inc., 1963).

R. C. Meier and S. H. Archer, *An Introduction to Mathematics for Business Analysis* (New York: McGraw-Hill Book Company, 1960).

P. Sanders, *Elementary Mathematics* (Scranton, Pa.: International Textbook Company, 1963).

chapter
eight

LINEAR PROGRAMMING: GRAPHIC AND ALGEBRAIC METHODS

$\mathbf{B}$usiness firms and their operations continue to increase in size and complexity. These increases have produced new variables, new problems, new uncertainties—all of which make new demands on today's managers. Increasingly, managers must turn to new tools and techniques if they are to cope with the many critical decisions which must be made.

Linear programming is one of the newer scientific aids to managerial decision making. Both the economist and the mathematician have had a part in its development. Its origins go back to the 1920s, to the input-output method of analysis developed by the economist Wassily W. Leontief. The present-day version stems primarily from the work of mathematician George B. Dantzig, who developed the simplex method of linear programming in 1947.

WHAT LINEAR PROGRAMMING IS

A problem confronting the typical business firm is the best allocation of the firm's limited resources. These resources include money, materials, machines, space, time, and personnel. Management's hope is to earmark or budget these resources so as to maximize dollar profits. Each resource is available in its own specific amount. This maximum availability (and it certainly *is* maximum at any given moment) operates as a limitation or a restriction. When, for example, every dollar of the firm's capital has been committed, then the manager must admit, however ruefully, "That's all there is—there isn't any more."

Linear programming is a mathematical technique for finding the best uses of a firm's limited resources. The adjective *linear* is used to describe a relationship between or among two or more variables, a relationship which is directly and precisely proportional. For example, linear means that a 10 per cent change in the number of productive hours used in some operation will cause a 10 per cent change in output. *Programming* refers to the use of certain mathematical techniques so as to get the best solution to a problem involving limited resources.

MAJOR REQUIREMENTS OF A LINEAR PROGRAMMING PROBLEM

Before looking at a linear programming solution, let us consider the major requirements of a linear programming problem in a specific firm.

198

Assume that the firm is a manufacturer of two types of furniture—tables and chairs.

First, there must be an objective the firm wants to achieve. The major objective of our manufacturer, obviously, is to maximize dollar profits. We recognize that profits are not linearly related to sales volume. The variable that *is* linearly related to sales volume is *total contribution*. You recall that total contribution is (selling price per unit less variable cost per unit) × (sales volume in units).

Second, there must be alternate courses of action, one of which will achieve the objective. For example, should our firm allocate its manufacturing capacity to tables and chairs in the ratio of 50:50? 25:75? 70:30? Some other ratio?

Third, resources must be in limited supply. Our furniture plant has a limited number of machine hours available; consequently, the more hours it schedules for tables, the fewer chairs it can make.

Fourth, the variables in the problem must be interrelated. For example, if profit per table is $8 and profit per chair is $6, total dollar profit will reflect the ratio of tables to chairs.

Fifth, we must be able to express the firm's objective and its limitations as mathematical equations or inequalities, and these must be linear equations or inequalities. Our furniture maker's objective, dollar profits, can be expressed in this simple equation:

Profit = $8(number of tables) + $6(number of chairs)

INEQUALITIES VERSUS EQUATIONS

Although less familiar than the equation, the *inequality* is an important relationship in linear programming. How are the two different? Equations, of course, are represented by the well-known equals sign: $=$. They are specific statements expressed in mathematical form. Remember our equation in the preceding paragraph: $P = \$8$(number of tables) $+ \$6$(number of chairs).

Many business problems, however, cannot be expressed in the form of nice, neat equations. Instead of being precise, specifications may provide only that minimum or maximum requirements be met. Here we need *inequalities;* these are another type of relationship expressed in mathematical form. For example, the statement that the cost of 5 tables and 4 chairs must not exceed $120 is $5T + 4C \le \$120$ when expressed as an inequality. The sign $\leq$ means "is equal to or less than." In this case any value equal to or less than \$120 satisfies the inequality. If this were an equation, the cost of 5 tables and 4 chairs would *equal* \$120— no more, no less. Hence an equation is much more restrictive than a corresponding inequality.

We might have expressed the cost of 5 tables and 4 chairs still another way. We could have said that the cost of 5 tables and 4 chairs *will be at least* \$120. Expressed as an inequality, this statement is $5T + 4C \geq$ \$120. The sign $\geq$ means "is equal to or greater than." Any value equal to or greater than \$120 would satisfy this inequality.

Most restrictions in a linear programming problem are expressed as inequalities. As will be seen, they set upper or lower limits; they do not express exact equalities. Thus they permit many possibilities.

LINEAR PROGRAMMING
BY GRAPHIC METHODS

Because we can draw in no more than three dimensions, graphic methods of linear programming can be used only where no more than three variables (products, in this case) are involved. Perhaps the graphic method is best demonstrated when applied to a manufacturer who wants to determine the most profitable combination of products to make and market.

Assume that our manufacturer makes two products, tables and chairs, which must be processed through two machine centers. Machine center 1 has up to 60 hours available. Machine center 2 can handle up to 48 hours of work. Manufacturing one table requires 4 hours in machine center 1 and 2 hours in machine center 2. Each chair requires 2 hours in machine center 1 and 4 hours in machine center 2.

If profit is \$8 per table and \$6 per chair, the problem is to determine the best possible combination of tables and chairs to produce and sell in order to realize the maximum profit. There are two limitations (also called *restraints*) in the problem: the time available in machine center 1, and the time available in machine center 2.

Let us use P_1 to represent the optimum number of tables to be made and P_2 to represent the optimum number of chairs to be made. The information needed to solve the problem is summarized in Table 8-1.

1. First step. To begin solving the problem, let us restate the information in mathematical form. In order to do this, we must intro-

Table 8-1

Manufacturing problem information		
Machine center	Hours required for one unit of product		Total hours available
	Tables P_1	Chairs P_2	
1	4	2	60
2	2	4	48
Profit per unit	$8	$6	

duce a new term, "objective function." This term refers to the equation which shows the relationship of output to profit:

$$Z = \text{profit}$$
$$\$8P_1 = \text{total profit from sale of tables}$$
$$\$6P_2 = \text{total profit from sale of chairs}$$
$$Z = \$8P_1 + \$6P_2$$

Time used in making the two products must certainly not exceed the total time available in the machine centers. In other words, the hours required to make one table times the number of tables produced— plus the hours required to make one chair times the number of chairs produced—must be equal to or less than the time available in each machine center. Mathematically, this is stated as

$$4P_1 + 2P_2 \leq 60 \text{ machine center 1}$$
$$2P_1 + 4P_2 \leq 48 \text{ machine center 2}$$

The first inequality above states that the hours required to produce one table (4 hours) times the number of tables produced (P_1), plus the hours required to produce one chair (2 hours) times the number of chairs produced (P_2), must be equal to or less than the 60 hours available in machine center 1. A similar explanation holds for the second inequality. Note that both inequalities represent capacity restrictions on output and, therefore, on profit.

In order to obtain meaningful answers, the values calculated for P_1 and P_2 must be positive; they must represent real tables and real chairs. Thus all elements of the solution to a linear programming problem must be equal to or greater than zero ($P_1 \geq 0$, $P_2 \geq 0$). This restraint means that the solution must lie in the quadrant in which both X and Y are positive (see Figure 6-6).

The problem can now be summarized in a mathematical form:

Maximize $\qquad\qquad Z = 8P_1 + 6P_2$

subject to these restraints:

$$4P_1 + 2P_2 \leq 60$$
$$2P_1 + 4P_2 \leq 48$$
$$P_1 \geq 0$$
$$P_2 \geq 0$$

2. Second step. Plot the restraints in the problem on a graph, with product P_1 shown on the x axis and product P_2 shown on the y axis. Figure 8-1 shows the P_1 and P_2 axes.

The inequality $4P_1 + 2P_2 \leq 60$ may be located on the graph by first locating its two terminal points and joining these points by a straight line. The two terminal points for the inequality can be found in the following manner:

a. If we assume that *all* the time available in machine center 1 is used in making chairs—that the production of tables is zero—then 30 chairs *could* be made. Thus, if we let $P_1 = 0$, then $P_2 \leq 30$.

Proof: $\qquad 4P_1 + 2P_2 \leq 60$
$\qquad\qquad 4(0) + 2P_2 \leq 60$
$\qquad\qquad\qquad P_2 \leq 30$ If we make the maximum number of chairs, then $P_2 = 30$.

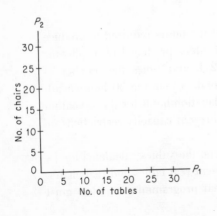

Figure 8-1

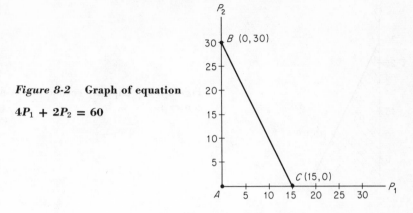

Figure 8-2 **Graph of equation**

$4P_1 + 2P_2 = 60$

Our first point, thus, is (0,30); this point denotes the production of 0 tables and 30 chairs.

b. In order to find the second point, we assume that all the time available in machine center 1 is used in making tables—that the production of chairs is zero. Under this assumption we *could* produce 15 tables. Thus, if we let $P_2 = 0$, then $P_1 \leq 15$.

Proof: $4P_1 + 2P_2 \leq 60$
           $4P_1 + 2(0) \leq 60$
                $P_1 \leq 15$ If we make the maximum number of
                            tables, then $P_1 = 15$.

Our second point, thus, is (15,0); this point denotes the production of 15 tables and 0 chairs.

Locating these two points (0,30) and (15,0) and joining them results in the straight line shown in Figure 8-2.

Now see the same straight line shown in Figure 8-3.

Any combination of tables and chairs on line *BC* will use up all the 60 hours available in machine center 1. For instance, producing 10 tables and 10 chairs (point 10,10 on the graph) will use up 10(4 hours) + 10(2 hours) = 60 hours. Suppose, however, that the firm can sell only 5 tables and 15 chairs (point 5,15 on the graph). This point is not on line *BC*—but this combination *can* be produced without exceeding the 60 hours available: 5(4 hours) + 15(2 hours) = 50 hours, and 50 hours ≤ 60 hours. This point (5,15), or indeed, *any* combination of tables and chairs which lies in the shaded area to the left of line *BC*, can

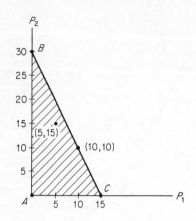

Figure 8-3 **Capacity restriction in machine center 1.**

be produced without exceeding the 60 hours available. The shaded area *ABC* and not the line *BC* is the graphic representation of the inequality $4P_1 + 2P_2 \leq 60$.

Here are some illustrations. Each of the following combinations of tables and chairs is shown as a point on Figure 8-4.

4 tables and 8 chairs: $4(4) + 2(8) = 32$ hours required
10 tables and 2 chairs: $4(10) + 2(2) = 44$ hours required
3 tables and 20 chairs: $4(3) + 2(20) = 52$ hours required
8 tables and 12 chairs: $4(8) + 2(12) = 56$ hours required
15 tables and 15 chairs: $4(15) + 2(15) = 90$ hours required

Note that the time requirements of the first four combinations fall within the 60 hours available in machine center 1. The fifth combination *cannot* be produced because the hours needed exceed the hours available.

A similar explanation applies to the graph of the restraint inequality

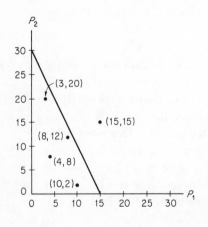

Figure 8-4 **Graph of equation**

$$4P_1 + 2P_2 = 60$$

with various combinations of P_1 and P_2 shown as points.

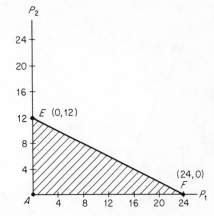

Figure 8-5 **Capacity restriction in machine center 2.**

for machine center 2: $2P_1 + 4P_2 \leq 48$. The line EF in Figure 8-5 represents all combinations of tables and chairs which will use up exactly 48 hours $(2P_1 + 4P_2 = 48)$. The shaded area AEF contains all possible combinations which do not exceed 48 hours $(2P_1 + 4P_2 \leq 48)$. Any point—any combination of tables and chairs falling within the shaded area AEF—will satisfy the time restriction in machine center 2. Thus the shaded area AEF, not the line EF, is the graphic representation of the inequality $2P_1 + 4P_2 \leq 48$.

In order to complete a table or chair, both machine centers must be used. This means that the best combination of tables and chairs must fall within an area to the left of line BC (Figure 8-3) and line EF (Figure 8-5); this best combination must not exceed the available time in either machine center. To find this common area we must plot the two original inequalities (see Figures 8-3 and 8-5) on the same P_1 and P_2 axes. See Figure 8-6.

The area that does not exceed either of the two machine center restraints—the shaded area $AEDC$ in Figure 8-6—contains *all* combinations of tables and chairs satisfying the inequalities

$4P_1 + 2P_2 \leq 60$
$2P_1 + 4P_2 \leq 48$

Here are some examples:

    a. 5 tables and 2 chairs

Machine center 1 $4P_1 + 2P_2 \leq 60$ hours available
                                $4(5) + 2(2) = 24$ hours required

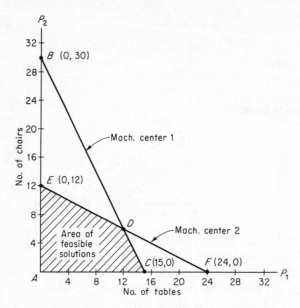

Figure 8-6 **Graphical representation of problem restraints.**

Machine center 2 $2P_1 + 4P_2 \leq 48$ hours available
                             $2(5) + 4(2) = 18$ hours required

     The time required to make 5 tables and 2 chairs falls within the time available in both machine centers (see Figure 8-7).

     b. 10 tables and 5 chairs

Machine center 1 $4P_1 + 2P_2 \leq 60$ hours available
                             $4(10) + 2(5) = 50$ hours required

Machine center 2 $2P_1 + 4P_2 \leq 48$ hours available
                             $2(10) + 4(5) = 40$ hours required

     The combination 10 tables and 5 chairs also satisfies the two restraints (see Figure 8-7).

     c. 8 tables and 12 chairs

Machine center 1 $4P_1 + 2P_2 \leq 60$ hours available
                             $4(8) + 2(12) = 56$ hours required

Machine center 2 $2P_1 + 4P_2 \leq 48$ hours available
$2(8) + 4(12) = 64$ hours required

The time required to make 8 tables and 12 chairs falls within the time available in machine center 1 but *exceeds* the time available in machine center 2. This combination falls outside the area common to both inequalities in Figure 8-7 and, therefore, is not possible.

3. Third step. Locate point *D*, because once that point is known, the shaded area *AEDC* will have been delineated precisely. This is true because we have already three points:

A (0,0)
E (0,12)
C (15,0)

How can we locate point *D*? One possibility is to read its location from an accurately drawn graph. Another method, the one we shall be using, is to solve simultaneously the equations of the two lines which in-

Figure 8-7   **Area of feasible solutions, with examples *a*, *b*, and *c* shown.**

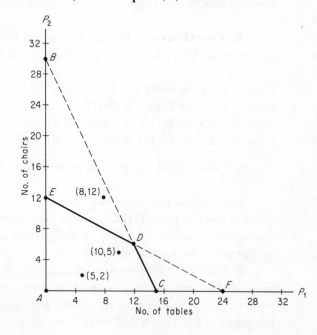

tersect to form point D, the only point common to both equations. The equations to be solved are

$$4P_1 + 2P_2 = 60$$
$$2P_1 + 4P_2 = 48$$

To solve these two equations simultaneously, we:

a. Multiply the first equation by -2:

$$-2(4P_1 + 2P_2 = 60) = -8P_1 - 4P_2 = -120$$

Add the second equation:
$$+ \quad \underline{2P_1 + 4P_2 = \quad 48}$$
$$-6P_1 \quad \quad = -72$$
$$P_1 = \quad 12$$

b. Now substitute 12 for P_1 in the second equation:

$$2P_1 + 4P_2 = 48 = 2(12) + 4P_2 = 48$$
$$24 + 4P_2 = 48$$
$$4P_2 = 24$$
$$P_2 = 6$$

Point D, thus, is   (12,6)

4. Fourth step.   Test the four points that delineate the shaded area to see which yields the greatest dollar profit.

Point A (0,0) $= \$8(0) + \$6(0) = \quad 0$
Point E (0,12) $= \$8(0) + \$6(12) = \$72$
Point C (15,0) $= \$8(15) + \$6(0) = \$120$
Point D (12,6) $= \$8(12) + \$6(6) = \$132$

The point which yields the greatest profit is point D—$132.

The concept that the most profitable combination of tables and chairs is found at point D (12,6) can be further amplified by first plotting the objective function $Z = \$8P_1 + \$6P_2$ (given in the first step) directly on a graph of the feasible solutions area.

To accomplish this, we first let profits equal some minimum dollar figure we know we can attain without violating a restriction. In this case we have elected to let profits equal \$48, a profit easily attainable. Then the objective function is $\$48 = \$8P_1 + \$6P_2$.

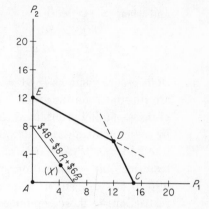

Figure 8-8 **Objective function plotted.**

We then plot this equation on the graph in Figure 8-8 in the same manner that we originally plotted our restrictions (Figure 8-2). First locate two terminal points and then join them with a straight line.

When
$$P_1 = 0$$
$$\$48 = \$8(0) + \$6P_2$$
$$P_2 = \$8$$

and when
$$P_2 = 0$$
$$\$48 = \$8P_1 + \$6(0)$$
$$P_1 = \$6$$

Figure 8-8 illustrates the area of feasible solutions (A E D C) with the profit equation $\$48 = \$8P_1 + \$6P_2$ drawn in. This line represents all the possible combinations of tables and chairs which would yield a total profit of $48. You might want to check one such combination. For example, point X represents the manufacture of 4 tables and 2⅔ chairs.

$$4(\$8) + 2\tfrac{2}{3}(\$6) = \$48$$

Suppose we now graph the line representing all combinations of tables and chairs which would produce a $96 profit:

$$\$96 = \$8P_1 + \$6P_2$$

when
$$P_1 = 0$$
$$\$96 = \$8(0) + \$6P_2$$
$$P_2 = \$16$$

and when $P_2 = 0$

$$\$96 = \$8P_1 + \$6(0)$$
$$P_1 = \$12$$

Both profit equations ($\$48 = \$8P_1 + \$6P_2$ and $\$96 = \$8P_1 + \$6P_2$) are illustrated on the graph in Figure 8-9. Now what is the significance of these parallel profit lines? Simply this: A $48 profit will be generated by manufacturing *any* combination of tables and chairs falling on the line $\$48 = \$8P_1 + \$6P_2$, and a $96 profit will be generated by manufacturing *any* combination of tables and chairs falling on the line $\$96 = \$8P_1 + \$6P_2$. [Note, however, that we are limited by problem restrictions to those combinations which fall within the area of feasible solutions (A E D C).]

It is also true that there is *one* parallel profit line which will pass through point D. This particular profit line (line 3) is illustrated in Figure 8-10, together with the first two profit lines. Although most of the combinations of tables and chairs on profit line 3 do not fall within the area of feasible solutions (A E D C), one point does—point D.

The second profit line drawn generated more profit than the first one ($96 versus $48). It is obvious, then, that the profit line which can be located farthest from the origin (point A) will contain all the combinations of tables and chairs which will generate the greatest possible profit, and as long as at least one point on this maximum profit line is still within the area of feasible solutions (A E D C), that point represents the most profitable combination of products. Point D lies on profit line 3 and is still within the area of feasible solutions; thus it represents the most profitable combination of tables (12) and chairs (6).

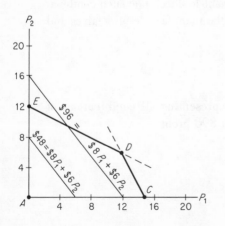

Figure 8-9   **Two profit lines plotted.**

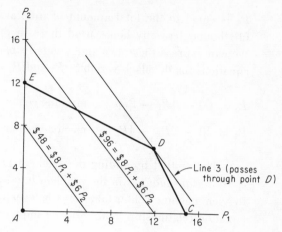

Figure 8-10 **Three profit lines plotted.**

LINEAR PROGRAMMING BY AN ALGEBRAIC METHOD

An algebraic solution to a linear programming problem can be demonstrated with the same simple manufacturing case we used in the graphic method.

Stated algebraically, the problem is

Maximize $Z = \$8P_1 + \$6P_2$

subject to:

$4P_1 + 2P_2 \leq 60$ (machine center 1)

$2P_1 + 4P_2 \leq 48$ (machine center 2)

The first step is to convert the inequalities into equations. Previously, we stated that the best combination of tables and chairs may not necessarily use all the time available in each machine center. We must, therefore, add to each inequality a variable which will take up the slack —the time not used in each machine center. This variable is called a *slack variable.* For example, let

P_3 = slack variable (unused time) in machine center 1

P_4 = slack variable (unused time) in machine center 2

P_3 is equal to the total amount of time available in machine center 1 (60 hours) less any hours used there in processing tables and chairs.

P_4 is equal to the total amount of time available in machine center 2 (48 hours) less any hours used there in processing tables and chairs. We can express these two statements in mathematical form by writing equations for the slack variables P_3 and P_4 as follows:

$$P_3 = 60 - 4P_1 - 2P_2 \qquad \text{machine center 1} \qquad (8\text{-}1)$$

$$P_4 = 48 - 2P_1 - 4P_2 \qquad \text{machine center 2} \qquad (8\text{-}2)$$

Notice that by adding the slack variables, we have converted the *constraint inequalities* in the problem into *equations*. The slack variable in each machine center takes on whatever value is required to make the equation relationship hold. Two examples will clarify this point.

Example 1. Assume that in machine center 1 we process 5 tables and 3 chairs.

$P_3 = 60$ hours $- 4(5) - 2(3)$
$\quad = 34$ hours unused time in machine center 1

Example 2. Assume that in machine center 2 we process 4 tables and 6 chairs.

$P_4 = 48$ hours $- 2(4) - 4(6)$
$\quad = 16$ hours unused time in machine center 2

Because these slack variables have no money value (no profit or loss is charged against idle machine time), the profit function can be rewritten to include the slack variables with zero profit contributions as follows:

$$\text{Profit} = \$8P_1 + \$6P_2 + \$0P_3 + \$0P_4 \qquad (8\text{-}3)$$

In the graphic method we found that the points in the feasible solutions area represented various combinations of tables and chairs (product mixes) which yielded a profit. We also found that the origin (0,0) resulted in a zero profit. This indicates that no tables and chairs were produced. In other words, (0,0) reflects only unused capacity.

We can illustrate this feasible (but zero-profit) solution in the algebraic method by referring back to the slack variable equations:

$$P_3 = 60 - 4P_1 - 2P_2 \qquad \text{machine center 1} \qquad (8\text{-}1)$$
$$P_4 = 48 - 2P_1 - 4P_2 \qquad \text{machine center 2} \qquad (8\text{-}2)$$

The essential value of these two equations is that they show the relationship between the variables in the first solution (P_3 and P_4, which represent unused time) and the other variables (P_1 and P_2, which represent products). For that reason we shall call them *relationship equations*.

First solution

$$P_1 = 0 \quad \text{(no tables)}$$
$$P_2 = 0 \quad \text{(no chairs)}$$
$$P_3 = 60 - 4(0) - 2(0) = 60 \text{ hours unused}$$
$$P_4 = 48 - 2(0) - 4(0) = 48 \text{ hours unused}$$

This solution contains only the slack variables P_3 and P_4. Substituting the quantities of P_1, P_2, P_3, and P_4 in the profit function gives the following profit:

$$\begin{aligned} \text{Profit} &= \$8P_1 + \$6P_2 + \$0P_3 + \$0P_4 \\ &= \$8(0) + \$6(0) + \$0(60) + \$0(48) \qquad (8\text{-}3) \\ &= \$0 \end{aligned}$$

This zero profit calls attention to one of the features of this algebraic method, namely, that the initial solution shows a zero profit. Thus this initial solution is technically possible but not financially attractive.

The next step is to examine the profit function to see if profits can be increased. Clearly, improvement is possible by manufacturing some tables (P_1) or chairs (P_2) in exchange for the unused time (P_3 or P_4), which has no value. To move toward the one best product mix, we first consider manufacturing only that product which contributes the highest profit per unit—tables. How many tables? Refer back to Eqs. (8-1) and (8-2). Assume that all the time available in each machine center is used to produce tables (P_1). This dictates that production of chairs (P_2) be zero. Equation (8-1), $P_3 = 60 - 4P_1 - 2P_2$, shows that in machine center 1 we have 60 hours available. The time required to process 1 table is 4 hours. Thus we can make

$$\frac{60 \text{ hours available}}{4 \text{ hours per table}} = 15 \text{ tables}$$

Equation (8-2), $P_4 = 48 - 2P_1 - 4P_2$, shows that 48 hours are available in machine center 2. The time required to process one table in center 2 is 2 hours. Thus the number of tables which can be processed in machine center 2 is

$$\frac{48 \text{ hours available}}{2 \text{ hours per table}} = 24 \text{ tables}$$

We see at once that only 15 tables can be made. To process 24 tables would require 96 hours in machine center 1, but total time available there is only 60 hours. Therefore machine center 1 is our *limiting center*; it limits the production of tables to 15 units. Production of 15 tables requires 60 hours in machine center 1 and 30 hours in machine center 2; this production is within the time restrictions in both centers.

Now we substitute the values $P_1 = 15$ and $P_2 = 0$ in Eqs. (8-1) and (8-2):

$$P_3 = 60 - 4(15) - 2(0) = 0$$
$$P_4 = 48 - 2(15) - 4(0) = 18$$

Second solution

$P_1 = 15$ tables
$P_2 = 0$ chairs
$P_3 = 0$ unused hours in center 1
$P_4 = 18$ unused hours in center 2

$$\begin{aligned} \text{Profit} &= \$8P_1 + \$6P_2 + \$0P_3 + \$0P_4 \\ &= \$8(15) + \$6(0) + \$0(0) + \$0(18) \\ &= \$120 \end{aligned} \tag{8-3}$$

This profit figure clearly is better than the zero profit of the first solution.

Again we must determine whether more improvement is possible. By producing 15 tables, the amount of unused time in machine center 1 (P_3) was reduced to zero. Equations (8-1) and (8-2) must be changed to reflect this fact. Here they are repeated before change:

$$P_3 = 60 - 4P_1 - 2P_2 \tag{8-1}$$

$$P_4 = 48 - 2P_1 - 4P_2 \tag{8-2}$$

Now that P_1 has replaced P_3, solve for P_1 in Eq. (8-1).

$$4P_1 = 60 - 2P_2 - P_3$$

Dividing through by 4 yields

$$P_1 = 15 - \tfrac{1}{2}P_2 - \tfrac{1}{4}P_3 \tag{8-4}$$

Putting this value for P_1 into Eq. (8-2) will give us a new equation, Eq. (8-5):

$$
\begin{aligned}
P_4 &= 48 - 2P_1 - 4P_2 \tag{8-2}\\
&= 48 - 2(15 - \tfrac{1}{2}P_2 - \tfrac{1}{4}P_3) - 4P_2 \\
&= 48 - 30 + P_2 + \tfrac{1}{2}P_3 - 4P_2 \\
&= 18 - 3P_2 + \tfrac{1}{2}P_3 \tag{8-5}
\end{aligned}
$$

The two new equations which reflect the relationship among all the variables in the second solution now are

$$P_1 = 15 - \tfrac{1}{2}P_2 - \tfrac{1}{4}P_3 \tag{8-4}$$

$$P_4 = 18 - 3P_2 + \tfrac{1}{2}P_3 \tag{8-5}$$

To learn whether a third solution will make a profit greater than $120, put the second-solution value for P_1 and P_4 into the profit function.

$$
\begin{aligned}
\text{Profit} &= \$8P_1 + \$6P_2 + \$0P_3 + \$0P_4 \tag{8-3}\\
&= \$8(15 - \tfrac{1}{2}P_2 - \tfrac{1}{4}P_3) + \$6P_2 + \$0P_3 \\
&\qquad\qquad\qquad\qquad\quad + \$0(18 - 3P_2 + \tfrac{1}{2}P_3) \\
&= \$120 - \$4P_2 - \$2P_3 + \$6P_2 \\
&= \$120 + \$2P_2 - \$2P_3 \tag{8-6}
\end{aligned}
$$

This new expression of the profit function (profit = $120 + $2P_2 - $2P_3) indicates that if we bring chairs (P_2) into the solution, we will make an additional profit of $2 for each chair we produce. This may be confusing—the original statement of the problem indicated that each chair made a profit of $6.

We must remember, however, that all the hours in machine center 1 have been committed; we cannot begin to make chairs except by sacrificing some of the tables now being made. A chair requires 2 hours in machine center 1. A table requires 4 hours in the same center. To introduce a chair into our product mix we must forgo the manufacture of ½ table. Thus, we lose ½($8) because we make ½ table less—but we gain $6 from each chair we process. A loss of $4 and a gain of $6 nets us $2. The revised profit function (profit = $120 + $2P_2 - $2P_3) shows this.

Now, what about $-$2P_3$ in the revised profit function? This simply means that if we want to take away 1 of the 60 hours in machine center 1 for some other purpose, this act will cost us $2. Why?

Each of the 15 tables we are now making requires 4 hours in center 1. To remove 1 hour makes us give up ¼ table—or ¼ of $8—or $2.

We now see that the revised profit function (profit = $120 + $2P_2 - $2P_3) states the total current profit and indicates the profit implications of the two courses of action available to us. It behooves us to make some chairs even at the sacrifice of some tables. How many chairs?

The new relationship equations can be used to determine the number of chairs to add. Note that the production of 15 tables uses all the hours available in machine center 1. But to make a chair, we must have some time in that center. We must give up some tables in order to produce chairs. For each table we give up, we can process 2 chairs. If we gave up all 15 tables in machine center 1, we could make 30 chairs:

$$\frac{15 \text{ tables now being made}}{½ \text{ table given up for 1 chair}} = 30 \text{ chairs}$$

But chairs must also go through machine center 2. We now must determine the maximum number of chairs that can be processed in machine center 2. We have already seen that 1 chair replaces ½ table in machine center 1. When table production is reduced by ½ table, one result is to free or release ½ of the 2 hours a table must have in machine center 2. Thus 1 hour is freed for every ½ table given up—but the chair that replaces the ½ table requires 4 hours in machine center 2. And 4 hours required for each chair less the 1 hour released or freed by cutting production back by ½ table equals a net requirement of 3 hours per chair in machine center 2. Remember that the second solution indicated 18 hours available in center 2. Consequently,

$$\frac{18 \text{ hours available in machine center 2}}{3 \text{ net hours required per chair}} = 6 \text{ chairs}$$

A general rule for finding the quantity to be added to the product mix calls for these two steps:

1. Divide the constant in each equation by the coefficient of the variable being added. Remember that the terms *constant, coefficient,* and *variable* refer to mathematical expressions such as these:

$$5X = 15$$

Coefficient ———⌐↑   ↑   ⌐—— Constant

Variable

2. Choose the smaller positive quotient in step 1 as the quantity to be added.

For example, the constant in Eq. (8-4) is 15; the coefficient of the variable to be added (P_2, chairs) is ½. $15/½ = 30$. Likewise, the constant in Eq. (8-5) is 18, and the coefficient of the variable to be added (P_2, chairs) is 3. $18/3 = 6$. We settled on 6 as the quantity of chairs to be added to the product mix. A figure larger than 6 would violate Eq. (8-5); that is, a value greater than 6 would require more time in machine center 2 than the available 18 hours.

We have now decided to make 6 chairs. What effects will this decision have on the production of tables, the availability of hours, and the generation of profit? The equations we calculated after the second solution can help here.

$$P_1 = 15 - ½P_2 - ¼P_3 \tag{8-4}$$

$$P_4 = 18 - 3P_2 + ½P_3 \tag{8-5}$$

Substituting 6 for P_2 and 0 for P_3 yields

$$P_1 = 15 - ½(6) - ¼(0)$$
$$= 12$$
$$P_4 = 18 - 3(6) + ½(0)$$
$$= 0$$

We now see that the production of 6 chairs reduces the production of tables to 12 and uses completely all the available hours in both machine centers.

What about profit?

$$\text{Profit} = \$8P_1 + \$6P_2 + \$0P_3 + \$0P_4 \qquad (8\text{-}3)$$
$$= \$8(12) + \$6(6) + \$0(0) + \$0(0)$$
$$= \$96 + \$36$$
$$= \$132$$

The new third solution which produces this profit is

Third solution

$P_1 = 12$ tables
$P_2 = 6$ chairs
$P_3 = 0$ unused hours in center 1
$P_4 = 0$ unused hours in center 2

The fact that all available hours in both machine centers have been utilized may be verified:

Products	Center 1 (60 hours available)	Center 2 (48 hours available)
P_1 (tables)	12×4 hours $= 48$	12×2 hours $= 24$
P_2 (chairs)	6×2 hours $= \underline{12}$	6×4 hours $= \underline{24}$
	60	48

Now see if there is a solution which yields a profit greater than $132. To do this, we proceed exactly as we did in going from the second solution to the third solution. First we repeat the two equations which show us the product mix just prior to the third solution:

$$P_1 = 15 - \tfrac{1}{2}P_2 - \tfrac{1}{4}P_3 \qquad (8\text{-}4)$$

$$P_4 = 18 - 3P_2 + \tfrac{1}{2}P_3 \qquad (8\text{-}5)$$

Then we reflect in these two equations the changes we made when we replaced P_4 with P_2 in order to get the third solution. We now solve for P_2 in Eq. (8-5):

$$P_4 = 18 - 3P_2 + \tfrac{1}{2}P_3$$
$$3P_2 = 18 + \tfrac{1}{2}P_3 - P_4 \tag{8-5}$$

Dividing through by 3 yields

$$P_2 = 6 + \tfrac{1}{6}P_3 - \tfrac{1}{3}P_4 \tag{8-7}$$

Now we substitute $(6 + \tfrac{1}{6}P_3 - \tfrac{1}{3}P_4)$ for P_2 in Eq. (8-4):

$$P_1 = 15 - \tfrac{1}{2}P_2 - \tfrac{1}{4}P_3 \tag{8-4}$$

$$= 15 - \tfrac{1}{2}(6 + \tfrac{1}{6}P_3 - \tfrac{1}{3}P_4) - \tfrac{1}{4}P_3$$
$$= 15 - 3 - \tfrac{1}{12}P_3 + \tfrac{1}{6}P_4 - \tfrac{1}{4}P_3$$
$$= 12 - \tfrac{1}{3}P_3 + \tfrac{1}{6}P_4 \tag{8-8}$$

The two new equations for the third solution are then

$$P_1 = 12 - \tfrac{1}{3}P_3 + \tfrac{1}{6}P_4 \tag{8-8}$$
$$P_2 = 6 + \tfrac{1}{6}P_3 - \tfrac{1}{3}P_4 \tag{8-7}$$

To find out whether another combination of products might generate a profit greater than \$132, we simply substitute the values for P_1 and P_2 [Eqs. (8-8) and (8-7)] into the profit function:

$$\text{Profit} = \$8P_1 + \$6P_2 + \$0P_3 + \$0P_4 \tag{8-3}$$
$$= \$8(12 - \tfrac{1}{3}P_3 + \tfrac{1}{6}P_4) + \$6(6 + \tfrac{1}{6}P_3 - \tfrac{1}{3}P_4) + \$0 + \$0$$
$$= \$96 - \tfrac{8}{3}P_3 + \tfrac{8}{6}P_4 + \$36 + P_3 - 2P_4$$
$$= \$132 - \$\tfrac{5}{3}P_3 - \$\tfrac{2}{3}P_4 \tag{8-9}$$

At this point an examination of the profit function shows that there are no positive coefficients for P_3 or P_4. This means that no further improvement is possible, because adding any units of P_3 or P_4 (unused time) would decrease profits. The negative signs show this. Hence, the third solution ($P_1 = 12$; $P_2 = 6$) is the optimal solution, and as we can see, it agrees with the graphic solution. The advantage of the algebraic solution is that it can be used where more than three possible products are involved, whereas the graphic solution is limited to three products or three dimensions.

PROBLEMS

8-1 The Jones Company manufactures two products, J_1 and J_2. Each J_1 sold contributes $6, and each J_2 contributes $5. In addition, each product must pass through two assembly points, A_1 and A_2. J_1 requires 4 hours in A_1 and 4 hours in A_2. J_2 requires 3 hours in A_1 and 5 hours in A_2.

There are 40 hours available in A_1 and 30 hours available in A_2. Using graphic linear programming, determine the optimum product mix.

8-2 Two products are manufactured by the Smith Company. Product 1 contributes $10, and product 2 contributes $6. Each product must go through two machine centers. Product 1 requires 12 hours in center 1 and 4 hours in center 2. Product 2 requires 4 hours in center 1 and 8 hours in center 2. There are 60 hours available in center 1 and 40 hours available in center 2. Using graphic linear programming, find the optimum product mix and the total contribution of this mix.

8-3 Given
2 products—X_1 and X_2
X_1 contribution $= \$9/\text{unit}$
X_2 contribution $= \$7/\text{unit}$

	Hours required per unit	
	Center 1	Center 2
X_1	12 hours	4 hours
X_2	4 hours	8 hours
Total hours available in each machine center	60	40

From the given information, find the optimum product mix using algebraic linear programming.

8-4 The ABC Company makes two products, Y_1 and Y_2. The contribution of each of these is as follows:
$Y_1 = \$15/\text{unit}$
$Y_2 = \$11/\text{unit}$

Each of the products is made from two raw materials, A and B; Y_1 and Y_2 require raw materials in the following amounts:

	A	B
Y_1	4 pounds	3 pounds
Y_2	2 pounds	1 pound

400 pounds of A are available—500 pounds of B.

Using the algebraic linear programming method, determine the combination of Y_1 and Y_2 which will maximize the total contribution.

8-5 Three products can be made by the Lee Company. The contribution of each of these is as follows:

W_1 contribution $= \$\ 9/\text{unit}$
W_2 contribution $= \$\ 6/\text{unit}$
W_3 contribution $= \$12/\text{unit}$

Each of these three products is manufactured from three raw materials. Production requirements are as follows:

	Material 1	Material 2	Material 3
W_1 requires	4 pounds/unit	8 pounds/unit	5 pounds/unit
W_2 requires	3 pounds/unit	6 pounds/unit	6 pounds/unit
W_3 requires	6 pounds/unit	12 pounds/unit	6 pounds/unit
Total pounds available	480	480	600

From the data given above, determine the optimum product mix and the maximum contribution; use algebraic linear programming.

BIBLIOGRAPHY

H. Bierman, L. E. Fouraker, and R. K. Jaedicke, *Quantitative Analysis for Business Decisions* (Homewood, Ill.: Richard D. Irwin, Inc., 1961).

R. W. Llewellyn, *Linear Programming* (New York: Holt, Rinehart and Winston, Inc., 1964).

T. H. Naylor and E. T. Byrne, *Linear Programming* (Belmont, Calif.: Wadsworth Publishing Company, Inc., 1963).

R. S. Stockton, *Introduction to Linear Programming* (Boston: Allyn and Bacon, Inc., 1960).

chapter
nine
LINEAR PROGRAMMING: SIMPLEX METHOD

$\mathbf{P}$roduct-mix problems in most firms involve many products and many machine centers. For example, picture a problem involving 10 products and 15 machine centers. In such a case, the algebraic solution to linear programming demonstrated in the last chapter becomes impractical because of the sheer size of the problem. There is another procedure, the simplex method, which offers a means of solving the more complicated linear programming problems.

In the simplex method, the computational routine is an *iterative* process. To iterate means to repeat; hence in working toward the optimum solution, the computational routine is repeated over and over, following a standard pattern. Successive solutions are developed in a systematic pattern until the best solution is reached.

Another characteristic of the simplex method is that each new solution will yield a profit as large as or larger than the previous solution. This important feature assures us that we are always moving closer to the optimum answer. Finally, the method indicates when the optimum solution has been reached.

RELATIONSHIP BETWEEN SIMPLEX AND ALGEBRAIC METHODS

Remember that we are introducing a second method of linear programming, the simplex method, because of the complexity of the typical calculations involved in algebraic linear programming.

The simplex method which follows uses algebra also—not ordinary algebra but *matrix* algebra, which was treated in Chapter 7. Instead of solving each set of relationship equations (Chapter 8) by simultaneous equations, the simplex method uses matrix algebra. You saw in Chapter 7 that any set of simultaneous equations can be solved easily by using the matrix algebra concept of the *inverse*.

In the simplex solution method to follow, we shall actually be forming an inverse to solve a set of simultaneous equations. True, the formation of the inverse will *not* be accomplished in the same manner as it was in Chapter 7, but it will be an inverse nevertheless.

SETTING UP THE INITIAL BASIC SOLUTION

To solve a problem by the simplex method requires (1) arranging the problem equations and inequalities in a special way, and (2) following systematic procedures and rules in calculating a solution. These steps will be demonstrated using the same product-mix problem of Chapter 8 —that is,

Maximize   Profit = $8P_1 + $6P_2$

subject to: $4P_1 + 2P_2 \leq 60$ hours   machine center 1
               $2P_1 + 4P_2 \leq 48$ hours   machine center 2

As in the algebraic solution, the first step is to convert the inequalities into equations by adding slack variables.

$$4P_1 + 2P_2 + P_3 = 60 \text{ hours} \tag{9-1}$$

$$2P_1 + 4P_2 + P_4 = 48 \text{ hours} \tag{9-2}$$

Except for arrangement, these equations are the same as Eqs. (8-1) and (8-2), which were used in setting up the algebraic solution.

In the simplex method, any unknown that occurs in one equation must appear in all equations. The unknowns that do not affect an equation are written with a zero coefficient. For example, since P_3 and P_4 represent unused time which yields no profit, these variables are added to the profit function with zero coefficients. Furthermore, since P_3 rep-

Table 9-1

Parts of the simplex tableau

C_j column (*profits per unit*)						

C_j	Product mix		$8	$6	$0	$0	←C_j row
		Quantity	P_1	P_2	P_3	P_4	←Variable row
$0	P_3	60	4	2	1	0	2 rows illustrating restraint equations (coefficients only)
$0	P_4	48	2	4	0	1	

Product-mix column
Constant column (*quantities of product in the mix*)
Variable columns
Body matrix
Identity matrix

resents unused time in machine center 1 only, it is added to the equation representing machine center 2 with a zero coefficient. For the same reason $0P_4$ is added to the equation representing the time constraint in machine center 1. Thus the equations are

Maximize   Profit $= \$8P_1 + \$6P_2 + \$0P_3 + \$0P_4$ (8-3)

subject to: $4P_1 + 2P_2 + P_3 + 0P_4 = 60$ hours   (9-1)

$2P_1 + 4P_2 + 0P_3 + P_4 = 48$ hours   (9-2)

To simplify handling the equations in the problem, they can be put into tabular form. In Chapter 7 we found that systems of equations can be solved by working with coefficients alone, and thus the variables need not be rewritten each time.

It will be helpful to describe the simplex tableau and to identify the parts and function of each. First, see Table 9-1. The two *restraint equations* are shown in the simplex tableau as:

	P_1	P_2	P_3	P_4
60	4	2	1	0
48	2	4	0	1

Note first that row 1 (4, 2, 1, 0) represents the coefficients of our first equation and row 2 (2, 4, 0, 1) the coefficients of our second equation. Second, each *variable column* contains all the coefficients of one unknown. For example, under P_1 is written $\binom{4}{2}$, under P_2 is written $\binom{2}{4}$, under P_3 is written $\binom{1}{0}$, and under P_4 is written $\binom{0}{1}$. Third, the constants (60 and 48) have been placed to the left of the equations. We have simply rearranged the terms in the constraint equations to form the simplex tableau.

As with the algebraic method of Chapter 8, we must establish an initial solution. Again the starting solution will be the zero-profit solution. This solution would be to make no tables or chairs, have all unused time, and hence realize no profit. We found in the algebraic method that if no tables and chairs were produced—if $P_1 = 0$ and $P_2 = 0$—then the first solution would be

$P_1 = 0$
$P_2 = 0$
$P_3 = 60$
$P_4 = 48$

This first feasible solution is shown in the initial simplex tableau as follows:

Product mix	Quantity	P_1	P_2	P_3	P_4
P_3	60	4	2	1	0
P_4	48	2	4	0	1

Note that the *product-mix column* contains the variables in the solutions. The variables in the first solution are P_3 and P_4 (the slack variables). In the *quantity column* we find the quantities of the variables that are in the solution.

$P_3 = 60$ hours available in machine center 1
$P_4 = 48$ hours available in machine center 2

Since the variables P_1 and P_2 do not appear in the mix, they are equal to zero.

The *C_j column* in Table 9-1 contains the profit per unit for the variables P_3 and P_4. For example, the zero appearing to the left of the P_3 row in Table 9-1 means that profit per unit of P_3 is zero.

The *identity matrix* in the initial simplex tableau consists of the coefficients of the slack variables that are added to the constraint inequalities to make them equations.

The *body matrix* consists of the coefficients of the real product variables, P_1 and P_2. For example, the element 4 in the P_1 column of the body matrix means that if we wanted to make 1 unit of P_1—to bring 1 table into the solution—we would have to give up 4 hours of P_3 in machine center 1.

Similarly, the element 2 in the P_2 column indicates that the manufacturing of 1 unit of P_2—bringing 1 chair into the solution—would force us to give up 2 hours of P_3 in machine center 1.

The elements in the body matrix, thus, represent rates of substitution.

The element 1 in the P_3 column tells us that to bring in 1 hour of P_3—to make 1 hour of P_3 available—we would have to give up 1 of the 60 hours of P_3 now in the solution. As there are only 60 hours in center 1 available, we must give up 1 of the 60 if we want an hour for some other purpose. This is just like taking one hour off the top of a pile and adding another to the bottom.

The zero in the P_4 column immediately under the P_4 means that making 1 hour in machine center 2 available for other purposes has no effect on P_3, the amount of slack time in center 1.

In our examination of substitution rates, we have treated two types of action:

1. The *addition* of real products, P_1 and P_2, into the production schedule or solution.

2. The *withdrawal* of time, P_3 and P_4, from the total amounts of time available in each of the two machine centers—withdrawal so as to make time available for other purposes.

Up to this point, setting up the initial simplex tableau has not involved any computations. We have simply rearranged the problem equations to form the first simplex tableau.

To find the profit for each solution and to determine whether the solution can be improved upon, we need to add two more rows to the initial simplex tableau: a Z_j row and a $C_j - Z_j$ row. This has been done in Table 9-2. The value in the Z_j row under the quantity column represents the total profit from this particular solution: zero, in this case. In this first solution, we have 60 hours of unused time in machine center 1

Table 9-2

C_j			$8	$6	$0	$0
	Product mix	Quantity	P_1	P_2	P_3	P_4
$0	P_3	60	4	2	1	0
$0	P_4	48	2	4	0	1
2 rows $\{$	Z_j	$0	$0	$0	$0	$0
added $\{$	$C_j - Z_j$		$8	$6	$0	$0

**INITIAL SIMPLEX TABLEAU COMPLETED
(two rows added)**

($P_3 = 60$) and 48 hours of unused time in machine center 2 ($P_4 = 48$). The total profit from this solution is found by multiplying the profit per unit of P_3 ($0) by the quantity of P_3 in the solution (60 hours), plus the profit per unit of P_4 ($0) times the quantity of P_4 in the solution (48 hours).

Total profit for first solution:

Number of unused hours of $P_3 = 60$
Times profit per unit of P_3 $\times$ $0 = $0

Number of unused hours of $P_4 = 48$
Times profit per unit of P_4 $\times$ $0 = $0

Total profit $0

The four values for Z_j under the variable columns (all $0) are the amounts by which profit would be reduced if 1 unit of any of the variables (P_1, P_2, P_3, P_4) were added to the mix. For example, if we want to make 1 unit of P_1, the elements $\begin{pmatrix} 4 \\ 2 \end{pmatrix}$ in the body matrix tell us we must give up 4 hours of P_3 and 2 hours of P_4. But unused time in each machine center is worth $0 per hour; consequently, there is *no* reduction in profit.

How much profit is lost by adding 1 unit of P_1 to the production schedule or solution?

Number of hours of P_3 given up $= 4$
Times profit per unit of P_3 $\times$ $0 = $0

Number of hours of P_4 given up $= 2$
Times profit per unit of P_4 $\times$ $0 = $0

Total profit given up $0

C_j has been defined as profit per unit; for tables (P_1), C_j is $8 per unit.

$C_j - Z_j$ is the *net* profit which will result from introducing—from adding—one unit of a variable to the production schedule or solution. For example, if 1 unit of P_1 adds $8 of profit to the solution *and* if its introduction causes no loss, then $C_j - Z_j$ for $P_1 = $8.

The calculation of Z_js for Table 9-2 follows:

Z_j (total profit) $= (\$0) (60) + (\$0) (48) = \$0$
Z_j for column $P_1 = (\$0) (4) + (\$0) (2) = \$0$
Z_j for column $P_2 = (\$0) (2) + (\$0) (4) = \$0$
Z_j for column $P_3 = (\$0) (1) + (\$0) (0) = \$0$
Z_j for column $P_4 = (\$0) (0) + (\$0) (1) = \$0$

Calculations of *net* profit per unit of each variable follow:

Variables	Profit/unit (C_j)	−	Profit lost/unit (Z_j)	=	Net profit/unit $(C_j - Z_j)$
P_1	$8	−	$0	=	$8
P_2	$6	−	$0	=	$6
P_3	$0	−	$0	=	$0
P_4	$0	−	$0	=	$0

By examining the numbers in the $C_j - Z_j$ row of Table 9-2, we can see, for example, that total profit can be increased by $8 for each unit of P_1 (tables) added to the mix or by $6 for each unit of P_2 (chairs) added to the mix. Thus a positive number in the $C_j - Z_j$ row ($8 in the case of the P_1 column) indicates that profits can be improved by that amount for each unit of P_1 added. On the other hand, a negative number in the $C_j - Z_j$ row would indicate the amount by which profits would *decrease* if 1 unit of the variable heading that column were added to the solution. Hence the optimum solution is reached when no positive numbers remain in the $C_j - Z_j$ row; that is, no more profit can be made.

DEVELOPING THE IMPROVED SOLUTIONS

Now that the initial simplex tableau is established, the next step is to determine if improvement is possible. The computational procedure for the second solution is as follows:

1. Determine which variable will add the most per unit to profit. The numbers in the $C_j - Z_j$ row tell exactly which product will increase profits most. As stated previously, the presence of positive numbers in the $C_j - Z_j$ row indicates that profit can be improved—the larger the positive number, the greater the improvement possible.

As in the algebraic method, we select as the variable to be added to the first solution that variable which contributes the *most* profit per unit. In Table 9-3, bringing in P_1 (tables) will add \$8 per unit to profit. The P_1 column is the optimum column.

Table 9-3

C_j	Product mix	Quantity	$8 P_1	$6 P_2	$0 P_3	$0 P_4
$0	P_3	60	4	2	1	0
$0	P_4	48	2	4	0	1
	Z_j	$0	$0	$0	$0	$0
	$C_j - Z_j$		$8	$6	$0	$0

Optimum column in initial simplex tableau

—Optimum column

By definition, the *optimum column* (Table 9-3) is that column which has the largest positive value in the $C_j - Z_j$ row or, stated in another way, that column whose product will contribute the most profit per unit. Inspection of the optimum column tells us that the variable P_1 (tables) should be added to the mix, replacing one of the variables presently in the mix.

2. The next step is to determine which variable will be replaced. This is done in the following manner: Divide 60 and 48 in the quantity column by their corresponding numbers in the optimum column and select the row with the smaller or smallest ratio as the row to be replaced. In this case, the ratios would be

P_3 row $\quad \dfrac{60 \text{ hours available}}{4 \text{ hours required per unit}} = 15$ units of P_1

P_4 row $\quad \dfrac{48 \text{ hours available}}{2 \text{ hours required per unit}} = 24$ units of P_1

Since the P_3 row has the smaller positive ratio (15:1 rather than 24:1), it is called the *replaced row* because it will be replaced in the next solution by 15 units of P_1. The elements common to both the P_3 and P_4 rows *and* the optimum column are called *intersectional elements*. Thus the intersectional element of the row to be replaced (P_3 row) is 4, and the intersectional element of the P_4 row is 2 (see Table 9-4). Row replacement means that in the next solution, the variable P_3 (unused time) will be replaced by 15 units of P_1 (15 tables).

Table 9-4

Replaced row and intersectional elements in initial simplex tableau

C_j	Product mix	Quantity	$8 P_1	$6 P_2	$0 P_3	$0 P_4	
$0	P_3	60	④	2	1	0	←Replaced row
$0	P_4	48	②	4	0	1	⌐ Intersectional elements
	Z_j	$0	$0	$0	$0	$0	
	$C_j - Z_j$		$8	$6	$0	$0	

└—Optimum column

3. Having selected the optimum column and the replaced row, we can develop the second simplex solution, an *improved* solution.

The first part of the new tableau to be developed is the P_1 row. The P_1 row appears in place of the replaced row (P_3) of Table 9-4. The P_1 row of the new tableau is computed as follows: Divide each number in the replaced row (the P_3 row) by the intersectional element (4) of the replaced row:

$$60/4 = 15 \quad 4/4 = 1 \quad 2/4 = \frac{1}{2} \quad 1/4 = \frac{1}{4} \quad 0/4 = 0$$

Thus the new P_1 row should be (15, 1, ½, ¼, 0).

Note in Table 9-5 that for the first time there is a dollar figure in the C_j column ($8 per unit). Also note that P_4 and its profit per unit ($0) remain in the new tableau.

Table 9-5

C_j	Product mix	Quantity	$8 P_1	$6 P_2	$0 P_3	$0 P_4	
$8	P_1	15	1	½	¼	0	← Replacing row
$0	P_4						
	Z_j						
	$C_j - Z_j$						

Replacing row in second simplex tableau

4. To complete the second tableau, we compute new values for the remaining rows. *All* remaining rows of the variables in the tableau are calculated using the following formula:

$$\begin{pmatrix}\text{Elements in}\\\text{the old row}\end{pmatrix} - \begin{pmatrix}\text{intersectional}\\\text{element of old row}\end{pmatrix} \times \begin{pmatrix}\text{corresponding}\\\text{elements in}\\\text{replacing row}\end{pmatrix} = \begin{matrix}\text{new}\\\text{row}\end{matrix}$$

Using this formula, the new P_4 row is:

$\begin{pmatrix}\text{Element in}\\\text{old } P_4 \text{ row}\end{pmatrix}$	$-$	$\begin{pmatrix}\text{intersectional}\\\text{element of}\\P_4 \text{ row}\end{pmatrix}$	$\times$	$\begin{pmatrix}\text{corresponding}\\\text{element in}\\\text{replacing row}\end{pmatrix}$	$=$	$\begin{matrix}\text{new } P_4\\\text{row}\end{matrix}$
48	—	(2	×	15)	=	18
2	—	(2	×	1)	=	0
4	—	(2	×	½)	=	3
0	—	(2	×	¼)	=	−½
1	—	(2	×	0)	=	1

The new P_4 row as it appears in the second tableau is shown in Table 9-6. The method for computing the Z_j and $C_j - Z_j$ rows (the profit opportunities) has already been demonstrated in developing the initial simplex tableau.

Table 9-6

C_j	Product mix	Quantity	$8 P_1	$6 P_2	$0 P_3	$0 P_4
$8	P_1	15	1	½	¼	0
$0	P_4	18	0	3	−½	1
	Z_j					
	$C_j - Z_j$					

Replacing row and new P_4 row in second tableau

The computation of the Z_j row of the second tableau is as follows:

Z_j (total profit) $= (\$8)\,(15) + (\$0)\,(18) = \$120 =$ total profit of second solution

$$\left.\begin{array}{l} Z_j \text{ for } P_1 = (\$8)\,(1) + (\$0)\,(0) = \$8 \\ Z_j \text{ for } P_2 = (\$8)\,(\tfrac{1}{2}) + (\$0)\,(3) = \$4 \\ Z_j \text{ for } P_3 = (\$8)\,(\tfrac{1}{4}) + (\$0)\,(-\tfrac{1}{2}) = \$2 \\ Z_j \text{ for } P_4 = (\$8)\,(0) + (\$0)\,(1) = \$0 \end{array}\right\} \begin{array}{l} \text{profits given up by intro-} \\ \text{ducing 1 unit of these} \\ \text{variables} \end{array}$$

Thus the computations above indicate that introducing a unit of P_1 would lose $8 for us. How can this be?

  a. We currently make 15 units of P_1.
  b. Production of 15 tables uses up all the time originally available in machine center 1.
  c. To introduce another P_1, we would have to give up 1 of the current 15 P_1s.
  d. Giving up a table would cost us $8.

The new $C_j - Z_j$ row (net profit per unit) is:

Variables	Profit/unit (C_j)	−	profit lost/unit (Z_j)	=	net profit/unit ($C_j - Z_j$)
P_1	$8	−	$8	=	$0
P_2	$6	−	$4	=	$2
P_3	$0	−	$2	=	$-2
P_4	$0	−	$0	=	$0

The completed second tableau is shown in Table 9-7. Certainly the total profit from this second solution ($120) is an improvement over the zero profit in the first solution.

Table 9-7

C_j	Product mix	Quantity	$8 P_1	$6 P_2	$0 P_3	$0 P_4
$8	P_1	15	1	½	¼	0
$0	P_4	18	0	3	−½	1
	Z_j	$120	$8	$4	$2	$0
	$C_j - Z_j$		$0	$2	$−2	$0

SECOND SIMPLEX TABLEAU COMPLETED

The presence of a positive number ($2) in the P_2 column of the $C_j - Z_j$ row of the second solution (Table 9-7) indicates that further improvement is possible. Therefore the same process used to develop the second solution must be repeated to develop a third solution.

1. A look at the $C_j - Z_j$ row of the second tableau (Table 9-7) shows that P_2, chairs, contributes a *net* profit of $2 per unit.

C_j	Profit per unit of P_2	$6
Z_j	Profit lost per unit of P_2	(−)$4
$C_j - Z_j$	Net profit per unit of P_2	$2

The optimum column, therefore, in Table 9-7 is the P_2 column. Chairs will now be added, replacing one of the variables, P_1 or P_4, in the second solution.

2. The replaced row is found as before by dividing 15 and 18 in the quantity column by their corresponding numbers in the optimum column and selecting the row with the smaller ratio as the replaced row.

$$P_1 \text{ row} \quad \frac{15}{\frac{1}{2}} = 30$$

$$P_4 \text{ row} \quad \frac{18}{3} = 6$$

Table 9-8

C_j	Product		$8	$6	$0	$0	
	mix	Quantity	P_1	P_2	P_3	P_4	
$8	P_1	15	1	½	¼	0	
$0	P_4	18	0	③	$-½$	1	←Replaced row (P_4)
	Z_j	$120	$8	$4	$2	$0	
	$C_j - Z_j$		$0	$2	$-2	$0	

Optimum column, replaced row, and intersectional elements of second tableau

Intersectional element of P_1 row

Intersectional element of P_4 row (replaced row)

Optimum column

The P_4 row, the one with the smaller ratio, is designated as the replaced row. The optimum column, replaced row, and intersectional elements of the second tableau are shown in Table 9-8.

3. The replacing row of the third tableau is computed by dividing each number in the replaced row by the intersectional element of the replaced row.

$$\frac{18}{3} = 6 \qquad \frac{0}{3} = 0 \qquad \frac{3}{3} = 1 \qquad \frac{-½}{3} = -⅙ \qquad \frac{1}{3} = ⅓$$

Thus the replacing row of the third tableau is $(6, 0, 1, -⅙, ⅓)$. It assumes the same row position as the replaced row of the second tableau (see Table 9-9).

Table 9-9

C_j	Product		$8	$6	$0	$0	
	mix	Quantity	P_1	P_2	P_3	P_4	
$8	P_1						
$6	P_2	6	0	1	$-⅙$	⅓	← Replacing row
	Z_j						
	$C_j - Z_j$						

Replacing row of third tableau

4. The new values of the P_1 row are

$\begin{pmatrix}\text{Element in}\\ \text{old } P_1 \text{ row}\end{pmatrix}$	$-$	$\begin{pmatrix}\text{intersectional}\\ \text{element}\\ \text{of } P_1 \text{ row}\end{pmatrix}$	$\times$	$\begin{pmatrix}\text{corresponding}\\ \text{element of}\\ \text{replacing row}\end{pmatrix}$	$=$	new P_1 row
15	$-$	($\frac{1}{2}$	$\times$	6)	$=$	12
1	$-$	($\frac{1}{2}$	$\times$	0)	$=$	1
$\frac{1}{2}$	$-$	($\frac{1}{2}$	$\times$	1)	$=$	0
$\frac{1}{4}$	$-$	($\frac{1}{2}$	$\times$	$-\frac{1}{6}$)	$=$	$\frac{1}{3}$
0	$-$	($\frac{1}{2}$	$\times$	$\frac{1}{3}$)	$=$	$-\frac{1}{6}$

The new P_1 row is $(12, 1, 0, \frac{1}{3}, -\frac{1}{6})$. In Table 9-10 it has been added to the third tableau.

Table 9-10

Replacing row and new P_1 row in third tableau

C_j	Product mix	Quantity	$8 P_1	$6 P_2	$0 P_3	$0 P_4
$8	P_1	12	1	0	$\frac{1}{3}$	$-\frac{1}{6}$
$6	P_2	6	0	1	$-\frac{1}{6}$	$\frac{1}{3}$
	Z_j					
	$C_j - Z_j$					

The Z_js of the third tableau are computed as follows:

$Z_{\text{total}} = (\$8)(12) + (\$6)(6) = \$132 = $ total profit from third solution
$Z_{P_1} = (\$8)(1) + (\$6)(0) = \$8$
$Z_{P_2} = (\$8)(0) + (\$6)(1) = \$6$
$Z_{P_3} = (\$8)(\frac{1}{3}) + (\$6)(-\frac{1}{6}) = \$5/3$
$Z_{P_4} = (\$8)(-\frac{1}{6}) + (\$6)(\frac{1}{3}) = \$2/3$

The new $C_j - Z_j$ row (net profit per unit) is computed on page 238.

Variables	Profit/unit (C_j)	$-$	profit lost/unit (Z_j)	$=$	net profit/unit $(C_j - Z_j)$
P_1	\$8	$-$	\$8	$=$	\$0
P_2	\$6	$-$	\$6	$=$	\$0
P_3	\$0	$-$	\$5/3	$=$	\$$-5/3$
P_4	\$0	$-$	\$2/3	$=$	\$$-2/3$

The completed third tableau is shown in Table 9-11. <u>As there is no positive $C_j - Z_j$ value, as no further profit improvement is possible, the optimum solution has been obtained.</u> It is

$$P_1 = 12$$
$$P_2 = 6$$
$$P_3 = 0$$
$$P_4 = 0$$

Profits will be maximized by making 12 tables and 6 chairs and having no unused time in either machine center. The variables P_1 and P_2 appear in the product-mix column with their values represented by the corresponding numbers in the quantity column. The variables P_3 and P_4 do not appear in the product-mix column and, therefore, are equal to zero.

Table 9-11

			THIRD SIMPLEX TABLEAU COMPLETED			
C_j	Product		\$8	\$6	\$0	\$0
	mix	Quantity	P_1	P_2	P_3	P_4
\$8	P_1	12	1	0	$\frac{1}{3}$	$-\frac{1}{6}$
\$6	P_2	6	0	1	$-\frac{1}{6}$	$\frac{1}{3}$
	Z_j	\$132	\$8	\$6	\$5/3	\$2/3
	$C_j - Z_j$		\$0	\$0	\$$-5/3$	\$$-2/3$

← Inverse of original body matrix

The Z_j total, \$132, represents the profit obtained under the optimum solution. The above solution also can be verified by substitution in the initial problem equations:

Profit function:

$$Z = \$8P_1 + \$6P_2 + \$0(P_3 + P_4)$$
$$= \$8(12) + \$6(6) + \$0$$
$$= \$132$$

Problem constraints:

$$4P_1 + 2P_2 \leq 60 \qquad \text{machine center 1}$$
$$4(12) + 2(6) \leq 60$$
$$60 \leq 60$$

$$2P_1 + 4P_2 \leq 48 \qquad \text{machine center 2}$$
$$2(12) + 4(6) \leq 48$$
$$48 \leq 48$$

GENERAL INTERPRETATION OF ALL ELEMENTS IN SIMPLEX TABLEAU

Up to now, the discussion has centered on the mechanics or rules and procedures involved in solving a simplex problem. In addition to the solution, however, the simplex method provides us with important information concerning various alternative solutions and the effect of changes in the basic data upon the solutions. Frequently, this information is as valuable and revealing as the answer itself.

Thus our objective in this section will be to explain the economic significance of all the elements in the simplex tableau—to give meaning to the procedures learned thus far.

In Table 9-12 we have reproduced the second simplex tableau from the preceding section (see Table 9-7) and have numbered each element. Our general interpretation, keyed to each circled number, is as follows.

The quantity column

(1) In the initial simplex tableau (Table 9-2) we noted that P_1 (tables) made the larger contribution per unit to profit and thus should

Table 9-12

Second simplex tableau with each element numbered						
C_j	Product		$8	$6	$0	$0
	mix	Quantity	P_1	P_2	P_3	P_4
		(1)		(12)	(16)	(4)	(8)
$8	P_1	15	1	½	¼	0
		(2)		(13)	(17)	(5)	(9)
$0	P_4	18	0	3	−½	1
		(3)		(14)	(18)	(6)	(10)
	Z_j	$120	$8	$4	$2	$0
			(15)	(19)	(7)	(11)
	$C_j - Z_j$		$0	$2	$−2	$0

be added to the second solution. To find the quantity to be added, we proceeded as follows:

$$\frac{60 \text{ hours available in center 1}}{4 \text{ hours required per table}} = 15 \text{ tables}$$

We found that 15 was the largest quantity which could be made without violating any of the time restrictions in both centers.

Making 15 tables required all the hours available in center 1 (4 hours per unit $\times$ 15 units = 60 hours). Thus P_1 replaced P_3 in the solution.

(2) Each of the 15 tables requires 2 hours in machine center 2. Thus to make 15 tables requires 30 hours (2 hours per unit $\times$ 15 units). Since 48 hours are available and only 30 hours are required, we have 18 hours left in center 2.

In the quantity column we see 15 tables, 18 hours, and $120. Including three different types of item in the same column may seem confusing. This quantity column, however, will never be added. The figure 15 is significant as an element of the P_1 row and not as an element of the quantity column. In similar fashion, 18 is an element of the P_4 row, and $120 is an element of the Z_j row.

③ The $120 represents the total profit from the variables in the product mix.

Number of units of P_1 (tables) $= 15$
Times profit per unit of P_1 $\times \underline{\$\ 8} = \$120$

Number of units of P_4 (unused hours) $= 18$
Times profit per unit of P_4 $\times \underline{\$\ 0} = \underline{0}$

Total profit of second mix $\$120$

The body and identity matrices

The elements within the body matrix and the identity matrix of the simplex tableau represent substitution rates. These are explained below.

④ Since 1 unit of P_1 (1 table) requires 4 hours in center 1, the second solution uses up all the 60 hours in center 1. Therefore, the production of anything else in this machine center would require that some of the tables be given up. For example, if 1 unit of P_3 (1 hour) is made available for other purposes, ¼ table would have to be given up; or stated in another way, every hour of P_3 added to the solution reduces the production of P_1 (tables) by ¼ unit.

⑤ Reducing the production of P_1 (tables) by ¼ unit certainly must have an effect on center 2 because *chairs and tables* must be processed through both machine centers. Because P_1 requires 2 hours per unit in center 2 and because adding 1 unit of P_3 reduces the production of P_1 (tables) by ¼ unit, then ¼ $\times$ 2 $=$ ½ hour is freed in center 2. We can illustrate this another way:

Units of P_1 now in mix	15
If 1 unit of P_3 is added to the mix, P_1 is reduced by	$-$ ¼
New quantity of P_1	14¾
2 hours per unit of P_1 required in center 2	$\times$ 2
Total hours required to make 14¾ units of P_1 (in center 2)	29½
Total hours required to make $15P_1$ (2×15)	30
Total hours freed by adding 1 unit of P_3	½

(8) Adding 1 unit of P_4 has no effect (0) on P_1. Why? Since machine center 1 is the limiting center (all hours have been used), making available 1 hour of P_4 in machine center 2 will have no effect on the production of tables. Since 18 hours are still available in center 2, we can make one of them available without reducing our production of tables.

(9) Withdrawing 1 unit of P_4 removes 1 unit of P_4. Why? Since there are only 18 hours available in center 2 in the second solution, we can withdraw 1 hour ($1P_4$) only if we remove 1 hour ($1P_4$) from the 18 hours now available. Adding 1 hour ($1P_4$) would increase the time available in center 2 by 1 hour, making the total 49 hours. But this is impossible, because the total time available in center 2 is 48 hours. Thus in the second solution, if we add 1 hour ($1P_4$), we must subtract 1 hour ($1P_4$) in order not to exceed the 48 hours.

(12) Here again we have a 1-for-1 substitution, that is, each unit of P_1 added to the production schedule replaces 1 unit of P_1 in the solution. From (1) we found that 15 was the largest quantity of tables that could be processed in center 1. Thus in order to add another table ($1P_1$) and at the same time satisfy the time restriction in center 1 (60 hours available), we must subtract or give up 1 table to make the necessary time available.

(13) Adding 1 unit of P_1 to the production schedule has no effect on P_4. Why? From (12) we found that adding 1 table ($1P_1$) required giving up 1 table ($1P_1$), so that the net change in center 2 must be zero $(1 - 1 = 0)$. Since there is no real change in center 1, neither is there any change in center 2; no additional hours are required.

(16) Adding 1 unit of P_2 (chair) to the program replaces $\frac{1}{2}P_1$ (table). A chair ($1P_2$) requires 2 hours per unit in center 1, and a table ($1P_1$) requires 4 hours. Now, because center 1 is the limiting center (time is exhausted), processing 1 chair would require giving up $\frac{2}{4}$, or $\frac{1}{2}$, table ($\frac{1}{2}P_1$). Stated in another way, processing a chair in center 1 takes 2 of the 4 hours required to make a table. Thus for every chair processed in center 1, $\frac{1}{2}$ table must be given up to provide the necessary 2 hours.

(17) Adding 1 unit of P_2 (chair) replaces 3 units of P_4 (3 hours). The problem originally stated that $1P_2$ required 4 hours in center 2.

How can we justify this apparent inconsistency? First note that adding 1 chair $(1P_2)$ replaces ½ table (from ⑯). Second, a table requires 2 hours in center 2. Thus giving up ½ table frees 1 hour in center 2 (½ × 2 hours required per unit of P_1 = 1 hour). The 4 hours required to make a chair in center 2 minus the 1 hour freed equals 3 hours net change. Processing a chair still requires 4 hours per unit: 3 hours plus the 1 hour freed equals the 4 hours required. The inconsistency, therefore, disappears when we consider the effect of a change in not *one* center but *both* centers. Chairs and tables must be processed in both machine centers in order to make a completed unit. Thus any change in center 1 must have an effect in center 2.

In summary, the elements within the body and identity matrices of the simplex tableau represent marginal rates of substitution between the variables in the product mix and the variables heading the column. We found that a positive rate of substitution, for example, ⑯, indicates the decrease in P_1 that occurs if 1 unit of P_2 is added to the program. On the other hand, a negative rate of substitution, for example, ⑤, indicates the increase in P_4 (i.e., ½ hour freed) that occurs if 1 unit of P_3 is added to the program.

The Z_j row

We turn now to an explanation of the elements in the Z_j row; these represent the loss of profit that results from the addition of 1 unit of the variable heading the column.

⑥ Adding 1 unit of P_3 results in two changes: First, P_1 is decreased by ¼ unit (see ④); second, P_4 is increased by ½ unit (½ hour freed; see ⑤). How much profit would we lose if these two changes took place? Since profit per unit of P_1 is \$8 and P_1 is decreased by ¼ unit, the profit lost from this change would be \$8 × ¼P_1 = \$2. Because profit per unit of P_4 is \$0, the increase in P_4 by ½ unit results in no loss (\$0 × ½P_4 = \$0). The *total* profit lost, then, is the sum of the losses resulting from the two changes, or \$2 + \$0 = \$2.

The same reasoning process applies to the other elements of the Z_j row. We want to know first, the changes which occur when 1 unit of the variable heading the column is added; second, the loss of profit from each change; and third, the total profit lost—the sum of the losses of each change.

⑩ With the addition of 1 unit of P_4:

Change 1. No change in P_1 (see **⑧**)	0
Profit per unit of P_1	× $8
Loss	$0

Change 2. $1P_4$ given up (see **⑨**)	1
Profit per unit of P_4	× $0
Loss	$0

Total loss $0

⑭ With the addition of 1 unit of P_1:

Change 1. $1P_1$ given up (see **⑫**)	1
Profit per unit of P_1	× $8
Loss	$8

Change 2. No change in P_4 (see **⑬**)	0
Profit per unit of P_4	× $0
Loss	$0

Total loss $8

⑱ With the addition of 1 unit of P_2:

Change 1. ½P_1 given up (see **⑯**)	½
Profit per unit of P_1	× $8
Loss	$4

Change 2. $3P_4$ given up (see **⑰**)	3
Profit per unit of P_4	× $0
Loss	$0

Total loss $4

The $C_j - Z_j$ row

Each positive number in the $C_j - Z_j$ row represents the net profit obtainable if 1 unit of the variable heading that column were added to the solution. The following examples help to illustrate this point.

19 The positive number 2 represents the net profit if 1 unit of P_2 (1 chair) were added.

Total profit per unit of P_2	$6
Less total profit per unit lost (see **18**)	− 4
Net profit	$2

So long as there is a positive dollar figure in the $C_j - Z_j$ row, further improvement in profit can and should be made. Why? Because for each unit of P_2 added, we can increase the profit of $120 by $2. Element **2** (18 hours) and element **17** (3 hours per chair) indicate that 18/3, or 6, chairs can be added.

15 Total profit per unit of P_1	$8
Total profit per unit lost (see **14**)	− 8
Net profit	$0

For every unit of P_1 added, total profit will not change. The explanation is that we are already producing as many tables as possible under the time restrictions in machine center 1. If we add $1P_1$ to the solution, we must give up $1P_1$. Adding 1 unit of P_1 results in a profit increase of $8, but giving up 1 unit of P_1 results in a profit decrease of $8. Thus nothing is added to total profit.

11 Total profit per unit of P_4	$0
Total profit per unit lost (see **10**)	− 0
Net profit	$0

Each unit of P_4 added to the program will not change total profit. Again the explanation is that center 1 limits the production of tables to 15. Therefore adding 1 unit of P_4 has no effect on P_1 (see **8**). Total profit, then, cannot be increased by adding any units of P_4.

7 Total profit per unit of P_3	$0
Less total profit per unit lost (see **6**)	− 2
Net loss	$−2

A negative number (a net loss) in the $C_j - Z_j$ row indicates the decrease in total profit if 1 unit of the variable heading that column were added to the product mix. In this case, each unit of P_3 added to the program will decrease total profit by \$2. Why? From $\textcircled{4}$ we found that for every unit of P_3 added, $\frac{1}{4}$ table would have to be given up. Profit per unit of P_3 is \$0, but profit per unit of P_1 is \$8. So each P_3 added would result in a \$2 loss (\$8 $\times$ $\frac{1}{4}$ = \$2).

A negative number in the $C_j - Z_j$ row under one of the columns representing time (P_3 or P_4) has another interpretation. A negative number here represents the amount of increase in total profit if the number of hours available in that center could be increased by 1. For example, in $\textcircled{7}$ if 1 more hour ($1P_3$) were available in machine center 1 (i.e., if $P_3 = 61$ instead of 60 in the initial solution, Table 9-2), then total profit could be *increased* by \$2. This can be proved by using the equation representing the time restriction in center 1 altered to reflect the addition of 1 hour.

If $\qquad 4P_1 + 2P_2 + P_3 = 61$ $\qquad\qquad\qquad\qquad$ (9-3)

and we let $\qquad P_3 = 0 \qquad$ Since P_2 and P_3 are not in the
$\qquad\qquad\qquad\quad P_2 = 0 \qquad$ second solution, they are equal to 0.

then $4P_1 + 2(0) + 0 = 61$
$$4P_1 = 61 - 2(0) - 0$$
$$= 61$$
$$P_1 = 61/4$$

Substituting $P_1 = 61/4$ for P_1 in the profit function yields the following total profit:

Profit $= \$8P_1 + \$6P_2 + \$0P_3 + \$0P_4 \qquad\qquad$ (8-3)
$$= \$8(61/4) + \$6(0) + \$0 + \$0$$
$$= \$122$$

Note that making available 1 additional hour in center 1 would increase total profit by \$2.

With this information, the manager may want to investigate the possibilities of expanding the capacity in center 1.

In summary, a *positive number* in the $C_j - Z_j$ row indicates the amount of increase in total profit possible if 1 unit of the variable heading that column were added to the solution. A *negative number* in the

$C_j - Z_j$ row indicates the amount of decrease in total profit if 1 unit of the variable heading that column were added to the solution. A negative number in the $C_j - Z_j$ row *under the identity matrix also* can be thought of as the amount of increase in total profit obtainable if 1 more hour in the center heading that column were available.

A MINIMIZATION PROBLEM

Up to this point the discussion has involved a profit maximization problem. The simplex method can also be used in problems where the objective is to minimize costs.

For example, an animal feed company must produce 200 pounds of a mixture consisting of ingredients X_1 and X_2. X_1 costs \$3 per pound, and X_2 \$8 per pound. No more than 80 pounds of X_1 can be used, and at least 60 pounds of X_2 must be used. The problem then is to find how much of each ingredient should be used if the company wants to minimize cost.

The cost function can now be written as

$$\text{Cost} = \$3X_1 + \$8X_2$$

One restriction or constraint in the problem is that we must produce 200 pounds of the mixture—no more, no less. Stated mathematically, this statement becomes

$$X_1 + X_2 = 200 \text{ pounds}$$

This equation means that the number of pounds of X_1 plus the number of pounds of X_2 must equal 200 pounds.

The second restriction is that no more than 80 pounds of X_1 can be used. We may use less than 80 pounds but must not exceed 80 pounds. In mathematical language this is written as follows:

$$X_1 \leq 80 \text{ pounds}$$

The third restriction is that at least 60 pounds of X_2 must be used. We may use more than 60 pounds but not less than 60 pounds. Mathematically, this is expressed as follows:

$$X_2 \geq 60$$

In summary, then, the problem stated in mathematical form is

Minimize $\quad$ Cost $= \$3X_1 + \$8X_2$

subject to: $\quad X_1 + X_2 = 200$ pounds $\qquad\qquad$ (9-4)

$\qquad\qquad\quad X_1 \leq 80$ pounds

$\qquad\qquad\quad X_2 \geq 60$ pounds

At this point, it might be helpful to state that irrespective of whether the goal is to maximize profits or minimize costs, the steps in setting up the problem are similar, and once the first solution is formulated, the procedure is much the same.

Now consider the first restriction in this minimization problem represented by an equality:

$X_1 + X_2 = 200$ pounds

Remember from the manufacturing problem that our first need was for a solution—*any* technically feasible solution—so that we could start moving toward the final, the optimum, solution. Our first solution in the manufacturing problem netted us zero profit. This was a ridiculous solution profitwise, *but* it served as a starting point or base for improvement and refinement.

In this cost minimization problem, we once again need a starting solution. It too will be ridiculous costwise. It too will be a point of departure in our search for the lowest cost mixture.

Suppose we decide to let $X_1 = 0$ and $X_2 = 200$. We have observed all restrictions; our solution is

$\qquad X_1 + X_2 = 200$

$\qquad 0 + 200 = 200$

$\qquad\qquad 200 = 200 \qquad$ (Restriction is satisfied.)

$\qquad\qquad X_1 \leq 80$

$\qquad\qquad\quad 0 \leq 80 \qquad$ (Restriction is satisfied.)

$\qquad\qquad X_2 \geq 60$

$\qquad\qquad 200 \geq 60 \qquad$ (Restriction is satisfied.)

In a more realistic problem, one involving 12 ingredients (and each with its own restrictions), finding a first solution by inspection is almost impossible. Our need, then, is for a simple procedure which will generate a first solution in all problems, no matter how complicated.

Let us start by not putting any X_1 or X_2 into our first solution. Instead, start with 200 pounds of X_3—an artificial variable representing a new ingredient.

$$X_1 + X_2 + X_3 = 200$$
$$0 + 0 + 200 = 200$$
$$200 = 200 \qquad \text{(Restriction is satisfied.)}$$

Just what is X_3? It can be thought of as a very expensive substance ($100 a pound) which could substitute satisfactorily for our end product.

Our first solution, then, consists entirely of 200 pounds of X_3 at $100 per pound. Although this is ridiculous costwise, it does represent a technically feasible solution in that the product would fill our customers' needs.

Because of its high price ($100 versus $8 and $3), X_3 must not be present in our optimum solution.

In linear programming terminology, this type of variable (X_3) is called an *artificial variable*. It is only of value as a computational device; it allows two types of restrictions to be treated: the equality type and the greater-than-or-equal-to type.

The second restriction in this problem is of a type with which we are familiar.

$$X_1 \leq 80 \text{ pounds}$$

Because X_1 in the final solution may turn out to be less than 80 pounds, we must add a slack variable in order to form an equation.

$$X_1 + X_4 = 80 \text{ pounds}$$

The slack variable X_4 represents the difference between 80 pounds of X_1 and the actual number of pounds of X_1 in the final solution.

Finally, there is a third restriction:

$$X_2 \geq 60 \text{ pounds}$$

To convert this inequality into an equation, we must *subtract* a slack variable.

$$X_2 - X_5 = 60 \text{ pounds}$$

The negative slack variable X_5 represents the amount by which X_2 will exceed 60 pounds in the final solution. For example, if X_2 in the final solution equals 130 pounds, then X_5 must equal 70 pounds in order for the equation to hold. Of course, if X_2 equals 60 pounds in the final solution, then the value of X_5 would have to be 0.

We see at once that if $X_2 = 0$ in the first solution, then $0 - X_5 = 60$, or $X_5 = -60$. This equation is not a feasible one in the first solution because -60 pounds of an ingredient is not possible: -60 pounds makes no more sense than -12 tables or -6 chairs. What shall we do?

One approach is to prevent X_5 from appearing in the first solution. But what takes its place to keep the equation in balance? If X_2 is zero and X_5 is zero in the first solution, then we must introduce a new ingredient—one that is an acceptable substitute for X_2, one that will take the place of X_2 in the first solution. As in the case of X_3, this new ingredient (X_6) can be thought of as a very expensive substance—$100 a pound. The high price of X_6 assures us that it will never appear in our final solution. Thus the original restriction of $X_2 \geq 60$ was first changed to $X_2 - X_5 = 60$ by the addition of a slack variable; now the present change revises this into $X_2 - X_5 + X_6 = 60$ by the inclusion of an artificial variable. The equation in the first solution still holds because $X_2 = 0$ and $X_5 = 0$.

We stated that the artificial variables X_3 and X_6 would be assigned a very high cost, $100 a pound. To avoid having to work with extremely large numbers, we let the letter M represent $100. This will simplify the calculations to follow.

The cost function and the restriction equations ready for the initial simplex tableau are shown below:

$$
\begin{aligned}
\text{Minimize} \quad & \text{Cost} = \$3X_1 + \$8X_2 \\
\text{subject to:} \quad & X_1 + X_2 + X_3 && = 200 \\
& X_1 \qquad\qquad + X_4 && = 80 \qquad\qquad (9\text{-}5) \\
& \quad X_2 \qquad\quad - X_5 + X_6 && = 60
\end{aligned}
$$

We must show zero cost for the slack variables X_4 and X_5, and we must show $M cost for the artificial variables X_3 and X_6. These we include in our cost function:

$$
\text{Cost} = \$3X_1 + \$8X_2 + \$MX_3 + \$0X_4 - \$0X_5 + \$MX_6
$$

As was noted when the first restraint equations, Eqs. (9-1) and (9-2), were introduced, any unknown that occurs in one restraint equation must appear in all equations. Consequently we must now insert the appropriate variables with zero coefficients into the restraint equations.

Here is our problem ready for the simplex solution:

Minimize Cost $= \$3X_1 + \$8X_2 + \$MX_3 + \$0X_4 - \$0X_5 + \$MX_6$
subject to: $X_1 + X_2 + X_3 + 0X_4 + 0X_5 + 0X_6 = 200$
$$X_1 + 0X_2 + 0X_3 + X_4 + 0X_5 + 0X_6 = 80 \qquad (9\text{-}6)$$
$$0X_1 + X_2 + 0X_3 + 0X_4 - X_5 + X_6 = 60$$

The first simplex tableau is shown in Table 9-13. Note that the total cost of the first solution, $260M, is extremely high. Since the objective is to minimize costs, the optimum column is found by selecting that column which has the largest *negative* value in the $C_j - Z_j$ row (that column whose value will decrease costs the most). A glance at the $C_j - Z_j$ row shows only two negative values, $3 - M and $8 - 2M. As $8 - 2M is the larger negative number in the $C_j - Z_j$ row ($8 - 2M is $-192, while $3 - M is only $-97), X_2 is the optimum column.

Table 9-13

C_j	Product mix	Quantity	$3 X_1	$8 X_2	$M X_3	$0 X_4	$0 X_5	$M X_6	
$M	X_3	200	1	1	1	0	0	0	
$0	X_4	80	1	0	0	1	0	0	
$M	X_6	60	0	1	0	0	-1	1	← Replaced row
	Z_j	$260M	$M	$2M	$M	$0	$-M	$M	
	$C_j - Z_j$		$3 - M	$8 - 2M	$0	$0	$M	$0	

Initial simplex tableau: minimization problem

— Optimum column

The computational procedures for finding the replaced row, the replacing row, all other new rows, the Z_j row, and the $C_j - Z_j$ row are exactly the same as those for the maximization problem.

Computations for the initial tableau Table 9-13 are as follows:

Z_j row:

$$Z_{TOTAL} = (\$M)(200) + (\$0)(80) + (\$M)(60) = \$260M$$
$$Z_{X_1} = (\$M)(1) + (\$0)(1) + (\$M)(0) = \$M$$
$$Z_{X_2} = (\$M)(1) + (\$0)(0) + (\$M)(1) = \$2M$$
$$Z_{X_3} = (\$M)(1) + (\$0)(0) + (\$M)(0) = \$M$$
$$Z_{X_4} = (\$M)(0) + (\$0)(1) + (\$M)(0) = \$0$$
$$Z_{X_5} = (\$M)(0) + (\$0)(0) + (\$M)(-1) = \$-M$$
$$Z_{X_6} = (\$M)(0) + (\$0)(0) + (\$M)(1) = \$M$$

$C_j - Z_j$ row:

$$C_{X_1} - Z_{X_1} = \$3 - \$M = \$3 - M$$
$$C_{X_2} - Z_{X_2} = \$8 - \$2M = \$8 - 2M$$
$$C_{X_3} - Z_{X_3} = \$M - \$M = \$0$$
$$C_{X_4} - Z_{X_4} = \$0 - \$0 = \$0$$
$$C_{X_5} - Z_{X_5} = \$0 - (\$-M) = \$M$$
$$C_{X_6} - Z_{X_6} = \$M - \$M = \$0$$

Replaced row:

X_3 row $200/1 = 200$
X_4 row $80/0$ (Since $80/0$ is not a mathematical concept, this row
              is not considered.)
✓ X_6 row $60/1 = 60$ replaced row (smallest quotient)

The second solution is shown in Table 9-14.   Computations for the second simplex tableau are as follows.

Replacing row (X_2):

$$60/1 = 60$$
$$0/1 = 0$$
$$1/1 = 1$$
$$0/1 = 0$$
$$0/1 = 0$$
$$-1/1 = -1$$
$$1/1 = 1$$

Table 9-14

Second simplex tableau: minimization problem

C_j Product mix		Quantity	$3	$8	$M	$0	$0	$M	
			X_1	X_2	X_3	X_4	X_5	X_6	
$M	X_3	140	1	0	1	0	1	−1	Replaced
$0	X_4	80	1	0	0	1	0	0	row
$8	X_2	60	0	1	0	0	−1	1	
	Z_j	$140M + 480	$M	$8	$M	$0	$M − 8	$8 − M	
	$C_j − Z_j$		$3 − M	$0	$0	$0	$8 − M	$2M − 8	

Optimum column

X_3 *row:*

$$200 - 1\,(60) = 140$$
$$1 - 1\,(0) = 1$$
$$1 - 1\,(1) = 0$$
$$1 - 1\,(0) = 1$$
$$0 - 1\,(0) = 0$$
$$0 - 1\,(-1) = 1$$
$$0 - 1\,(1) = -1$$

X_4 *row:*

$$80 - 0\,(60) = 80$$
$$1 - 0\,(0) = 1$$
$$0 - 0\,(1) = 0$$
$$0 - 0\,(0) = 0$$
$$1 - 0\,(0) = 1$$
$$0 - 0\,(-1) = 0$$
$$0 - 0\,(1) = 0$$

Z_j *row:*

$$Z_{\text{TOTAL}} = \$M\,(140) + \$0\,(80) + \$8\,(60) = \$140M + 480$$
$$Z_{X_1} = \$M\,(1) + \$0\,(1) + \$8\,(0) = \$M$$
$$Z_{X_2} = \$M\,(0) + \$0\,(0) + \$8\,(1) = \$8$$
$$Z_{X_3} = \$M\,(1) + \$0\,(0) + \$8\,(0) = \$M$$
$$Z_{X_4} = \$M\,(0) + \$0\,(1) + \$8\,(0) = \$0$$
$$Z_{X_5} = \$M\,(1) + \$0\,(0) + \$8\,(-1) = \$M - 8$$
$$Z_{X_6} = \$M\,(-1) + \$0\,(0) + \$8\,(1) = \$8 - M$$

$C_j − Z_j$ *row:*

$$C_{X_1} - Z_{X_1} = \$3 - \$M = \$3 - M$$
$$C_{X_2} - Z_{X_2} = \$8 - \$8 = \$0$$
$$C_{X_3} - Z_{X_3} = \$M - \$M = \$0$$
$$C_{X_4} - Z_{X_4} = \$0 - \$0 = \$0$$
$$C_{X_5} - Z_{X_5} = \$0 - \$(M - 8) = \$8 - M$$
$$C_{X_6} - Z_{X_6} = \$M - \$(8 - M) = \$2M - 8$$

Replaced row:

X_3 row $140/1 = 140$

X_4 row $80/1 = 80$ (replaced row)

X_2 row $60/0$ (not defined)

Table 9-15

C_j	Product mix	Quantity	$3 X_1	$8 X_2	$M X_3	$0 X_4	$0 X_5	$M X_6	

Third simplex tableau: minimization problem

C_j	Product mix	Quantity	$3 X_1	$8 X_2	$M X_3	$0 X_4	$0 X_5	$M X_6
\$M	X_3	60	0	0	1	-1	1	-1
\$3	X_1	80	1	0	0	1	0	0
\$8	X_2	60	0	1	0	0	-1	1
	Z_j	\$60M + 720	\$3	\$8	\$M	\$3 − M	\$M − 8	\$8 − M
	$C_j - Z_j$		\$0	\$0	\$0	\$M − 3	\$8 − M	\$2M − 8

Replaced row ←

Optimum column

The third simplex tableau is shown in Table 9-15. Computations for the third simplex tableau are as follows.

Replacing row (X_1):

$80/1 = 80$
$1/1 = 1$
$0/1 = 0$
$0/1 = 0$
$1/1 = 1$
$0/1 = 0$
$0/1 = 0$

X_3 *row:* X_2 *row:*

$140 - 1\,(80) = 60$ $60 - 0\,(80) = 60$
$1 - 1\,(1) = 0$ $0 - 0\,(1) = 0$
$0 - 1\,(0) = 0$ $1 - 0\,(0) = 1$
$1 - 1\,(0) = 1$ $0 - 0\,(0) = 0$
$0 - 1\,(1) = -1$ $0 - 0\,(1) = 0$
$1 - 1\,(0) = 1$ $-1 - 0\,(0) = -1$
$-1 - 1\,(0) = -1$ $1 - 0\,(0) = 1$

Z_j *row:*

$Z_{\text{TOTAL}} = \$M\,(60) + \$3\,(80) + \$8\,(60) = \$720 + \$60M$
$Z_{X_1} = \$M\,(0) + \$3\,(1) + \$8\,(0) = \$3$

$$Z_{X_2} = \$M\ (0) + \$3\ (0) + \$8\ (1) = \$8$$
$$Z_{X_3} = \$M\ (1) + \$3\ (0) + \$8\ (0) = \$M$$
$$Z_{X_4} = \$M\ (-1) + \$3\ (1) + \$8\ (0) = \$3 - M$$
$$Z_{X_5} = \$M\ (1) + \$3\ (0) + \$8\ (-1) = \$M - 8$$
$$Z_{X_6} = \$M\ (-1) + \$3\ (0) + \$8\ (1) = \$8 - M$$

$C_j - Z_j$ row:

Replaced row:

$$C_{X_1} - Z_{X_1} = \$3 - \$3 = \$0$$

X_3 row $60/1 = 60$ (replaced row)

$$C_{X_2} - Z_{X_2} = \$8 - \$8 = \$0$$

X_1 row $80/0$ (not defined mathematically)

$$C_{X_3} - Z_{X_3} = \$M - \$M = \$0$$

$$C_{X_4} - Z_{X_4} = \$0 - \$(3 - M) = \$M - 3$$ X_2 row $60/(-1) = -60$

$$C_{X_5} - Z_{X_5} = \$0 - \$(M - 8) = \$8 - M$$

$$C_{X_6} - Z_{X_6} = \$M - \$(8 - M) = \$2M - 8$$

The fourth simplex tableau is shown in Table 9-16. Computations for the fourth tableau are as follows.

Replacing row (X_5):

$$60/1 = 60$$
$$0/1 = 0$$
$$0/1 = 0$$
$$1/1 = 1$$
$$-1/1 = -1$$
$$1/1 = 1$$
$$-1/1 = -1$$

X_1 row:

$$80 - 0\ (60) = 80$$
$$1 - 0\ (0) = 1$$
$$0 - 0\ (0) = 0$$
$$0 - 0\ (1) = 0$$
$$1 - 0\ (-1) = 1$$
$$0 - 0\ (1) = 0$$
$$0 - 0\ (-1) = 0$$

X_2 row:

$$60 - (-1)\ (60) = 120$$
$$0 - (-1)\ (0) = 0$$
$$1 - (-1)\ (0) = 1$$
$$0 - (-1)\ (1) = 1$$
$$0 - (-1)\ (-1) = -1$$
$$-1 - (-1)\ (1) = 0$$
$$1 - (-1)\ (-1) = 0$$

Table 9-16

C_j	Product mix	Quantity	$3 X_1	$8 X_2	$M X_3	$0 X_4	$0 X_5	$M X_6
			Fourth simplex tableau (optimum solution): minimization problem					
$0	X_5	60	0	0	1	-1	1	-1
$3	X_1	80	1	0	0	1	0	0
$8	X_2	120	0	1	1	-1	0	0
	Z_j	$1,200	$3	$8	$8	$-5	$0	$0
	$C_j - Z_j$		$0	$0	$M - 8	$5	$0	$M

Z_j row:

$$Z_{TOTAL} = \$0\,(60) + \$3\,(80) + \$8\,(120) = \$1{,}200$$
$$Z_{X_1} = \$0\,(0) + \$3\,(1) + \$8\,(0) = \$3$$
$$Z_{X_2} = \$0\,(0) + \$3\,(0) + \$8\,(1) = \$8$$
$$Z_{X_3} = \$0\,(1) + \$3\,(0) + \$8\,(1) = \$8$$
$$Z_{X_4} = \$0\,(-1) + \$3\,(1) + \$8\,(-1) = \$-5$$
$$Z_{X_5} = \$0\,(1) + \$3\,(0) + \$8\,(0) = \$0$$
$$Z_{X_6} = \$0\,(-1) + \$3\,(0) + \$8\,(0) = \$0$$

$C_j - Z_j$ row:

$$C_{X_1} - Z_{X_1} = \$3 - \$3 = \$0$$
$$C_{X_2} - Z_{X_2} = \$8 - \$8 = \$0$$
$$C_{X_3} - Z_{X_3} = \$M - \$8 = \$M - 8$$
$$C_{X_4} - Z_{X_4} = \$0 - \$(-5) = \$5$$
$$C_{X_5} - Z_{X_5} = \$0 - \$0 = \$0$$
$$C_{X_6} - Z_{X_6} = \$M - \$0 = \$M$$

Since in the fourth tableau (Table 9-16) no negative values remain in the $C_j - Z_j$ row, we have reached the optimum solution. It is to use 80 pounds of X_1 and 120 pounds of X_2. This results in a cost of $1,200, the minimum cost combination of X_1 and X_2 which satisfies the restrictions in the problem. We have the 200 pounds of our mixture

(120 + 80) required. Note that the slack variable X_5 is also in the solution. X_5 represents the amount of X_2 used over the minimum quantity required (60 pounds). Substituting the values for X_2 and X_5 in the constraint equation (9-5) $X_2 - X_5 + X_6 = 60$, we have

$$120 - 60 + 0 = 60$$
$$60 = 60$$

Since the artificial variable X_6 is not in the solution, it is equal to zero.

LINEAR PROGRAMMING SOLUTION TO THE TRANSPORTATION PROBLEM

In Chapter 1 we noted a certain type of management problem which lends itself particularly well to a quantitative solution. This kind of problem is generally referred to as the transportation problem and is illustrated by the following example:

The Ajax Company has two factories A and B, located some distance apart, and three regional warehouses R, S, and T, to which finished goods are shipped. The transportation manager must schedule shipments for the coming week according to the following schedule.

Factory A has 100 tons on hand.
Factory B has 200 tons on hand.

Warehouse S requires 60 tons.
Warehouse R requires 70 tons.
Warehouse T requires 50 tons.

The shipping costs are as follows.

A	to	R	$3/ton	B	to	R	$2/ton
A	to	S	$1/ton	B	to	S	$4/ton
A	to	T	$5/ton	B	to	T	$6/ton

There are many possible solutions which will satisfy the needs of the warehouses and at the same time not exceed the stocks at either of the two factories. Our manager is in a quandary as to which *one* of many solutions offers the lowest total weekly shipping cost. For instance, if he were to ship as follows:

A	to	R	70 tons	@	$3 = $210
A	to	S	0 tons		
A	to	T	0 tons		
B	to	R	0 tons		
B	to	S	60 tons	@	$4 = $240
B	to	T	50 tons	@	$6 = $300
	Total cost				$750

Altering the shipping plan as follows would reduce the total cost substantially.

A	to	R	0 tons		
A	to	S	60 tons	@	$1 = $ 60
A	to	T	0 tons		
B	to	R	70 tons	@	$2 = $140
B	to	S	0 tons		
B	to	T	50 tons	@	$6 = $300
	Total cost				$500

Of course, we could play with this problem until we had exhausted all the hundreds of shipping combinations in our search for the least expensive one.

Instead, let us use linear programming to find the *least-cost* solution. We might begin by viewing the problem as follows.

Warehouses					
R	S	T			
			A	100 tons	
					Factories
			B	200 tons	
70 tons	60 tons	50 tons			

We are searching for the optimum quantities of finished product to be shipped from each factory to each warehouse. Therefore let a series of Xs represent these quantities.

Let X_1 represent that quantity shipped from A to R.
Let X_2 represent that quantity shipped from A to S.
Let X_3 represent that quantity shipped from A to T.
Let X_4 represent that quantity shipped from B to R.
Let X_5 represent that quantity shipped from B to S.
Let X_6 represent that quantity shipped from B to T.

Now the problem appears as follows.

	Warehouses				
R	S	T			
X_1	X_2	X_3	A	100 tons	Factories
X_4	X_5	X_6	B	200 tons	
70	60	50			

We will develop our restrictions for the linear programming simplex solution as follows.

Since warehouse R needs 70 tons, $X_1 + X_4$ must $= 70$.
Since warehouse S needs 60 tons, $X_2 + X_5$ must $= 60$.
Since warehouse T needs 50 tons, $X_3 + X_6$ must $= 50$.

and

Because factory A has only 100 tons, $X_1 + X_2 + X_3$ must ≤ 100.
Because factory B has only 200 tons, $X_4 + X_5 + X_6$ must ≤ 200.

Thus our optimum solution must satisfy all five of these conditions.

In our first statement of this problem in linear programming language, we attach the cost coefficients per ton to each of the unknown variables as follows.

Minimize $\$3X_1 + \$1X_2 + \$5X_3 + \$2X_4 + \$4X_5 + \$6X_6$

subject to: $X_1 + X_4 = 70$

$X_2 + X_5 = 60$

$X_3 + X_6 = 50$ (9-7)

$X_1 + X_2 + X_3 \leq 100$

$X_4 + X_5 + X_6 \leq 200$

We can change the two inequalities into equations by adding slack variables X_7 and X_8 as follows.

$$X_1 + X_4 = 70$$
$$X_2 + X_5 = 60$$
$$X_3 + X_6 = 50$$
$$X_1 + X_2 + X_3 + X_7 = 100$$
$$X_4 + X_5 + X_6 + X_8 = 200$$

Now all that remains is to add artificial variables (X_9, X_{10}, and X_{11}) to the first three equations to generate an initial solution.

$$X_1 + X_4 + X_9 = 70$$
$$X_2 + X_5 + X_{10} = 60$$
$$X_3 + X_6 + X_{11} = 50$$
$$X_1 + X_2 + X_3 + X_7 = 100$$
$$X_4 + X_5 + X_6 + X_8 = 200$$

(9-8)

Initial solution:

$$X_9 = 70$$
$$X_{10} = 60$$
$$X_{11} = 50$$
$$X_7 = 100$$
$$X_8 = 200$$

The restrictions for the first simplex tableau appear as follows.

$$X_1 + 0X_2 + 0X_3 + X_4 + 0X_5 + 0X_6$$
$$+ 0X_7 + 0X_8 + X_9 + 0X_{10} + 0X_{11} = 70$$

$$0X_1 + X_2 + 0X_3 + 0X_4 + X_5 + 0X_6$$
$$+ 0X_7 + 0X_8 + 0X_9 + X_{10} + 0X_{11} = 60$$

$$0X_1 + 0X_2 + X_3 + 0X_4 + 0X_5 + X_6$$
$$+ 0X_7 + 0X_8 + 0X_9 + 0X_{10} + X_{11} = 50$$
$$X_1 + X_2 + X_3 + 0X_4 + 0X_5 + 0X_6$$
$$+ X_7 + 0X_8 + 0X_9 + 0X_{10} + 0X_{11} = 100$$
$$0X_1 + 0X_2 + 0X_3 + X_4 + X_5 + X_6$$
$$+ 0X_7 + X_8 + 0X_9 + 0X_{10} + 0X_{11} = 200$$

The first simplex tableau is shown in Table 9-17. Whereas it may first appear that a simplex tableau of this size presents a prodigious amount of work, you must recall from earlier minimization problems that the calculations involved are drastically simplified because the entire body of the tableau is composed of zeros and ones. Actually, the answer to this problem is obtained in four steps. The optimum shipping schedule works out to be

A ships   0   to   R
           60   to   S
           40   to   T

and

B ships   70   to   R
            0   to   S
           10   to   T

yielding a total shipping cost of $460.

The simplex algorithm is quite useful in a wide range of problems which call for one choice to be made from a group of choices too numerous to handle by normal arithmetic methods. This particular application to the transportation problem is given because it is widely used in industry today.

Stepping-stone method

Transportation problems of the type we have just worked *can* be solved by another method sometimes called the stepping-stone method. The stepping-stone method does not require the use of the simplex algorithm and thus *on smaller problems* is somewhat faster.

Table 9-17

Initial simplex tableau: transportation problem

			$3	$1	$5	$2	$4	$6	$0	$0	$M	$M	$M
C_j	Shipping mix	Quantity	X_1	X_2	X_3	X_4	X_5	X_6	X_7	X_8	X_9	X_{10}	X_{11}
$0	X_7	100	1	0	0	1	0	0	0	0	1	0	0
$0	X_8	200	0	1	0	0	1	0	0	0	0	1	0
$M	X_9	70	0	0	1	0	0	1	0	0	0	0	1
$M	X_{10}	60	1	1	1	0	0	0	1	0	0	0	0
$M	X_{11}	50	0	0	0	1	1	1	0	1	0	0	0
	Z_j	$180M	$M	$M	$2M	$M	$M	$2M	$M	$M	$0	$0	$M
	$C_j - Z_j$		$3 − M	$1 − M	$5 − 2M	$2 − M	$4 − M	$6 − 2M	−$M	−$M	$0	$0	$M

↑ Optimum column
(largest negative $C_j - Z_j$)

← Replaced row

262

Originally, the initial solution in the stepping-stone method was obtained by trial and error. This can be quite time-consuming. More recently, timesaving ways of obtaining these initial solutions have appeared.

Because you have already been introduced to the simplex method (universally applicable *regardless* of the size of the problem), the authors do not feel it necessary to present the details of another method.

PROBLEMS

9-1 The Ajax Manufacturing Company makes three products; contribution per unit for each is as follows:

X_1 \$2
X_2 4
X_3 3

Each of these products passes through three manufacturing centers as a part of the production process. Time required in each center to produce 1 unit of each of the three products is as follows:

Product	Center 1	Center 2	Center 3
X_1	3 hours/unit	2 hours/unit	1 hour/unit
X_2	4 hours/unit	1 hour/unit	3 hours/unit
X_3	2 hours/unit	2 hours/unit	2 hours/unit

Each of the three centers has time available for next week as follows:

Center 1   60 hours
Center 2   40 hours
Center 3   80 hours

Determine the optimum product mix for next week's production schedule.

9-2 Maximize $2X_1 + 4X_2 + X_3 + X_4$
subject to these restrictions:

$X_1 + 3X_2 + X_4 \leq 4$
$2X_1 + X_2 \leq 3$
$X_2 + 4X_3 + X_4 \leq 3$

9-3 A customer of the Regal Corporation needs 1,000 pounds of a chemical mixture consisting of three raw materials. Cost per pound for each of these is given as follows:

X_1 \$2/pound
X_2 3/pound
X_3 4/pound

The customer requires the mixture to meet the following conditions:

a. The mix must contain at least 200 pounds of X_2.
b. The mix cannot contain more than 400 pounds of X_1.
c. The mix must contain at least 100 pounds of X_3.

Determine the least-cost mixture for the batch of 1,000 pounds which will satisfy the customer's requirements.

9-4   A producer of dolomitic limestone for agricultural use has three lime quarries which supply five regional warehouses. The inventory position of each of the quarries this week is as follows:

Quarry	Tons lime on hand
1	200
2	100
3	150

Transportation costs per ton from each quarry to each of the regional warehouses are shown in the following table:

Quarries	Warehouses				
	1	2	3	4	5
1	$5/ton	$1/ton	$6/ton	$3/ton	$1/ton
2	$2/ton	$3/ton	$4/ton	$5/ton	$4/ton
3	$4/ton	$2/ton	$3/ton	$2/ton	$3/ton

The warehouses need lime for next week in the following quantities:

Warehouse 1	80 tons
Warehouse 2	90 tons
Warehouse 3	100 tons
Warehouse 4	70 tons
Warehouse 5	60 tons

Determine the shipping schedule for next week that will minimize the total cost of satisfying the requirements of each of the five warehouses.

9-5   During the coming week a factory can manufacture combinations of the following products:

Product	Contribution per unit
X_1	$3
X_2	4
X_3	5
X_4	2
X_5	6

The manufacturing facilities of the firm are divided into four centers through which the products may or may not have to pass, depending on individual manufacturing requirements. Individual requirements for each product in terms of hours and the total number of available hours in each center are given below:

Product	Center 1	Center 2	Center 3	Center 4
X_1	3 hours/unit	8 hours/unit	2 hours/unit	6 hours/unit
X_2	4 hours/unit	3 hours/unit	1 hour/unit	0 hours/unit
X_3	2 hours/unit	2 hours/unit	0 hours/unit	2 hours/unit
X_4	2 hours/unit	1 hour/unit	3 hours/unit	4 hours/unit
X_5	5 hours/unit	4 hours/unit	4 hours/unit	3 hours/unit
Total hours available	700	600	400	900

In addition to the above manufacturing restrictions on output, the following list represents the maximum sales anticipated for each of the five products during the coming week. No production is scheduled for inventory.

X_1 100 units
X_2 50 units
X_3 90 units
X_4 70 units
X_5 30 units

Each of the five products is made from five raw materials, A, B, C, D, and E. The following table illustrates the per unit requirements in pounds for each product and the total availability of each raw material for the coming week:

Product	A	B	C	D	E
X_1	4 lb/unit	2 lb/unit	0 lb/unit	1 lb/unit	3 lb/unit
X_2	7 lb/unit	4 lb/unit	4 lb/unit	0 lb/unit	4 lb/unit
X_3	6 lb/unit	2 lb/unit	5 lb/unit	7 lb/unit	0 lb/unit
X_4	1 lb/unit	1 lb/unit	6 lb/unit	4 lb/unit	2 lb/unit
X_5	3 lb/unit	0 lb/unit	2 lb/unit	3 lb/unit	4 lb/unit
Total pounds available	1,000	900	300	400	1,600

If the company desires to maximize the contributions of the products to overhead and profit, what should the optimum manufacturing schedule be for next week?

BIBLIOGRAPHY

A. Chung, *Linear Programming* (Columbus, Ohio: Charles E. Merrill Books, Inc., 1963).

S. I. Gass, *Linear Programming* (New York: McGraw-Hill Book Company, 1958).

A. Kaufmann, *Methods and Models of Operations Research* (Englewood Cliffs, N.J.: Prentice-Hall, Inc., 1963).

R. W. Llewellyn, *Linear Programming* (New York: Holt, Rinehart and Winston, Inc., 1964).

T. H. Naylor and E. T. Byrne, *Linear Programming* (Belmont, Calif.: Wadsworth Publishing Company, Inc., 1963).

A. Shuchman, *Scientific Decision Making in Business* (New York: Holt, Rinehart and Winston, Inc., 1963).

R. S. Stockton, *Introduction to Linear Programming* (Boston: Allyn and Bacon, Inc., 1960).

chapter ten GAMES AND STRATEGIES

The generic term "games" is used in this chapter to refer to general situations of conflict over time. Most of us are familiar with certain parlor games (bridge, poker, checkers, chess) the objectives and rules of which are known to the participants. We know, in addition, that experience often enables one player to predict with some accuracy the reactions of opponents to some particular strategy he might pursue. In games, the participants are competitors; the success of one is normally at the expense of the others. Each player selects and executes those strategies and tactics which he believes will result in his winning the game.

Certain characteristics of simple games are also characteristics of many situations of business conflict. In games, players make use of deductive and inductive mathematical techniques in attempting to determine an optimum strategy for winning. The mathematics of the theory of games is of interest to us for this reason.

TWO-PERSON ZERO-SUM GAMES

Our treatment of the theory of games will be limited to two-person games: to situations of conflict where there are only two participants. Many management situations, obviously, involve the participation of many persons and thus are not examples of two-person games. The mathematics for three-person and larger games, however, is too complex to include in a text of this type. Just remember that the basics underlying the generation of optimum or winning strategies in conflict situations must respect the same principles of inductive and deductive logic, regardless of the number of participants.

A two-person game is illustrated in Table 10-1. The players, X and Y, are equal in intelligence and ability. Each has a choice of two strat-

Table 10-1

A two-person game		
	Player Y	
Player X	Strategy Q	Strategy R
Strategy M	X wins 2 points	X wins 3 points
Strategy N	Y wins 1 point	Y wins 2 points

egies. Each knows the outcomes (referred to as payoffs) for every possible combination of strategies; these are shown in the body of the table. Note that the game is biased against player Y; but since he is required to play, he will do his best. This is roughly equivalent to the business situation in which short-run loss is inevitable; these losses must be minimized by good strategy. The solution to this simple game is easily obtained by analyzing the possible strategies of each player:

1. X wins the game only by playing his strategy M; thus he plays M all the time.

2. Y realizes that X will play strategy M all the time and, in an effort to minimize X's gains, plays his strategy Q.

3. The solution to the game is thus M, Q (strategy M and strategy Q).

4. X wins 2 points (Y loses 2 points) each time the game is played; thus the value of the game to X is 2; the value of the game to Y is −2.

The term "value of the game" used in this sense is the average winnings per play over a long series of plays. Though player Y loses in this game, he is still playing his optimum strategy, i.e., minimizing his losses. If he had adopted strategy R, his losses would have been 3 points per play, on the average.

The simple game illustrated in Table 10-1 is a two-person zero-sum game. The term "zero-sum" is used because the sum of the gains (X wins 2 points in each play) exactly equals the sum of the losses (Y loses 2 points in each play). Our discussion of games will focus on this two-person zero-sum type, a type which can be solved with ordinary algebra or matrix algebra.

STANDARD LANGUAGE FOR GAMES

Using certain universal language, games can be written in a much more concise form than that used in Table 10-1. Here is the same game in abbreviated form:

$$ \begin{array}{c} \ Y \\ X \begin{pmatrix} 2 & 3 \\ -1 & -2 \end{pmatrix} \end{array} \qquad (10\text{-}1) $$

The game has now been expressed as a matrix. This matrix is called the *payoff* or *payout* matrix. The four individual payoff possibilities are expressed as numbers; a positive number indicates a payoff to the player who plays the rows (X); a negative number indicates a payoff to the player who plays the columns (Y). The possible strategies for player X are row 1 and row 2 (reading from top to bottom as in standard matrix form); the possible strategies for Y are column 1 and column 2 (reading from left to right as in standard matrix form).

Below are illustrated several payoff matrices, with a detailed explanation of the payoff possibilities to the right of each example.

$a.$ X $\begin{pmatrix} 2 & 4 \\ 1 & -3 \end{pmatrix}$ Ⓧ

	Q	R
M	X wins 2 points	X wins 4 points
N	X wins 1 point	Y wins 3 points

(Columns labeled Y, with Ⓨ above, Q and R)

$b.$ X $\begin{pmatrix} 2 & 0 & 4 \\ 1 & -3 & 2 \end{pmatrix}$ Ⓧ

	Q	R	S
M	X wins 2 points	Neither player wins	X wins 4 points
N	X wins 1 point	Y wins 3 points	X wins 2 points

(Columns labeled Y, with Ⓨ above, Q, R, S)

$c.$ X $\begin{pmatrix} 1 & -3 \\ 2 & 4 \\ -1 & 5 \end{pmatrix}$ Ⓧ

	Q	R
M	X wins 1 point	Y wins 3 points
N	X wins 2 points	X wins 4 points
O	Y wins 1 point	X wins 5 points

(Columns labeled Y, with Ⓨ above, Q and R)

$d.$ X $\begin{pmatrix} 3 & 2 & -2 \\ 1 & -3 & -4 \\ 0 & 1 & -3 \end{pmatrix}$ Ⓧ

	Q	R	S
M	X wins 3 points	X wins 2 points	Y wins 2 points
N	X wins 1 point	Y wins 3 points	Y wins 4 points
O	Neither player wins	X wins 1 point	Y wins 3 points

(Columns labeled Y, with Ⓨ above, Q, R, S)

$e.$ X $\begin{pmatrix} 1 & -3 \\ 4 & 0 \\ 3 & -1 \end{pmatrix}$ Ⓧ

	Q	R
M	X wins 1 point	Y wins 3 points
N	X wins 4 points	Neither player wins
O	X wins 3 points	Y wins 1 point

(Columns labeled Y, with Ⓨ above, Q and R)

In cases b, c, d, and e, one or both players had more than two choices of strategies. All these games are still two-person games, regardless of the number of strategies open to each player.

The matrices shown above are now repeated below, with an explanation of how the optimum strategies for each player were determined. In each case the value of the game is circled.

a. X $\begin{pmatrix} ② & 4 \\ 1 & -3 \end{pmatrix}$ Y

Y observes that his only chance to win, -3, occurs if X plays row 2; he realizes X will never play row 2 for that reason, but will play row 1. Y then must play column 1 to reduce his average loss to 2 points instead of 4. The final strategies are X, 1; Y, 1.

b. X $\begin{pmatrix} 2 & ⓪ & 4 \\ 1 & -3 & 2 \end{pmatrix}$ Y

X observes that Y's only chance to win, -3, occurs if X plays row 2; hence X plays row 1 each time. To minimize his losses, Y then plays column 2. Neither player wins. Strategies: X, 1; Y, 2.

c. X $\begin{pmatrix} 1 & -3 \\ ② & 4 \\ -1 & 5 \end{pmatrix}$ Y

X observes that Y cannot win if X plays row 2; hence X plays row 2 each time. Y then plays column 1 to minimize his losses. Strategies: X, 2; Y, 1.

d. X $\begin{pmatrix} 3 & 2 & ⊖② \\ 1 & -3 & -4 \\ 0 & 1 & -3 \end{pmatrix}$ Y

Y observes that X cannot win if Y plays column 3, hence Y plays column 3 each time. To minimize his losses, X must then play row 1. Strategies: X, 1; Y, 3.

e. X $\begin{pmatrix} 1 & -3 \\ 4 & ⓪ \\ 3 & -1 \end{pmatrix}$ Y

Y observes that he can keep X from winning by playing column 2 on each play. X counters by playing row 2 each time to ensure against losing. Neither player wins. Strategies: X, 2; Y, 2.

PURE STRATEGIES AND SADDLE POINTS

In each of the cases above, there is *one* strategy for player X and *one* strategy for player Y that will eventually be played each time. They may experiment for a while, but in time they will adopt the strategy we have illustrated; this assumes, of course, that each player desires to win (or to minimize his losses if he cannot win). In each of these games, each player has a *pure strategy*, one he plays all the time. The payoff which is obtained when each player plays his pure strategy is called a *saddle point*; or expressed a little differently, the saddle point is the *value* of a game in which each player has a pure strategy.

A saddle point can be recognized because it is *both* the smallest numerical value in its row *and* the largest numerical value in its column. Ponder for a moment the significance of this. Player Y would rather have as a payoff the smallest numerical value in any row. Player X would rather have as a payoff the largest numerical value in any column. Naturally, when there is one numerical value which satisfies both these conditions (a saddle point), both players will be playing optimally if each chooses that value. Of course, not all two-person games have a saddle point. Examination of the game matrix will reveal whether one is present. When a saddle point is present, complex calculations to determine optimum strategies and game value are unnecessary.

Now let us look at other games, some of which have saddle points. In cases where saddle points exist, they are circled and the strategies and value of the game are shown.

$a.$ $\begin{pmatrix} 1 & 0 \\ -4 & 3 \end{pmatrix}$ No saddle point (There is no payoff which is *both* the smallest value in its row *and* the largest value in its column.)

$b.$ $\begin{pmatrix} 6 & ② \\ -1 & -4 \end{pmatrix}$ Strategies: X, 1; Y, 2
Game value: $+2$ (The payoff, 2, is the smallest value in its row and the largest value in its column.)

$c.$ $\begin{pmatrix} -7 & 7 & 8 \\ ④ & -3 & -2 \end{pmatrix}$ Strategies: X, 2; Y, 1
Game value: -4

$d.$ $\begin{pmatrix} 4 & -2 & 3 \\ 0 & 5 & 6 \end{pmatrix}$ No saddle point

$$e. \begin{pmatrix} 1 & 2 \\ 3 & 4 \\ 5 & -6 \end{pmatrix}$$
No saddle point

$$f. \begin{pmatrix} ⓪ & 2 \\ -3 & -6 \\ -4 & -3 \end{pmatrix}$$
Strategies: X, 1; Y, 1
Game value: 0

$$g. \begin{pmatrix} ① & 7 & 6 \\ -4 & 3 & -5 \\ 0 & -2 & 7 \end{pmatrix}$$
Strategies: X, 1; Y, 1
Game value: $+1$

$$h. \begin{pmatrix} 1 & 6 & 8 \\ 2 & 7 & -9 \\ -4 & 9 & 12 \end{pmatrix}$$
No saddle point

MIXED STRATEGIES

In the cases where no saddle point exists, the players resort to a mixed strategy: To optimize his winnings, player X will play each of his rows a certain part of the time, and player Y will play each of his columns a certain part of the time. X must determine what proportion of the time he should play each row, and Y must determine what proportion of the time he should play each column.

Following is a simple two-person zero-sum game. Because there is no saddle point in this game, there are no pure strategies that the players may use to play optimally.

$$\begin{matrix} & Y \\ X & \begin{pmatrix} 5 & 1 \\ 3 & 4 \end{pmatrix} \end{matrix}$$

There is no payoff which is both the smallest value in its row and the largest value in its column.   (10-2)

Our tasks are to determine what portion of his time player X should spend playing each of his rows and what portion of the time player Y should spend playing each of his columns. Since we are dealing in portions of time, we need to differentiate between the time player X spends playing row 1 and the time he spends playing row 2. The same type of breakdown must be made for player Y.

Suppose we let Q equal the fractional proportion of the time player X spends playing the first row; then, since 1 equals all the time available, $1 - Q$ must equal the proportion of the time he would spend playing the second row. For example, if player X plays the first row ¾ of the time, then $1 - ¾$ or ¼ must equal the time he spends playing the second row. The same concept, of course, applies to player Y and his distribution of time between his columns. These representations of the proportional distribution of time between the rows and between the columns are illustrated as follows:

$$
\begin{array}{c}
 \quad P \quad\ 1 - P \\
Q \begin{pmatrix} 5 & 1 \\ 3 & 4 \end{pmatrix} \\
1 - Q
\end{array}
\qquad\qquad (10\text{-}2)
$$

This indicates to us that:

1. Player X plays the first row Q of the time (Q is between 0 and 100 per cent).
2. Player X plays the second row $100\% - Q$ of the time.
3. Player Y plays the first column P of the time (P is between 0 and 100 per cent).
4. Player Y plays the second column $100\% - P$ of the time.

Now let us solve for the unknown fractions P and Q. Consider player X first. Logically, X wants to divide his plays between his rows so that his expected winnings from playing the first row will exactly equal his expected winnings from playing the second row—no matter what Y does. Business provides an analogy. A certain firm follows course of action A until B looks more profitable, at which point it switches to B. Later, should B become less attractive than A, the firm switches back to A. Of course, X's opponent Y is assumed to be just as intelligent and will adopt *his* optimum strategy. If, on the other hand, Y was incompetent and adopted a stupid strategy, X would hardly reason out his strategy in this manner; he would simply look for the obvious loopholes in Y's strategy and play accordingly.

Table 10-2 represents X's expected winnings from playing his first row Q of the time and his second row $(1 - Q)$ of the time.

Table 10-2

	X's expected winnings	
	If Y plays column 1	If Y plays column 2
X plays row 1 Q of the time	X wins 5 points Q of the time	X wins 1 point Q of the time
X plays row 2 $(1 - Q)$ of the time	X wins 3 points $(1 - Q)$ of the time	X wins 4 points $(1 - Q)$ of the time
X's expected winnings	$5Q + 3(1-Q)$ when Y plays column 1	$1Q + 4(1-Q)$ when Y plays column 2

To make X's expected winnings when Y plays column 1 equal to X's expected winnings when Y plays column 2, we let $5Q + 3(1 - Q)$ equal $1Q + 4(1 - Q)$ and solve for the one particular Q which *does* equate the two expectations:

$$5Q + 3(1 - Q) = 1Q + 4(1 - Q) \tag{10-3}$$
$$5Q + 3 - 3Q = 1Q + 4 - 4Q$$
$$5Q = 1$$
$$Q = \tfrac{1}{5}$$

Therefore, $1 - Q = \tfrac{4}{5}$.

Our algebraic solution thus indicates that player X plays the first row $\tfrac{1}{5}$ of the time and the second row $\tfrac{4}{5}$ of the time.

Now all that remains is to solve for player Y's optimal strategies by using the same algebraic method. Player Y wants to divide his time between his columns so that no matter what X does about the rows, Y will maximize his winnings over time. By so doing, Y puts himself in a position where he does not care which strategy X chooses, since Y maximizes his winnings (or minimizes his losses) regardless of X's choice of strategies. These observations about Y's choice of strategies between the columns can be represented in algebraic form to allow us to solve for the strategies. Table 10-3 represents Y's expectations from playing his first column P of the time and his second column $(1 - P)$ of the time, *regardless* of what X does.

Table 10-3

	Y's expected losses		Y's expected losses
	Y plays col. 1 P of the time and col. 2 $(1 - P)$ of the time		
If X plays row 1	Y loses 5 points P of the time	Y loses 1 point $(1 - P)$ of the time	$5P + 1(1-P)$ when X plays row 1
If X plays row 2	Y loses 3 points P of the time	Y loses 4 points $(1 - P)$ of the time	$3P + 4(1-P)$ when X plays row 2

Now equate Y's expected losses when X plays row 1 with Y's expected losses when X plays row 2:

$$5P + 1(1 - P) = 3P + 4(1 - P) \tag{10-4}$$

and solve for P:

$$5P + 1 - P = 3P + 4 - 4P$$
$$4P + 1 = 4 - P$$
$$5P = 3$$
$$P = \tfrac{3}{5}$$

Therefore, $1 - P = \tfrac{2}{5}$.

Our solution for Y's best strategy is for him to play the first column $\tfrac{3}{5}$ of the time and the second column $\tfrac{2}{5}$ of the time. Of course, when we indicate that a player should play each of his choices a certain proportion of the time, we realize that this division of time between the rows or columns must be done at random, without any discernible pattern. If one of the players begins to notice a pattern in the play of his opponent—if X notices that Y plays column 1 three times and then column 2 twice, over and over again in that order—that player will then adjust his strategy to take advantage of his opponent's disclosure of his future pattern. On the other hand, if both players play their best strategies *but* without a discernible pattern, then the strategies we have determined represent the *best* possible divisions of time between the rows or columns.

Now that we can solve for the optimum mixed strategies, we are in a position to calculate the value of this game. Our original game, together with the optimum strategies for each of the players, is presented below:

$$\begin{array}{ccc} & & \text{Y} \\ & & \tfrac{3}{5} \quad \tfrac{2}{5} \\ \text{X} & \begin{array}{c} \tfrac{1}{5} \\ \tfrac{4}{5} \end{array} & \begin{pmatrix} \mathbf{5} & \mathbf{1} \\ \mathbf{3} & \mathbf{4} \end{pmatrix} \end{array} \qquad (10\text{-}2)$$

Looking at the game from player X's point of view, we can reason as follows:

1. During the $\tfrac{3}{5}$ of the time that Y plays column 1, X wins 5 points $\tfrac{1}{5}$ of the time and 3 points $\tfrac{4}{5}$ of the time.
2. During the $\tfrac{2}{5}$ of the time that Y plays column 2, X wins 1 point $\tfrac{1}{5}$ of the time and 4 points $\tfrac{4}{5}$ of the time.

Therefore, X's total expected winnings over time are the sum of statements 1 and 2 above:

$$\begin{array}{lcl} \quad 1 & & \quad 2 \\ \tfrac{3}{5}\,[5(\tfrac{1}{5}) + 3(\tfrac{4}{5})] & + & \tfrac{2}{5}\,[1(\tfrac{1}{5}) + 4(\tfrac{4}{5})] \\ \tfrac{3}{5}\,(\tfrac{5}{5} + \tfrac{12}{5}) & + & \tfrac{2}{5}\,(\tfrac{1}{5} + \tfrac{16}{5}) \\ \tfrac{3}{5}\,(\tfrac{17}{5}) & + & \tfrac{2}{5}\,(\tfrac{17}{5}) \\ \quad = \tfrac{17}{5} = \text{value of the game} & & \end{array}$$

This means that player X, if he plays his optimal strategies, can expect to win an average payoff of $3\tfrac{2}{5}$ points for each play of the game. From our earlier observation, we know that X will be the winner of this game, since the value is a positive number. If the value of the game had been a negative number, Y would have been the winner. This, of course, could not be true in this particular game, since the game was slanted in X's favor in that it contained no negative payoffs in the original matrix.

We could have arrived at the same value of the game looking at it from Y's point of view:

1. During the $\tfrac{1}{5}$ of the time that X plays row 1, Y loses 5 points $\tfrac{3}{5}$ of the time and 1 point $\tfrac{2}{5}$ of the time.
2. During the $\tfrac{4}{5}$ of the time that X plays row 2, Y loses 3 points $\tfrac{3}{5}$ of the time and 4 points $\tfrac{2}{5}$ of the time.

Therefore, Y's total expected losses over time are the sum of statements 1 and 2:

$$
\begin{array}{ll}
1 & 2 \\
\tfrac{1}{5}\,[5(\tfrac{3}{5}) + 1(\tfrac{2}{5})] & + \tfrac{4}{5}\,[3(\tfrac{3}{5}) + 4(\tfrac{2}{5})] \\
\tfrac{1}{5}\,(\tfrac{15}{5} + \tfrac{2}{5}) & + \tfrac{4}{5}\,(\tfrac{9}{5} + \tfrac{8}{5}) \\
\tfrac{1}{5}\,(\tfrac{17}{5}) & + \tfrac{4}{5}\,(\tfrac{17}{5}) \\
= \tfrac{17}{5}
\end{array}
$$

Again we see that the value of the game is $\tfrac{3}{5}$; since it is a positive number, we know that X wins. The term "value of the game" does not mean that X will win $\tfrac{3}{5}$ points each time these two players play; it means instead that X's winnings over many plays of the game will average $\tfrac{3}{5}$ points per game.

ALTERNATE SOLUTION METHODS FOR 2 × 2 GAMES

Arithmetic method for finding optimum strategies

There is a very simple arithmetic method of solving for the optimum strategies of each of the players in a 2×2 game. To illustrate it, let us reproduce the original game from the previous section:

$$
\begin{array}{c}
\quad Y \\
X \begin{pmatrix} 5 & 1 \\ 3 & 4 \end{pmatrix}
\end{array}
\tag{10-2}
$$

The first step in the arithmetic solution method is to subtract the smaller payoff in each row from the larger payoff, and the smaller payoff in each column from the larger payoff:

$$
\begin{array}{c}
\quad Y \\
X \begin{pmatrix} 5 & 1 \\ 3 & 4 \end{pmatrix} \quad \begin{array}{l} 4 \\ 1 \end{array} \quad \begin{array}{l} 5-1=4 \\ 4-3=1 \end{array} \qquad \begin{array}{cc} 5 & 4 \\ -3 & -1 \\ \hline 2 & 3 \end{array} \\
\qquad\quad 2 \quad 3
\end{array}
\tag{10-5}
$$

The next step is to interchange each of these pairs of subtracted numbers:

$$
\text{X} \begin{matrix} & \text{Y} & \\ \begin{pmatrix} 5 & 1 \\ 3 & 4 \end{pmatrix} & \begin{matrix} 1 \\ 4 \end{matrix} \\ \begin{matrix} 3 & 2 \end{matrix} & \end{matrix}
\tag{10-6}
$$

To find the strategies for player X, simply add 1 and 4 and place each in turn over the sum.   To find the strategies for player Y, add 3 and 2 and place each in turn over the sum:

$$
\text{X} \begin{pmatrix} 5 & 1 \\ 3 & 4 \end{pmatrix} \begin{matrix} \dfrac{1}{1+4} \\ \dfrac{4}{1+4} \end{matrix} \quad = \quad \text{X} \begin{pmatrix} 5 & 1 \\ 3 & 4 \end{pmatrix} \begin{matrix} \dfrac{1}{5} \\ \dfrac{4}{5} \end{matrix} \quad \begin{matrix} \text{X} = \tfrac{1}{5}, \tfrac{4}{5} \\ \text{Y} = \tfrac{3}{5}, \tfrac{2}{5} \end{matrix}
\tag{10-7}
$$

$$
\dfrac{3}{3+2} \ \dfrac{2}{3+2} \qquad\qquad \dfrac{3}{5} \ \dfrac{2}{5}
$$

You can verify the accuracy of these arithmetic strategies by using the more involved algebraic method.   This arithmetic technique is a very useful one because it is less complex than the algebraic method.   It is often used to solve for the strategies in 2×2 games; unfortunately, it cannot be applied to larger games.

Matrix algebra method for finding optimum strategies and game value

From our discussion of matrix algebra, we can get some very useful computational methods which allow us to solve for the optimum strategies *and* the values of 2×2 games.

Using the same payoff matrix as before,

$$
\text{X} \begin{matrix} \text{Y} \\ \begin{pmatrix} 5 & 1 \\ 3 & 4 \end{pmatrix} \end{matrix} \quad \text{original game matrix A}
\tag{10-2}
$$

the optimum strategies for each of the players and the value of this game may be found by solving the following matrix fractions:

X's optimum strategies are $\dfrac{(1 \quad 1)(\text{adjoint of } \mathbf{A})}{(1 \quad 1)(\text{adjoint of } \mathbf{A})\begin{pmatrix}1\\1\end{pmatrix}}$ (10-8)

Y's optimum strategies are $\dfrac{(1 \quad 1)(\text{transpose of adjoint of } \mathbf{A})}{(1 \quad 1)(\text{adjoint of } \mathbf{A})\begin{pmatrix}1\\1\end{pmatrix}}$ (10-9)

Value of the game is $\dfrac{|\text{determinant of } \mathbf{A}|}{(1 \quad 1)(\text{adjoint of } \mathbf{A})\begin{pmatrix}1\\1\end{pmatrix}}$ (10-10)

Value of the game may also be obtained by solving

$$(\text{X's strategies}) \quad \begin{pmatrix}\text{Game}\\\text{matrix}\end{pmatrix} \quad \begin{pmatrix}\text{Y's}\\s\\t\\r\\a\\t\\e\\g\\i\\e\\s\end{pmatrix} \quad (10\text{-}11)$$

A row   A   A column
vector   matrix   vector

Using the matrix algebra solution methods outlined above, let us solve first for X's optimum strategies:

$$X = \dfrac{(1 \quad 1)(\text{adjoint of } \mathbf{A})}{(1 \quad 1)(\text{adjoint of } \mathbf{A})\begin{pmatrix}1\\1\end{pmatrix}} \qquad (10\text{-}8)$$

The adjoint of the original matrix $\begin{pmatrix}5 & 1\\3 & 4\end{pmatrix}$ can be calculated using the method outlined in Chapter 7. This method tells us quickly that the adjoint of the original matrix is

$$\begin{pmatrix} 4 & -1 \\ -3 & 5 \end{pmatrix}$$

The calculation of X's strategies then involves some simple matrix multiplication as follows:

$$\frac{(1 \quad 1) \begin{pmatrix} 4 & -1 \\ -3 & 5 \end{pmatrix}}{(1 \quad 1) \begin{pmatrix} 4 & -1 \\ -3 & 5 \end{pmatrix} \begin{pmatrix} 1 \\ 1 \end{pmatrix}}$$

which reduces to $\dfrac{(1 \quad 4)}{(1 \quad 4) \begin{pmatrix} 1 \\ 1 \end{pmatrix}}$

and finally, $\dfrac{(1 \quad 4)}{(5)}$

This can be broken down into X's two optimum strategies for his rows as follows:

⅕   ⅘

To solve for Y's optimum strategies, we solve

$$Y = \frac{(1 \quad 1) \begin{pmatrix} \text{transpose of} \\ \text{the adjoint} \\ \text{of A} \end{pmatrix}}{(1 \quad 1) \begin{pmatrix} \text{adjoint of} \\ \text{A} \end{pmatrix} \begin{pmatrix} 1 \\ 1 \end{pmatrix}} \qquad (10\text{-}9)$$

The transpose of the adjoint is obtained by interchanging the rows and columns in the matrix $\begin{pmatrix} 4 & -1 \\ -3 & 5 \end{pmatrix}$, which yields $\begin{pmatrix} 4 & -3 \\ -1 & 5 \end{pmatrix}$. The calculation of Y's strategies then involves some simple matrix multiplication as follows:

$$\frac{(1 \quad 1) \begin{pmatrix} 4 & -3 \\ -1 & 5 \end{pmatrix}}{(1 \quad 1) \begin{pmatrix} 4 & -1 \\ -3 & 5 \end{pmatrix} \begin{pmatrix} 1 \\ 1 \end{pmatrix}}$$

which reduces to $\dfrac{(3 \quad 2)}{(1 \quad 4)\begin{pmatrix}1\\1\end{pmatrix}}$

and finally, $\dfrac{(3 \quad 2)}{(5)}$

This can be broken down into Y's optimum strategies for his columns as follows:

⅗   ⅖

The matrix algebra solution to the *value of the game* may be accomplished in either of two ways:

$$\text{Value} = \frac{|\text{determinant of } \mathbf{A}|}{(1 \quad 1)(\text{adjoint of } \mathbf{A})\begin{pmatrix}1\\1\end{pmatrix}} \tag{10-10}$$

or

$$\text{Value} = (\text{X's strategies})(\mathbf{A})\begin{pmatrix}\text{Y's}\\\text{s}\\\text{t}\\\text{r}\\\text{a}\\\text{t}\\\text{e}\\\text{g}\\\text{i}\\\text{e}\\\text{s}\end{pmatrix} \tag{10-11}$$

Solving for the value using Eq. (10-10) requires the solution of

$$\text{Value} = \frac{\begin{vmatrix}5 & 1\\3 & 4\end{vmatrix}}{(1 \quad 1)\begin{pmatrix}4 & -1\\-3 & 5\end{pmatrix}\begin{pmatrix}1\\1\end{pmatrix}}$$

which reduces to

$$\frac{17}{(1 \quad 4)\begin{pmatrix}1\\1\end{pmatrix}}$$

and finally, $\frac{17}{5}$, or $3\frac{2}{5}$

Solving for the value of the game using Eq. (10-11) requires the solution of

$$\text{Value} = (\tfrac{1}{5} \quad \tfrac{4}{5})\begin{pmatrix}5 & 1\\3 & 4\end{pmatrix}\begin{pmatrix}\tfrac{3}{5}\\\tfrac{2}{5}\end{pmatrix}$$

$$= (1\tfrac{7}{5} \quad 1\tfrac{7}{5})\begin{pmatrix}\tfrac{3}{5}\\\tfrac{2}{5}\end{pmatrix}$$

$$= 1\tfrac{7}{5}, \text{ or } 3\tfrac{2}{5}$$

The matrix algebra solution method shown in Eq. (10-10) is generally limited to 2×2 games. The method shown in Eq. (10-11) is effective for finding game value regardless of the dimensions of the game matrix.

Joint probability method for obtaining game value

If we reproduce the original game matrix and the optimum strategies for the game we have been discussing in this chapter as follows:

$$\begin{array}{cc} & \text{Y} \\ & \tfrac{3}{5} \quad \tfrac{2}{5} \\ \text{X} \begin{array}{c}\tfrac{1}{5}\\\tfrac{4}{5}\end{array} & \begin{pmatrix}5 & 1\\3 & 4\end{pmatrix}\end{array} \qquad (10\text{-}2)$$

we can see that each of the player's strategies consists of two probabilities, i.e., a $\frac{1}{5}$ probability that player X will play row 1 and a $\frac{4}{5}$ probability that player X will play row 2. Similarly, the probability that player Y will play column 1 is $\frac{3}{5}$ and the probability that Y will play column 2 is $\frac{2}{5}$. Since both players play independently in that neither knows what the other will play for the next move, the probabilities for player X are independent of the probabilities for player Y.

Each of the payoffs in the game (5, 1, 3, and 4) is attained only if a particular column and a particular row are played simultaneously. For instance, player X wins 5 points only if he plays row 1 at the same time that player Y plays column 1. The probability that row 1 and column 1 will both be played simultaneously is a joint probability under conditions of statistical independence: $P(\text{row 1, column 1}) = P(\text{row 1}) \times P(\text{column 1})$, or in this case, $\frac{1}{5} \times \frac{3}{5}$, or $\frac{3}{25}$. The probability that 5 will be the payoff after the play of the game is then $\frac{3}{25}$.

Using this same reasoning, we can compute the joint probabilities that each of the payoffs will be obtained.

Payoff value	Strategies which produce this payoff	Probability of this payoff
5	row 1, column 1	$\frac{1}{5} \times \frac{3}{5} = \frac{3}{25}$
1	row 1, column 2	$\frac{1}{5} \times \frac{2}{5} = \frac{2}{25}$
3	row 2, column 1	$\frac{4}{5} \times \frac{3}{5} = \frac{12}{25}$
4	row 2, column 2	$\frac{4}{5} \times \frac{2}{5} = \frac{8}{25}$
Total		1.0

Now we can compute the value of the game by multiplying each of the payoffs by the probability that it will occur:

Payoff		Probability of this payoff		
5	×	$\frac{3}{25}$	=	$\frac{15}{25}$
1	×	$\frac{2}{25}$	=	$\frac{2}{25}$
3	×	$\frac{12}{25}$	=	$\frac{36}{25}$
4	×	$\frac{8}{25}$	=	$\frac{32}{25}$
Total				$\frac{85}{25}$ or $3\frac{2}{5}$ Value of the game

This last step is nothing more than obtaining the mean of a random variable, the random variable in this case being the value of the payoffs.

$2 \times M$ AND $M \times 2$ GAMES

A game in which one player has more than two choices but the other player is limited to two choices is referred to as a $2 \times M$ or $M \times 2$ game, according to whether the player who plays the columns or the player who plays the rows is the one with more than two choices. Two such games with their dimensions indicated beside each of them are shown below:

$$\begin{matrix} & Y \\ X & \begin{pmatrix} 1 & 2 \\ -1 & -4 \\ 3 & 1 \end{pmatrix} \end{matrix} \qquad M \times 2 \quad \begin{matrix} \text{More than 2 rows; exactly} \\ \text{2 columns} \end{matrix} \quad (10\text{-}12)$$

$$\begin{matrix} & Y \\ X & \begin{pmatrix} -1 & -6 & 3 & 1 \\ -7 & -4 & 2 & 0 \end{pmatrix} \end{matrix} \quad 2 \times M \quad \begin{matrix} \text{Exactly 2 rows; more} \\ \text{than 2 columns} \end{matrix} \quad (10\text{-}13)$$

None of the solution methods we have discussed so far will allow us to solve for the optimum strategies and game values of games such as the two shown above—unless, of course, we happened to find saddle points in these games; in such cases we would have the strategies and the values nicely defined. Neither of these two games contains a saddle point.

Solution by dominance

If there were a way to reduce each of the above games to a 2×2 game for which we know a solution method, the games could be solved easily. A further look at Eq. (10-12):

$$\begin{matrix} & Y \\ X & \begin{pmatrix} 1 & 2 \\ -1 & -4 \\ 3 & 1 \end{pmatrix} \end{matrix} \qquad (10\text{-}12)$$

raises the question "Why would player X play row 2, when that would give his opponent his only chance to win?" Clearly, he never would play row 2, since he can do much better playing rows 1 and 3. We can say then that row 2 is *dominated;* i.e., it is discarded because another strategy or other strategies will *always* return player X a better payoff than the dominated strategy, regardless of his opponent's actions.

Thus through the evaluation of the possibility of dominance in Eq. (10-12), we can reduce it from

$$\begin{array}{cc} & Y \\ X & \begin{pmatrix} 1 & 2 \\ -1 & -4 \\ 3 & 1 \end{pmatrix} \end{array}$$

$$\text{to} \quad \begin{array}{cc} & Y \\ X & \begin{pmatrix} 1 & 2 \\ 3 & 1 \end{pmatrix} \end{array}$$

for which we can easily obtain the strategies and value, as follows: X = ⅔, 0, ⅓; Y = ⅓, ⅔; value of the game = 5/3. To obtain these answers, we could use any one of the 2 × 2 methods we learned previously, except, of course, the method of saddle points. Even though X never plays his second row, his optimum strategies include a strategy for each of the three rows, the strategy for the second row being zero.

Turning our attention to the 2 × *M* game,

$$\begin{array}{cc} & Y \\ X & \begin{pmatrix} -1 & -6 & 3 & 1 \\ -7 & -4 & 2 & 0 \end{pmatrix} \end{array} \tag{10-13}$$

we find that we can again apply our method of dominance to this game. Player Y will never play his third or fourth columns, for that would give his opponent a chance to win. If player Y plays only his first and second columns, all the payoffs are negative, and Y will always win this particular game. The 2 × *M* game above can thus be reduced to

$$\begin{array}{cc} & Y \\ X & \begin{pmatrix} -1 & -6 \\ -7 & -4 \end{pmatrix} \end{array}$$

for which the solutions (by one of our previously discussed methods) are as follows: X = 3/8, 5/8; Y = 2/8, 6/8, 0, 0; value of the game = $-4\frac{3}{4}$.

Even though Y does not play columns 3 and 4, zeros have been entered as the optimum strategies for these columns to indicate that Y has an optimum strategy for each of his columns, even though it may be not to play some of them.

Several $2 \times M$ and $M \times 2$ games are shown below. Beside each is the 2×2 game which results when the games are analyzed for dominance and each dominated row or column is removed.

$$a. \quad \text{X} \begin{pmatrix} 6 & 4 & -1 & 0 & -3 \\ 3 & 2 & -4 & 2 & -1 \end{pmatrix} \qquad 2 \times M \qquad \begin{pmatrix} -1 & -3 \\ -4 & -1 \end{pmatrix}$$

with Y labeled above the first matrix.

Player Y will not play column 1, 2, or 4, since these give his opponent X an opportunity to win. In each case column 3 or column 5 is a better choice. Player Y will still divide his time between columns 3 and 5 because neither of these is *always* better than the other.

$$b. \quad \text{X} \begin{pmatrix} 4 & 1 \\ 2 & 3 \\ -1 & 1 \end{pmatrix} \qquad M \times 2 \qquad \begin{pmatrix} 4 & 1 \\ 2 & 3 \end{pmatrix}$$

with Y labeled above the first matrix.

Player X will not play row 3, since this would give Y a chance to win 1 point. In each case row 1 or row 2 is a better choice than row 3. Player X will still divide his time between rows 1 and 2, since neither of these is always better than the other.

$$c. \quad \text{X} \begin{pmatrix} 3 & -5 & -6 \\ 0 & -7 & 0 \end{pmatrix} \qquad 2 \times M \qquad \begin{pmatrix} -5 & -6 \\ -7 & 0 \end{pmatrix}$$

with Y labeled above the first matrix.

Player Y will not play column 1, since this would give X a chance to win 3 points. Columns 2 and 3 are both better choices for player Y than column 1. Player Y will divide his time between columns 2 and 3 because neither of these is always better than the other.

$$d. \quad \text{X} \begin{pmatrix} -2 & 4 \\ -1 & 4 \\ 3 & 1 \end{pmatrix} \qquad M \times 2 \qquad \begin{pmatrix} -1 & 4 \\ 3 & 1 \end{pmatrix}$$

with Y labeled above the first matrix.

Player X will not play row 1, since playing row 2 would be better; X's winnings if Y plays column 2 are 4 points in each case, but X stands to lose 2 points instead of 1 point should Y play column 1. Player X will, of course, play row 3, since he wins on both payoffs in that row. X will divide his time between rows 2 and 3, since neither of them is always better than the other.

Solution by method of subgames

Many $2 \times M$ or $M \times 2$ games can be reduced by the method of dominance to a 2×2 game which is easily solved. There are, however, many other cases where such a reduction is impossible or only partially successful; this leaves a game to be solved which is still larger than 2×2. For instance, in the following example, the original game

$$\begin{matrix} & & Y & & & \\ X & \begin{pmatrix} -6 & -1 & 1 & 4 & 4 & 3 \\ 7 & -2 & 6 & 3 & -5 & 7 \end{pmatrix} \end{matrix} \tag{10-14}$$

can be reduced by dominance to

$$\begin{matrix} & & Y & \\ X & \begin{pmatrix} -6 & -1 & 4 \\ 7 & -2 & -5 \end{pmatrix} \end{matrix} \tag{10-15}$$

by reasoning that player Y would not play columns 3, 4, and 6 in the original game since these columns guarantee a payoff to his opponent. Unfortunately our method of dominance cannot go any further, and we are still left with a game larger than 2×2 to solve.

The 2×3 game $\begin{pmatrix} -6 & -1 & 4 \\ 7 & -2 & -5 \end{pmatrix}$ can be thought of as actually being three 2×2 games as follows:

Subgame 1. $\begin{pmatrix} -6 & -1 \\ 7 & -2 \end{pmatrix}$ columns 1 and 2

Subgame 2. $\begin{pmatrix} -6 & 4 \\ 7 & -5 \end{pmatrix}$ columns 1 and 3

Subgame 3. $\begin{pmatrix} -1 & 4 \\ -2 & -5 \end{pmatrix}$ columns 2 and 3

In each of the three 2 × 2 games above, player Y has chosen *not* to play one of his columns.   For example, in subgame 1, column 3 has been omitted; in subgame 2, column 2 has been omitted; and in subgame 3, column 1 has been omitted.

Since it is player Y who has the choice of not playing one of the columns, what he in fact is really doing is trying to determine which combination of a two-column strategy is best for him.   As to why he is convinced that some two-column strategy is better than a three-column strategy (playing all three columns in some proportion), the reason is seen by observing the original game matrix:

$$X \begin{array}{c} Y \\ \begin{pmatrix} -6 & -1 & 4 \\ 7 & -2 & -5 \end{pmatrix} \end{array} \qquad\qquad (10\text{-}15)$$

When player X plays his first row, Y would rather choose between the first column (-6) and the second column (-1) than consider the third column (4), because a mixed strategy for player Y between -6 and -1 when X plays row 1 pays off considerably better than a mixed strategy between any other two columns.   Similarly, when player X plays row 2, Y would rather play a mixed strategy between columns 2 and 3, where the payoffs would be -2 and -5, respectively, instead of involving column 1, where the payoff is 7 points to his opponent.   Thus, given a mixed strategy for player X, Y observes that some two-column strategy is better than a three-column strategy.   The job remaining is to determine which of the possible two-column strategies is *best* for player Y, since it is he who must decide which one to play.   In any event, we can now see that Y will not play one of his columns.

To choose player Y's best two-column strategy, let us solve all three of the 2 × 2 games for their strategies and their values and then pick the one pattern which is truly optimum.   Each of the games with its solution appears below.   Note that when a column is not to be played, it is represented in Y's strategy with a zero.

Subgame 1. $\begin{pmatrix} -6 & -1 \\ 7 & -2 \end{pmatrix}$ $\quad$ $X = (\%_{14}, \frac{5}{14})$ $\qquad$ Third column of original
$\qquad\qquad\qquad\qquad\qquad\qquad$ $Y = (\frac{1}{14}, \frac{13}{14}, 0)$ $\qquad$ game is not played.

$\qquad\qquad\qquad\qquad\qquad\qquad\qquad$ Value $= -\frac{19}{14}$

Subgame 2. $\begin{pmatrix} -6 & 4 \\ 7 & -5 \end{pmatrix}$ $X = (^{12}\!\!/_{22}, \, ^{10}\!\!/_{22})$ Second column of original

$Y = (^9\!\!/_{22}, \, 0, \, ^{13}\!\!/_{22})$ game is not played.

Value $= -^1\!\!/_{11}$

Subgame 3. $\begin{pmatrix} -1 & 4 \\ -2 & -5 \end{pmatrix}$ $X = (1, 0)$ First column of original

$Y = (0, 1, 0)$ game is not played.

Value $= \boxed{-1}$

↑
Saddle
point

It would then appear that subgame 1, with a value to player Y of $-^{19}\!\!/_{14}$, would offer Y the best alternative among the three subgames and that Y's optimum strategy is to play the first column $^1\!\!/_{14}$ of the time, the second column $^{13}\!\!/_{14}$ of the time, and the third column 0 of the time.

It is not difficult at all to *prove* that the two-column strategy we have selected for player Y is clearly optimum. To do this, we need to observe the original 2 × 3 game:

$$
\begin{array}{cc}
 & Y \\
 & \begin{array}{ccc} Y_1 & Y_2 & Y_3 \end{array} \\
X \begin{array}{c} X_1 \\ X_2 \end{array} & \begin{pmatrix} -6 & -1 & 4 \\ 7 & -2 & -5 \end{pmatrix}
\end{array}
$$

Let X_1 = proportion of time X plays row 1

X_2 = proportion of time X plays row 2   (10-15)

From this game we see that when Y plays his first column, X loses 6 points from playing row 1 and wins 7 points from playing row 2. From our earlier explanation of how a mixed strategy is actually chosen by equating expectations, we remember that X's expectations from playing a mixed strategy between his rows are the same regardless of which column Y plays. Put another way, X chooses his mixed strategy in such a way that he wins (or loses) the same regardless of Y's choice of column. This can be expressed algebraically as follows:

X's expected winnings

Y plays column 1	$-6X_1 + 7X_2 \geq -^{19}\!\!/_{14}$	X expects to lose $^{19}\!\!/_{14}$ points
Y plays column 2	$-1X_1 - 2X_2 \geq -^{19}\!\!/_{14}$	regardless of Y's choice; the
Y plays column 3	$4X_1 - 5X_2 \geq -^{19}\!\!/_{14}$	$\geq$ sign indicates he may

lose *less* if Y chooses poor strategies.

The first inequality above states that if X plays row 1 X_1 of the time and row 2 X_2 of the time, he will lose no more than $^{19}\!/_{14}$ points (the value of the game). He may in fact lose *less* than $^{19}\!/_{14}$ points *if* Y's strategies are not good ones; hence the $\geq$ inequality sign. If the strategies we found for X in the solution of subgame 1 ($^9\!/_{14}$, $^5\!/_{14}$) are indeed optimum ones, they should satisfy the three inequalities above. Let us test them to see if they do:

$$-6\,(^9\!/_{14}) + 7\,(^5\!/_{14}) \geq -^{19}\!/_{14} \qquad -^{54}\!/_{14} + ^{35}\!/_{14} = -^{19}\!/_{14}$$
$$-1\,(^9\!/_{14}) - 2\,(^5\!/_{14}) \geq -^{19}\!/_{14} \qquad -^9\!/_{14} - ^{10}\!/_{14} = -^{19}\!/_{14}$$
$$4\,(^9\!/_{14}) - 5\,(^5\!/_{14}) \geq -^{19}\!/_{14} \qquad ^{36}\!/_{14} - ^{25}\!/_{14} = \ \ ^{11}\!/_{14}$$
$$^{11}\!/_{14} > -^{19}\!/_{14}$$

Since all three inequalities are satisfied by the values we inserted for X's strategies, these must have been X's optimum strategies. Notice that when Y played column 3, X lost less than $-^{19}\!/_{14}$ points; this seems to indicate that column 3 should not be played by player Y, a decision that we already made by assigning a zero in the solution of subgame 1 to the chances that column 3 should be played.

We still must test for Y's strategies to see if *they* were optimum for subgame 1. Referring again to the original game [Eq. (10-15)], we must remember that Y has chosen his mixed strategies in such a way that his expectations from each of his columns are identical regardless of his opponent's choice. In other words, Y has chosen his strategies in such a way that he wins at least the value of the game from each column. This can be expressed algebraically as follows:

$$Y\text{'s expected winnings}$$

X plays row 1 $\quad -6Y_1 - 1Y_2 + 4Y_3 \leq -^{19}\!/_{14}$ $\qquad$ Y expects to win $^{19}\!/_{14}$

X plays row 2 $\quad 7Y_1 - 2Y_2 - 5Y_3 \leq -^{19}\!/_{14}$ $\qquad$ points regardless of X's choice; the $\leq$ sign indicates Y may win *more* if X chooses poor strategies

The first inequality above states that if Y plays column 1 Y_1 of the time, column 2 Y_2 of the time, and column 3 Y_3 of the time, he will win at least $^{19}\!/_{14}$ points; the $\leq$ inequality sign indicates that Y may indeed do even better than this (win a more negative value) if X's strategies are

not good ones. Thus if Y's strategies are optimum, they should satisfy
the two inequalities above:

$$-6 \left(\tfrac{1}{14}\right) - 1 \left(\tfrac{13}{14}\right) + 4 \,(0) \leq -\tfrac{19}{14} \qquad -\tfrac{6}{14} - \tfrac{13}{14} = -\tfrac{19}{14}$$
$$7 \left(\tfrac{1}{14}\right) - 2 \left(\tfrac{13}{14}\right) - 5 \,(0) \leq -\tfrac{19}{14} \qquad \tfrac{7}{14} - \tfrac{26}{14} = -\tfrac{19}{14}$$

Since both inequalities are satisfied by the strategies we found for
player Y, these must have been his optimum strategies. We could have
saved all this trouble by picking that subgame with the greatest value to
Y; but without verification that our decision was an optimum one, we
would never have been sure that Y had chosen correctly in refusing to
play column 3.

Another example of the solution of $2 \times M$ or $M \times 2$ games by the
subgame method will be useful. In the following example, it is player X
who must choose which two of the rows he will play. The original 3×2
game, its subgames, and their solutions follow.

$$\text{Original game} \qquad \begin{pmatrix} 4 & 2 \\ 3 & 8 \\ 0 & 9 \end{pmatrix} \qquad\qquad (10\text{-}16)$$

Having first satisfied ourselves that there is no saddle point in the original game, we proceed to break it down into its three subgames:

Subgame 1	Subgame 2	Subgame 3
$\begin{pmatrix} 4 & 2 \\ 3 & 8 \end{pmatrix}$	$\begin{pmatrix} 4 & 2 \\ 0 & 9 \end{pmatrix}$	$\begin{pmatrix} 3 & 8 \\ 0 & 9 \end{pmatrix}$
X strategy $= (\tfrac{5}{7}, \tfrac{2}{7}, 0)$	X strategy $= (\tfrac{9}{11}, 0, \tfrac{2}{11})$	X strategy $= (0, 1, 0)$
Y strategy $= (\tfrac{6}{7}, \tfrac{1}{7})$	Y strategy $= (\tfrac{7}{11}, \tfrac{4}{11})$	Y strategy $= (1, 0)$
Value $= 3\tfrac{5}{7}$	Value $= 3\tfrac{9}{11}$	Value $= 3$
		$\uparrow$
		Saddle point

Having solved for the strategies and values of the three subgames,
we can observe that the optimum game for player X is the one in which
he plays rows 1 and 2 of the original game and omits row 3, thereby
playing subgame 1. This offers him the greatest possible number of
points.

To assure ourselves that subgame 1 is *the* optimum game, we may set up the inequalities as we did before and test the strategies and value for subgame 1 in these inequalities:

$4X_1 + 3X_2 + 0X_3 \geq$ value of the game
$2X_1 + 8X_2 + 9X_3 \geq$ value of the game

$4Y_1 + 2Y_2 \leq$ value of the game
$3Y_1 + 8Y_2 \leq$ value of the game
$0Y_1 + 9Y_2 \leq$ value of the game

Substituting the strategies and the game value for subgame 1 into the above inequalities, we obtain

$4(\frac{5}{7}) + 3(\frac{2}{7}) + 0(0) \geq 3\frac{5}{7}$
$2(\frac{5}{7}) + 8(\frac{2}{7}) + 9(0) \geq 3\frac{5}{7}$

$4(\frac{6}{7}) + 2(\frac{1}{7}) \leq 3\frac{5}{7}$
$3(\frac{6}{7}) + 8(\frac{1}{7}) \leq 3\frac{5}{7}$
$0(\frac{6}{7}) + 9(\frac{1}{7}) \leq 3\frac{5}{7}$

All five of these inequalities *are* satisfied by the values we inserted for the strategies and the game value. In the fifth inequality, notice that if X played row 3, he would expect to win only $\frac{9}{7}$ points, *far* less than the game value; obviously he would avoid that row, in preference to a mixed strategy between the first and second rows. The 0 strategy we have assigned player X proves this point.

Graphic solution method for 2 × M and M × 2 games

Up to this point, we have discussed two methods for solving 2 × M and M × 2 games, i.e., saddle points and the method of subgames. These types of games can also be reduced to a graphic representation that points out which of the 2 × 2 subgames is the optimum one for the player who has to make the choice. In addition, the graphic method will indicate the value of that optimum game. The advantage of this method is that it will enable us to solve for the strategies in the optimum 2 × 2 game once we have decided which of the three or more possible games is optimum.

If we use for our example the game

$$X \begin{pmatrix} 4 & 2 \\ 3 & 8 \\ 0 & 9 \end{pmatrix} \quad \text{Y}$$

(10-16)

we can see that if player X elects to play the first row, his winnings will be either 4 points or 2 points, depending upon his opponent's choice of columns. This observation can be represented by graphing X's winnings or payoffs as in Figure 10-1.

Similarly, if X elects to play row 2, his winnings will be either 3 points or 8 points, depending upon his opponent's choice of columns. This observation has been added to the graph in Figure 10-2.

And of course, we can add a third line representing X's winnings if he elects to play the third row, as in Figure 10-3.

Observing the completed graph of the game, it might appear that row 3 offers X the best chance, since he *can* win 9 points; but we must remember that Y would immediately shift to his first column. The expectation of winning 9 points would then turn into the reality of a zero payoff for X.

If, on the other hand, X chose the second-row strategy, it might appear that he could win 8 points as a payoff. Of course he might, but the

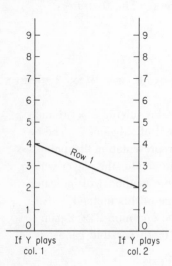

Figure 10-1   **X's winnings if he plays row 1.**

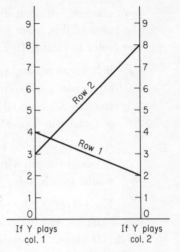

Figure 10-2 **X's winnings. Row 2 added.**

8-point payoff would again be turned into only a 3-point payoff as soon as Y began playing his first column.

If X elected to play the first-row strategy, he could win 4 points as the payoff, but only when Y played his first column. If Y elected to play his second column, X's winnings would be reduced to only 2 points.

If, however, X elected to play a mixed strategy between the first row and the second row, he can see that he cannot win less than 2 points and will not win more than 8 points, no matter what strategy his oppo-

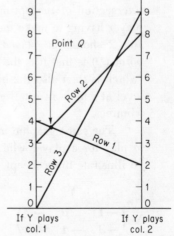

Figure 10-3 **X's winnings. All three rows and** *Q,* **value of the game.**

nent chooses. In fact, if X plays intelligently, he can ensure his winning the value of this game (3⅝ points). Here is how the players might reason (refer to Figure 10-2):

> If X began playing row 1 in expectation of winning 4 points, Y would obviously play column 2 to reduce X's payoff to 2 points. As soon as X observed this happening, he would switch to his second row and win 8 points as long as Y continued playing column 2.

> As soon as player Y switched back to his first column (hoping that X would remain with his second row and thus win only 3 points), X would switch to his first row and win 4 points.

For player X, the play of this game thus vacillates between rows 1 and 2 and around the point labeled Q (the value of the game) in Figure 10-3. If player Y chooses his column strategies carefully (using one of our previously discussed methods), he can hold X's winnings to an average between 3 and 4 points. He does this essentially by offensively countering X's moves. When X plays row 1 in expectation of winning 4 points, Y plays column 2. When X plays row 2 in expectation of winning 8 points, Y plays column 1 so that X wins only 3 points. The proportion of the time each player devotes to his rows and columns respectively is, of course, determined by methods we have previously covered. Thus our point Q is actually the value of this game, since it is the average payoff around which the game revolves.

Selecting the optimum two strategies from among many choices is accomplished by observing the intersection points (such as point Q). In Figure 10-4, the lowest intersection point in the shaded area denotes the intersection of the optimum two rows which should be played by the player having to make the choice among many rows; in this case rows 1 and 2 should be played. The significance of the *lowest* intersection point (Q) is that it is the lowest level at which Y can hold X's winnings (which is then also the highest payoff X can expect), and indeed is the level at which an intelligent opponent, Y, *will* succeed in holding X's winnings.

The same graphic method can be used to choose the two columns to play for a player who is faced with a choice among many columns. To illustrate this concept, let us consider the game

$$X \begin{pmatrix} -1 & 0 & -7 \\ -3 & -4 & -2 \end{pmatrix} \quad \overset{\text{Y}}{} \qquad (10\text{-}17)$$

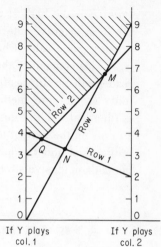

Figure 10-4 X's winnings showing three intersection points. *Q* is the lowest level at which Y can hold X's winnings; therefore it is the highest payoff X can expect.

Having first satisfied ourselves that no saddle point exists, we must then determine which two of Y's columns offer him the optimum mixed strategy. As before, we first plot all three of Y's columns—using, of course, negative numbers to represent payoffs to Y. Refer to Figure 10-5. The point *R*, which denotes the intersection of columns 2 and 3, indicates that Y should play some mixed strategy between those two columns in preference to any other two columns. The optimum subgame, then, is

$$\begin{pmatrix} 0 & -7 \\ -4 & -2 \end{pmatrix}$$
X strategies = (⅔, ⅞)
Y strategies = (0, ⅝, ⅘)
Value of game = −2⁸⁄₉

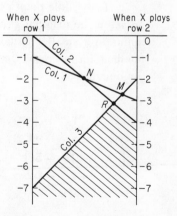

Figure 10-5 Y's winnings. *R* is the value of the game.

Point *R* is the highest intersection in the shaded area. The concept of the least negative intersection in this case indicates that point *R* is the greatest game value which X will allow Y to obtain.

This concept of the highest or lowest point (an extreme point), the reader will recall, was first developed in our treatment of linear programming by graphic methods. The concept as applied to game theory is identical. The lines representing the strategies are actually the restraints on the play of the game. The solution is thus obtained by determining just how far one player can go before he is restrained by his opponent's defensive strategy.

3 × 3 AND LARGER GAMES

In the solution to 3 × 3 and larger games, the first step, as in smaller games, is to look for a saddle point, for if one exists it will obviate more difficult solution methods. In the following game, for instance, a saddle point exists and is, of course, the solution to the optimum strategies and the value of the game.

$$\begin{pmatrix} 14 & 10 & \textcircled{9} \\ 4 & -2 & -6 \\ 8 & 6 & 4 \end{pmatrix}$$

X strategy = (1, 0, 0)
Y strategy = (0, 0, 1)
Value = 9
    ↑
  Saddle point

(10-18)

If no saddle point exists, one might utilize the method of dominance to see if the original game can be reduced by eliminating rows or columns to a smaller game, which can then be solved by the arithmetic method, for instance. In the following game, reduction has been obtained by dominance.

$$\text{X} \begin{pmatrix} 4 & -7 & 2 \\ 2 & -3 & -5 \\ 3 & -4 & -6 \end{pmatrix}$$

Y

Since the first column always offers player X a guaranteed chance to win, Y will not play that column.

(10-19)

The game is then reduced to

$$
X \begin{pmatrix} -7 & 2 \\ -3 & -5 \\ -4 & -6 \end{pmatrix}
$$

Y

Player X always loses more when he plays his third row than he does when he plays the second row; so he would never play the third row.

The game is further reduced to

$$
X \begin{pmatrix} -7 & 2 \\ -3 & -5 \end{pmatrix}
$$

Y

X strategy $= (\frac{2}{11}, \frac{9}{11}, 0)$
Y strategy $= (0, \frac{7}{11}, \frac{4}{11})$
Value $= -\frac{41}{11}$

If there is no saddle point and if dominance is unsuccessful in reducing the original game to a smaller game, linear programming offers the best solution method for larger games. In the following game, for instance, there is no saddle point, and dominance will not reduce the game to a more manageable size.

$$
\begin{array}{c} X_1 \\ X_2 \\ X_3 \end{array}
\begin{array}{ccc} Y_1 & Y_2 & Y_3 \end{array}
\begin{pmatrix} 3 & 2 & 3 \\ 2 & 3 & 4 \\ 5 & 4 & 2 \end{pmatrix}
\qquad (10\text{-}20)
$$

From our earlier discussion of $2 \times M$ and $M \times 2$ games (see the section Solution by Method of Subgames), we can write the inequalities which express the expectations of player Y as follows:

$$
\begin{aligned}
3Y_1 + 2Y_2 + 3Y_3 &\leq V \\
2Y_1 + 3Y_2 + 4Y_3 &\leq V \qquad (V = \text{game value}) \\
5Y_1 + 4Y_2 + 2Y_3 &\leq V
\end{aligned}
\qquad (10\text{-}21)
$$

The proportion of the time spent playing all three columns must, of course, sum to unity:

$$
Y_1 + Y_2 + Y_3 = 1 \qquad (10\text{-}22)
$$

To remove the Vs from the right-hand side of the three inequalities, we can divide all the terms by V:

$$\frac{3Y_1}{V} + \frac{2Y_2}{V} + \frac{3Y_3}{V} \leq 1$$

$$\frac{2Y_1}{V} + \frac{3Y_2}{V} + \frac{4Y_3}{V} \leq 1 \tag{10-23}$$

$$\frac{5Y_1}{V} + \frac{4Y_2}{V} + \frac{2Y_3}{V} \leq 1$$

To remove the Vs in the denominators of the Y terms, let us define a new Y variable:

$$\bar{Y} = \frac{Y}{V} \tag{10-24}$$

and solve the game in terms of $\bar{Y}$s instead of Ys. Then when we are done, we can multiply our $\bar{Y}$s by V to get the original Ys. (If $\bar{Y} = Y/V$, then $Y = \bar{Y} \times V$; this is just a helpful bit of mathematical juggling.)

Our three inequalities then become

$$3\bar{Y}_1 + 2\bar{Y}_2 + 3\bar{Y}_3 \leq 1$$
$$2\bar{Y}_1 + 3\bar{Y}_2 + 4\bar{Y}_3 \leq 1 \tag{10-25}$$
$$5\bar{Y}_1 + 4\bar{Y}_2 + 2\bar{Y}_3 \leq 1$$

To get our one equation $[Y_1 + Y_2 + Y_3 = 1$, Eq. (10-22)] into the same $\bar{Y}$ form, divide all its terms by V:

$$\frac{Y_1}{V} + \frac{Y_2}{V} + \frac{Y_3}{V} = \frac{1}{V} \tag{10-26}$$

and once again let $\bar{Y} = Y/V$, as we did above. Our equation now becomes

$$\bar{Y}_1 + \bar{Y}_2 + \bar{Y}_3 = \frac{1}{V} \tag{10-27}$$

Repeating all four restrictions, we now have

$$\bar{Y}_1 + \bar{Y}_2 + \bar{Y}_3 = \frac{1}{V} \tag{10-27}$$

$$3\bar{Y}_1 + 2\bar{Y}_2 + 3\bar{Y}_3 \le 1$$
$$2\bar{Y}_1 + 3\bar{Y}_2 + 4\bar{Y}_3 \le 1 \tag{10-25}$$
$$5\bar{Y}_1 + 4\bar{Y}_2 + 2\bar{Y}_3 \le 1$$

Y's objective must be to minimize the value of the game V; this is the same as maximizing $1/V$. We can write the linear programming problem to solve for Y's optimum strategies by adding a slack variable to each inequality.

Maximize $\quad \bar{Y}_1 + \bar{Y}_2 + \bar{Y}_3$
subject to: $\quad 3\bar{Y}_1 + 2\bar{Y}_2 + 3\bar{Y}_3 + \bar{Y}_4 + 0\bar{Y}_5 + 0\bar{Y}_6 = 1$
$\qquad\qquad\; 2\bar{Y}_1 + 3\bar{Y}_2 + 4\bar{Y}_3 + 0\bar{Y}_4 + \bar{Y}_5 + 0\bar{Y}_6 = 1 \quad (10\text{-}28)$
$\qquad\qquad\; 5\bar{Y}_1 + 4\bar{Y}_2 + 2\bar{Y}_3 + 0\bar{Y}_4 + 0\bar{Y}_5 + \bar{Y}_6 = 1$

Just for exercise, let us solve for Y's strategies by using the simplex algorithm. Because the simplex method was treated in detail in Chapter 9, we shall omit the explanations and show in Table 10-4 only the three tableaus necessary to solve for Y's strategies. Since all $C_j - Z_j$s in the third tableau are zero or negative, no further improvement is possible, and we have finished. The optimum $\bar{Y}$ strategies are

$$\bar{Y}_3 = \frac{3}{16}$$
$$\bar{Y}_1 = \frac{1}{8}$$

($\bar{Y}_4$ is a slack variable and has no real meaning.)

How can we convert $\bar{Y}_3$ and $\bar{Y}_1$ back into the real Y column strategies? Multiply them by V [see Eq. (10-24)]. What is V? Well, we maximized $1/V$ and found it to be $\frac{5}{16}$ (Z_j row under the quantity column). If $1/V = \frac{5}{16}$, then $V = \frac{16}{5}$.

$$Y_1 = \bar{Y}_1 \times V$$
$$= \frac{1}{8} \times \frac{16}{5}$$
$$= \frac{16}{40}$$
$$= \frac{2}{5}$$

$$Y_3 = \bar{Y}_3 \times V$$
$$= \frac{3}{16} \times \frac{16}{5}$$
$$= \frac{3}{5}$$

Y_2 is not played.

Table 10-4

Simplex algorithm for Y's strategies

C_j	Mix	Quantity (Column strategies)	1 $\bar{Y}_1$	1 $\bar{Y}_2$	1 $\bar{Y}_3$	0 $\bar{Y}_4$	0 $\bar{Y}_5$	0 $\bar{Y}_6$
0	$\bar{Y}_4$	1	3	2	3	1	0	0
0	$\bar{Y}_5$	1	2	3	4	0	1	0
0	$\bar{Y}_6$	1	5	4	2	0	0	1
	Z_j	0	0	0	0	0	0	0
	$C_j - Z_j$		1	1	1	0	0	0
			↑ Optimum column					

(Notice that in the $C_j - Z_j$ row of this step, there is a *tie;* $(1 = 1 = 1)$. Let us start with the column closest to the quantity column.)

0	$\bar{Y}_4$	$2/5$	0	$-2/5$	$9/5$	1	0	$-3/5$
0	$\bar{Y}_5$	$3/5$	0	$7/5$	$16/5$	0	1	$-2/5$
1	$\bar{Y}_1$	$1/5$	1	$4/5$	$2/5$	0	0	$1/5$
	Z_j	$1/5$	1	$4/5$	$2/5$	0	0	$1/5$
	$C_j - Z_j$		0	$1/5$	$3/5$	0	0	$-1/5$
					↑ Optimum column			

0	$\bar{Y}_4$	$1/16$	0	$-19/16$	0	1	$9/16$	$-3/8$
1	$\bar{Y}_3$	$3/16$	0	$7/16$	1	0	$5/16$	$-1/8$
1	$\bar{Y}_1$	$1/8$	1	$5/8$	0	0	$-1/8$	$1/4$
	Z_j	$5/16$	1	$17/16$	1	0	$3/16$	$1/8$
	$C_j - Z_j$		0	$-1/16$	0	0	$-3/16$	$-1/8$

Now what of X's row strategies? We can set up the inequalities which represent X's expectations as before:

$$\begin{aligned} 3X_1 + 2X_2 + 5X_3 &\geq V \\ 2X_1 + 3X_2 + 4X_3 &\geq V \\ 3X_1 + 4X_2 + 2X_3 &\geq V \end{aligned} \qquad (10\text{-}29)$$

and of course, $X_1 + X_2 + X_3 = 1$ (10-30)

Dividing through by V, we get $\bar{X}$ terms as follows:

$$3\bar{X}_1 + 2\bar{X}_2 + 5\bar{X}_3 \geq 1$$
$$2\bar{X}_1 + 3\bar{X}_2 + 4\bar{X}_3 \geq 1 \tag{10-31}$$
$$3\bar{X}_1 + 4\bar{X}_2 + 2\bar{X}_3 \geq 1$$

$$\bar{X}_1 + \bar{X}_2 + \bar{X}_3 = \frac{1}{V} \qquad \text{[see (10-26), (10-27)]}$$

Player X desires to maximize V, which is the same as minimizing $1/V$, so that our linear programming problem becomes

Minimize $\quad \bar{X}_1 + \bar{X}_2 + \bar{X}_3$
subject to: $\quad 3\bar{X}_1 + 2\bar{X}_2 + 5\bar{X}_3 \geq 1$
$\qquad\qquad\; 2\bar{X}_1 + 3\bar{X}_2 + 4\bar{X}_3 \geq 1 \qquad (10\text{-}32)$
$\qquad\qquad\; 3\bar{X}_1 + 4\bar{X}_2 + 2\bar{X}_3 \geq 1$

Adding slack variables and artificial variables, we get the problem in its final form:

Minimize $\quad \bar{X}_1 + \bar{X}_2 + \bar{X}_3$
subject to: $\quad 3\bar{X}_1 + 2\bar{X}_2 + 5\bar{X}_3 - \bar{X}_4 + 0\bar{X}_5$
$\qquad\qquad\qquad\qquad\qquad + 0\bar{X}_6 + \bar{X}_7 + 0\bar{X}_8 + 0\bar{X}_9 = 1$
$\qquad\qquad\; 2\bar{X}_1 + 3\bar{X}_2 + 4\bar{X}_3 + 0\bar{X}_4 - \bar{X}_5$
$\qquad\qquad\qquad\qquad\qquad + 0\bar{X}_6 + 0\bar{X}_7 + \bar{X}_8 + 0\bar{X}_9 = 1$
$\qquad\qquad\; 3\bar{X}_1 + 4\bar{X}_2 + 2\bar{X}_3 + 0\bar{X}_4 + 0\bar{X}_5$
$\qquad\qquad\qquad\qquad\qquad - \bar{X}_6 + 0\bar{X}_7 + 0\bar{X}_8 + \bar{X}_9 = 1$
$$\tag{10-33}$$

where $\qquad \bar{X}_4, \bar{X}_5,$ and $\bar{X}_6$ are slack variables
$\qquad\qquad \bar{X}_7, \bar{X}_8,$ and $\bar{X}_9$ are artificial variables

The solution to this linear programming problem turns out to be $\bar{X}_2 = \frac{3}{16}, \bar{X}_3 = \frac{1}{8}, \bar{X}_1 = 0$. Since $\bar{X} = X/V$, then $X = (\bar{X})(V)$, so that X's row strategies are

$$X_2 = \bar{X}_2 \times {}^{16}\!/_5$$
$$= \frac{3}{16} \times {}^{16}\!/_5$$
$$= \frac{3}{5}$$

$$X_3 = \bar{X}_3 \times {}^{16}\!/_5$$
$$= \frac{1}{8} \times {}^{16}\!/_5$$
$$= \frac{2}{5}$$

If this procedure seems long and tedious, remember that computer programs are available which will solve any linear programming problem in a matter of a few minutes once the applicable data have been programmed for the machine.

Linear programming will solve any size game; however, it is much easier to use one of our other methods on games less than 3×3 in size. On particularly large games which have no saddle point and which cannot be reduced by dominance, linear programming offers the most practical solution method.

MANAGEMENT USES OF THE THEORY OF GAMES

As we mentioned at the beginning of this chapter, the word "games" is a generic term that indicates situations of conflict in which the participants employ rational techniques to identify their best strategy. As such, games offer much in the way of insight into logical reasoning processes; however, their use in management decision making is still quite restricted. The most difficult task is obviously not the solution to the game, since we have discussed adequate methods by which to treat quite large two-person zero-sum games. Rather, it is our inability to fill in the values in the payoff matrix accurately.

It is not particularly difficult to establish, for instance, that one outcome is preferable to another, but it is quite another thing to state in numerical terms exactly how much more valuable it is. When the conflict situation is one involving a management decision, a precise calculation of the possible payoffs in dollars and cents is often impossible to obtain. This does not mean, however, that game theory cannot be used to advantage. Even though one of the participants may be unable to state in precise monetary terms the outcome for each possible combination of the strategies, he can generally rank the payoffs from best to worst in terms of their general appeal to him.

This idea of precise monetary payoffs versus ranked payoffs can best be illustrated by several examples.

Example 1. The case of payoffs ranked in order of preference may be illustrated by a marketing example. Two companies which compete, A and B, each prepare a display featuring one of its products in a supermarket once a week at the beginning of the week. Once the display has been set up, it cannot be changed for the remainder of the week.

Company A has three products, 1, 2, and 3, which it may display in competition with company B's products 4, 5, and 6. The promotion manager of company A has observed over a period of time that his net promotional effect from each of his choices is as follows:

$$
\begin{array}{c}
\text{B displays} \\
\begin{array}{ccc}
4 & 5 & 6
\end{array}
\end{array}
$$

$$
\text{A displays}
\begin{array}{c}
1 \\
2 \\
3
\end{array}
\left(
\begin{array}{ccc}
\text{good} & \text{fair} & \text{fair} \\
\text{fair} & \text{good} & \text{poor} \\
\text{poor} & \text{fair} & \text{good}
\end{array}
\right)
$$

If we let the promotional result "poor" take on a value to A of 1 point, "fair" take on a value of 2 points, and "good" take on a value of 3 points, our payoff matrix for this situation becomes

$$
\begin{array}{c}
\text{B} \\
\begin{array}{ccc}
4 & 5 & 6
\end{array}
\end{array}
$$

$$
\text{A}
\begin{array}{c}
1 \\
2 \\
3
\end{array}
\left(
\begin{array}{ccc}
3 & 2 & 2 \\
2 & 3 & 1 \\
1 & 2 & 3
\end{array}
\right)
$$

Testing first for a saddle point, we find there is none. We can verify that dominance will not be of use in reducing this game, either. Company A must then calculate a mixed strategy for his rows. A's best mixed strategy is as follows: Product 1 should be featured ½ of the time. Product 2 should be featured ⅙ of the time, and product 3 should be featured ⅓ of the time. The value of the game in this instance would represent the average promotional effect achieved by A; the game value in this case is $1\frac{3}{6}$ points, representing a promotional effect between fair and good.

Example 2. An example of a situation where rather precise monetary values might be calculated and used for the payoffs can be obtained from the area of finance—more precisely, investment portfolio management. Assume that an investor who possesses an amount of money (let us say $1,000) must invest it among three choices: common stocks, industrial bonds, and savings funds. The payoffs, in terms of (*a*) growth in capital and (*b*) returns to capital, are known for each of the investments under each of the three economic conditions which may prevail, i.e., recession, growth, and stability. Let us further assume that the investor must make his choice among the three portfolio choices for a period of one year in advance.

Under the above conditions, let us assume further that his expectations of the net earnings of his $1,000 portfolio after one year are represented by the following matrix:

	Recession	Growth	Stability
Stocks	−$150	$100	$50
Bonds	$ 40	$ 80	$50
Savings	$ 65	$ 50	$60

This 3×3 game can be solved for the investor's optimum strategies, which are as follows: stocks, .007, bonds .240, savings, .753. Thus the optimum division of his $1,000 investment, if the above matrix represents his expectations and if he must make his investment decision one year in advance, would be for him to invest $7 in stocks, $240 in bonds, and $753 in savings. If, however, he had some reason to believe that the market was headed in one direction or another, his decision would of course reflect his predictions. If he thought that market action would be random and fluctuating during the coming year, his best strategies are those we have calculated. The value of this game, incidentally, is $57.55, which represents a 5.75 per cent return for the investor.

Conclusion

Game theory is not a magic panacea for management's headaches. No one can now foretell its *future* applications and potential. It is, without question, good practice and good exercise for sharpening one's thinking about how to treat problems under uncertainty. Some of the other techniques (linear programming and inventory theory) assume a benign environment. Game theory, however, pits a player against an active opponent—against one who is an aggressive, hostile strategist. This is close to business experience—so close that the theory of games has an undeniable place in such a text as this.

PROBLEMS

10-1   Find the values of the following games:

$$a. \begin{pmatrix} 1 & 5 \\ 2 & 3 \end{pmatrix} \qquad b. \begin{pmatrix} 9 & -3 & -6 \\ 5 & 6 & -7 \\ -4 & 4 & -5 \end{pmatrix}$$

10-2   Use the arithmetic method for finding the optimum strategies for X and Y.

$$a.\ X \begin{matrix} Y \\ \begin{pmatrix} 3 & 4 \\ 4 & -1 \end{pmatrix} \end{matrix} \qquad b.\ X \begin{matrix} Y \\ \begin{pmatrix} -3 & 1 \\ 2 & -1 \end{pmatrix} \end{matrix}$$

10-3   Using the algebraic method, find the optimum strategies for X.

$$X \begin{matrix} Y \\ \begin{pmatrix} 1 & 6 \\ 3 & -4 \end{pmatrix} \end{matrix}$$

10-4   Use matrix algebra to find the optimum strategies for X and Y and the game value.

$$X \begin{matrix} Y \\ \begin{pmatrix} -3 & 1 \\ 2 & -1 \end{pmatrix} \end{matrix}$$

10-5   For the following game, use the arithmetic method to find the strategies, and use the joint probability method to determine the value of the game.

$$X \begin{matrix} Y \\ \begin{pmatrix} 1 & 4 \\ 2 & -2 \end{pmatrix} \end{matrix}$$

10-6   Reduce the following games by dominance and then restate the game that remains.

$$a. \begin{pmatrix} 1 & 3 \\ 4 & 1 \\ 2 & 4 \end{pmatrix} \quad b. \begin{pmatrix} 3 & 2 & 1 \\ 5 & 0 & 6 \\ -1 & 1 & -2 \end{pmatrix} \quad c. \begin{pmatrix} 3 & 3 & 4 & -3 & 4 \\ 2 & -1 & 2 & 1 & -3 \end{pmatrix}$$

10-7   Solve the following game for the optimum strategies and the value of the game.

$$\begin{pmatrix} 3 & -3 & 4 \\ -1 & 1 & -3 \end{pmatrix}$$

10-8   Find the optimum strategies and the value of this game.

$$X \begin{matrix} & & Y & \\ & & Y_1 & Y_2 \\ X_1 & \begin{pmatrix} -6 & 7 \\ X_2 & -1 & -2 \\ X_3 & 4 & -5 \end{pmatrix} \end{matrix}$$

10-9   For the game in problem 10-8, demonstrate that the optimum strategies satisfy the game inequalities.

10-10   Use a graphic solution to find X's average winnings.

$$X \begin{matrix} Y \\ \begin{pmatrix} 2 & 5 \\ 4 & 1 \end{pmatrix} \end{matrix}$$

BIBLIOGRAPHY

H. Bierman, L. E. Fouraker, and R. K. Jaedicke, *Quantitative Analysis for Business Decisions* (Homewood, Ill.: Richard D. Irwin, Inc., 1961).

S. Karlin, *Math Methods and Theory in Games, Programming and Economics* (Reading, Mass.: Addison-Wesley Publishing Company, Inc., 1959).

R. W. Llewellyn, *Linear Programming* (New York: Holt, Rinehart and Winston, Inc., 1964).

R. D. Luce and H. Raiffa, *Games and Decisions* (New York: John Wiley & Sons, Inc. 1958).

J. C. C. McKinsey, *Introduction to the Theory of Games* (New York: McGraw-Hill Book Company, 1952).

T. H. Naylor and E. T. Byrne, *Linear Programming* (Belmont, Calif.: Wadsworth Publishing Company, Inc., 1963).

J. D. Williams, *The Compleat Strategyst* (New York: McGraw-Hill Book Company, 1954).

chapter
eleven   **MARKOV**
ANALYSIS

The Markov process is a method of analyzing the *current* movement of some variable in an effort to predict the *future* movement of that same variable. The procedure was developed by the Russian mathematician A. Markov early in this century. He first used it to describe and predict the behavior of particles of gas in a closed container. As a management tool, the Markov process has been used in the last few years mainly as a marketing aid for examining and predicting the behavior of consumers in terms of their brand loyalty and their switching from one brand to another.

A full treatment of management's applications of the Markov process would require an extensive background in mathematics; however, using only the material developed in Chapter 7 on matrix algebra, we can illustrate the application of this technique to management problems, particularly to marketing problems.

We can best demonstrate the basic application of the Markov process by using a simple problem. Assume that A, B, and C are three dairies in a town and that they supply all the milk consumed in that town. It is known by all dairies that consumers switch from dairy to dairy over time because of advertising, dissatisfaction with service, and other reasons. If all three dairies maintain records concerning the number of their customers *and* the dairy from which they obtained each new customer, we have all the ingredients necessary for the application of this management tool.

Let us further suppose that Table 11-1 illustrates the movement of customers from one dairy to another over an observation period of one month. To further simplify the mathematics necessary, we shall assume that no new customers enter and no old customers leave the market during this period.

Table 11-1

Net changes in customers		
	Number of customers	
Dairy	June 1	July 1
A	200	220
B	500	490
C	300	290

Casual observation may suggest that a total of 20 customers switched during the month—10 from B to A and 10 from C to A. However, more detailed inspection may not support this initial inference. Suppose, for instance, that Table 11-2 is the true explanation of the exchange of customers among the three dairies. From it we see that 20 customers were gained by dairy A in a somewhat complex movement of customers involving all three dairies, a movement sometimes referred to in marketing as "brand switching."

Table 11-2

| | Actual exchanges of customers | | | |
| | | Changes during June | | |
Dairy	June 1 customers	Gain	Loss	July 1 customers
A	200	60	40	220
B	500	40	50	490
C	300	35	45	290

Each dairy needs details about brand switching if it is to do the best marketing job possible. If dairy B, for example, designs a promotional campaign under the impression that it is the only dairy losing customers *and* that it is losing them only to dairy A, B would be operating under a false assumption. In fact, dairy B is not just losing 10 customers per month; rather, each month it is *gaining 40* new customers from the other two dairies and *losing 50* old customers to the other two dairies.

Similarly, suppose that dairy A, noticing that it is gaining 20 customers each month, concentrates solely on efforts to lure additional customers away from its competitors. What dairy A has overlooked is its own losses of 40 customers per month. Perhaps some attempt to reduce this loss of 40 customers per month would be as effective dollarwise as efforts to capture additional customers from B and C.

The upshot of this whole matter is that simple analysis in terms of net gain or net loss of customers is inadequate for intelligent management. What management needs is a more detailed analysis concerning the rate of gains from and losses to *all competitors*. With such data, management can make an effort to:

1. Predict the share of market a seller will have at some future time
2. Predict the rate at which a seller will gain or lose his share of market in the future
3. Predict whether or not some market equilibrium (constant or level market shares) will obtain in the future
4. Analyze a seller's promotion efforts in terms of exactly what effects they are having on his gain and loss of market share

The Markov process offers us just such a tool for marketing analysis. By employing this tool of management, we are able to draw more accurate conclusions about our marketing position, both present and future. Without it, we tend to be in the position of dairy A when A knew he was gaining 20 customers per month but did not know that this gain was the net result of an interchange of customers among all three dairies.

To move beyond this simple analysis and into the use of the Markov process, we will have to compute *transition probabilities* for all three of our dairies. Transition probabilities are nothing more than the probability that a certain seller (a dairy, in this instance) will retain its customers. In other words, dairy B observes from Table 11-2 that it loses 50 customers this month; this is the same as saying that it has a probability of .9 of retaining customers; similarly, dairy A has a probability of .8 of retaining its customers; dairy C has a probability of .85 of retaining its customers. These transition probabilities for the retention of customers are calculated in Table 11-3.

At this point, we have some measure of the proportion of old customers each dairy retains each month, but we have not said anything

Table 11-3

	Transition probabilities for retention of customers			
Dairy	June 1 customers	Number lost	Number retained	Probability of retention
A	200	40	160	160/200 = .8
B	500	50	450	450/500 = .9
C	300	45	255	255/300 = .85

about the rates at which the three dairies gain new customers each month. Calculation of a complete set of these transition probabilities would require data on the flow of customers among all the dairies. Data of this sort demand good record keeping and take the form of Table 11-4.

Table 11-4

		Gains			Losses			
Dairy	June 1 customers	From A	From B	From C	To A	To B	To C	July 1 customers
A	200	0	35	25	0	20	20	220
B	500	20	0	20	35	0	15	490
C	300	20	15	0	25	20	0	290

Flow of customers

At this point, all the basic data are grouped in one table. We are able to observe not only the net gain or loss for any of the three dairies, but also the interrelationship between the gains and losses of customers by each of the dairies. For instance, it is now quite clear that dairy A gains the majority of its new customers from B. We can reason more intelligently from Table 11-4 concerning these interrelationships than we could when we knew only the net gain or loss by each of the dairies.

The next step in the application of the Markov process is to convert Table 11-4 into a more concise form, one wherein all the gains and losses take the form of transition probabilities. In our matrix of transition probabilities [Eq. (11-1)] we have included for each dairy the retention probability *and* the probability of its loss of customers to its two competitors. The rows in this matrix show the retention of customers and the gain of customers; the columns represent the retention of customers and the loss of customers. Note that the probabilities have been calculated to three decimal places.

Matrix of transition probabilities

$$
\begin{array}{c}
\\
A \\
B \\
C
\end{array}
\begin{array}{ccc}
A & B & C \\
.800 & .070 & .083 \\
.100 & .900 & .067 \\
.100 & .030 & .850
\end{array}
\qquad (11\text{-}1)
$$

Retention and gain $\longrightarrow$ Retention and loss $\downarrow$

Below is a matrix of the same dimensions as the one above illustrating exactly how each probability was determined.

$$
\begin{array}{c}
 \\
A \\
B \\
C
\end{array}
\begin{array}{ccc}
A & B & C \\
\left(\begin{array}{ccc}
160/200 = .800 & 35/500 = .070 & 25/300 = .083 \\
20/200 = .100 & 450/500 = .900 & 20/300 = .067 \\
20/200 = .100 & 15/500 = .030 & 255/300 = .850
\end{array} \right)
\end{array}
$$

The columns of the matrix of transition probabilities can be read as follows:

Column 1 indicates that dairy A retains .8 of its customers (160), loses .1 of its customers (20) to dairy B, and loses .1 of its customers (20) to dairy C.

Column 2 indicates that dairy B retains .9 of its customers (450), loses .07 of its customers (35) to dairy A, and loses .03 of its customers (15) to dairy C.

Column 3 indicates that dairy C retains .85 of its customers (255), loses .083 of its customers (25) to dairy A, and loses .067 of its customers (20) to dairy B.

Reading the rows yields the following information:

Row 1 indicates that dairy A retains .8 of its customers (160), gains .07 of B's customers (35), and gains .083 of C's customers (25).

Row 2 indicates that dairy B retains .9 of its customers (450), gains .1 of A's customers (20), and gains .067 of C's customers (20).

Row 3 indicates that dairy C retains .85 of its customers (255), gains .1 of A's customers (20), and gains .03 of B's customers (15).

With the information in this form, basic relationships can more easily be observed. In addition, through the use of matrix algebra we will be able to do the four management jobs listed on page 312.

STABILITY OF THE MATRIX OF TRANSITION PROBABILITIES

The Markov process is concerned with the *patronage* decisions of consumers; it involves how many consumers are buying from which dairies.

A basic assumption is that consumers do not shift their patronage from dairy to dairy to dairy at random; instead, we assume that choices of dairies to buy from in the future reflect choices made in the past.

A *first-order* Markov process is based on the assumption that the probability of the next event (customers' choices of vendors *next* month, in this case) depends upon the outcomes of the last event (customers' choices this month) and not at all on any earlier buying behavior. A *second-order* Markov process assumes that customer choices next month may depend upon their choices during the immediate past *two* months (or other buying period, if months are not used). In turn, *a third-order* process is based upon the assumption that customers' behavior is best predicted by observing and taking account of their behavior during the past *three* months (or other appropriate buying periods).

The mathematics of first-order chains is not difficult after you have studied the chapter on matrix algebra. In second- and third-order processes, however, the computations become more cumbersome and difficult. Studies suggest that using first-order assumptions for prediction purposes is not invalid, particularly if data appear to indicate that customer choices follow a fairly stable pattern—that is, if the matrix of transition probabilities remains stable. Because they are simple and because they have proved to be reliable predictors of future behavior, we shall limit our treatment to processes of the first order. For the reader who desires to expand this treatment to second- or third-order Markov processes, there are several excellent references available which go into the mathematical detail necessary for this advanced analysis.

PREDICTION OF MARKET SHARES
FOR FUTURE PERIODS

Let us return to our three dairies and assume that the matrix of transition probabilities remains fairly stable and that the July 1 market shares are these: A = 22 per cent, B = 49 per cent, C = 29 per cent. Managers of the three dairies would benefit, of course, from knowing the market shares that would obtain in some future period.

To calculate the probable share of the total market likely to be held by each of the dairies on August 1 (the month is our basic data-gathering period), we would simply set up the July 1 market shares as a matrix and multiply this matrix by the matrix of transition probabilities as follows:

<table>
<tr><td></td><td>Transition probabilities</td><td>July 1
market
shares</td><td>Probable
Aug. 1
market
shares</td><td></td></tr>
</table>

$$
\begin{matrix} A \\ B \\ C \end{matrix}
\begin{pmatrix} .800 & .070 & .083 \\ .100 & .900 & .067 \\ .100 & .030 & .850 \end{pmatrix}
\times
\begin{pmatrix} .22 \\ .49 \\ .29 \end{pmatrix}
=
\begin{pmatrix} .234 \\ .483 \\ .283 \end{pmatrix}
\quad (11\text{-}2)
$$

$$\overline{1.00} \qquad \overline{1.000}$$

The matrix multiplication is explained in detail below.

First row × first column
(A's propensity to retain its customers
     × A's share of market)   .8   × .22 = .176
(A's propensity to attract B's customers
     × B's share of market)   .070 × .49 = .034
(A's propensity to attract C's customers
     × C's share of market)   .083 × .29 = .024
    A's share of market on Aug. 1   .234

Second row × first column
(B's propensity to attract A's customers
     × A's share of market)   .1   × .22 = .022
(B's propensity to retain its customers
     × B's share of market)   .9   × .49 = .441
(B's propensity to attract C's customers
     × C's share of market)   .067 × .29 = .020
    B's share of market on Aug. 1   .483

Third row × first column
(C's propensity to attract A's customers
     × A's share of market)   .1 × .22 = .022
(C's propensity to attract B's customers
     × B's share of market)   .03 × .49 = .015
(C's propensity to retain its customers
     × C's share of market)   .85 × .29 = .246
    C's share of market on Aug. 1   .283

The probable market share on September 1 can be calculated by squaring the matrix of transition probabilities and multiplying the squared matrix by the July 1 market shares:

$$\text{Method 1} \quad \begin{pmatrix} .800 & .070 & .083 \\ .100 & .900 & .067 \\ .100 & .030 & .850 \end{pmatrix}^2 \times \begin{pmatrix} .22 \\ .49 \\ .29 \end{pmatrix} = \begin{matrix} \text{probable Sept. 1} \\ \text{market} \\ \text{shares} \end{matrix} \quad (11\text{-}3)$$

or by multiplying the matrix of transition probabilities by the market shares on August 1:

$$\text{Method 2} \quad \begin{pmatrix} .800 & .070 & .083 \\ .100 & .900 & .067 \\ .100 & .030 & .850 \end{pmatrix} \times \begin{pmatrix} .234 \\ .483 \\ .283 \end{pmatrix} = \begin{matrix} \text{probable Sept. 1} \\ \text{market} \\ \text{shares} \end{matrix} \quad (11\text{-}4)$$

Method 1. We can explain the logic behind method 1 this way. By squaring the original matrix of transition probabilities, we have in fact calculated the probabilities of retention, gain, and loss which can be multiplied by the original market shares (22, 49, and 29 per cent) to yield the market shares which will obtain on September 1. To obtain, for example, the first-column–first-row term X in the product, we multiply the first row by the first column:

$$\begin{pmatrix} .8 & .07 & .083 \end{pmatrix} \times \begin{pmatrix} .8 \\ .1 \\ .1 \end{pmatrix} = \begin{pmatrix} X \end{pmatrix}$$

First row × first column

A's propensity to retain its own customers × A's propensity to retain its own customers = that proportion of its original customers it retains after 2 periods = $.8 \times .8 = .64$

+

A's propensity to gain customers from B × B's propensity to gain customers from A = A's regain of its own customers from B = $.07 \times .1 = .007$

+

A's propensity to gain customers from C × C's propensity to gain customers from A = A's regain of its own customers from C = $.083 \times .1 = .0083$

We get the X term in the product by adding together the results of the three calculations:

.6400
.0070
.0083
——
.6553 = that portion of A's original customers A retains on Sept. 1

In similar fashion the other eight terms in the square of the matrix can be explained and calculated. The resulting matrix for use in method 1 is

$$
\begin{pmatrix}
.6553 & .1215 & .1416 \\
.1767 & .8200 & .1256 \\
.1680 & .0585 & .7328
\end{pmatrix}
$$

To complete method 1, we multiply the squared matrix by the July 1 market shares:

$$
\begin{pmatrix}
.6553 & .1215 & .1416 \\
.1767 & .8200 & .1256 \\
.1680 & .0585 & .7328
\end{pmatrix}
\times
\begin{pmatrix}
.22 \\
.49 \\
.29
\end{pmatrix}
$$

with the result

A	.244	
B	.478	probable market shares on Sept. 1
C	.278	
Total =	1.000	

For clarity, we shall explain the multiplication of the first row by the first column in detail:

$$
\begin{pmatrix}
.6553 & .1215 & .1416
\end{pmatrix}
\times
\begin{pmatrix}
.22 \\
.49 \\
.29
\end{pmatrix}
=
\begin{pmatrix}
.244
\end{pmatrix}
$$

A's propensity to retain its own customers after 2 periods $\times$ A's original market share = A's share of its original customers on September 1 = .6553 $\times$ .22 = .144

+

A's propensity to gain B's original customers after 2 periods × B's original market share = A's share of B's original customers on September 1 = .1215 × .49 = .059

+

A's propensity to gain C's original customers after 2 periods × C's original market share = A's share of C's original customers on September 1 = .1416 × .29 = .041

Adding the results of the three calculations, we get

.144
.059
.041
‾‾‾‾
.244 = A's probable market share on Sept. 1

Method 2. Multiplication of the original matrix of transition probabilities by the August 1 market shares yields the same result as method 1. We shall reproduce the two matrices and explain one of the multiplications, as follows:

$$\begin{pmatrix} .800 & .070 & .083 \\ .100 & .900 & .067 \\ .100 & .030 & .850 \end{pmatrix} \times \begin{pmatrix} .234 \\ .483 \\ .283 \end{pmatrix} = \begin{array}{l} \text{probable market shares} \\ \text{on Sept. 1} \end{array}$$

First row × first column
A's propensity to retain its own customers × A's share of market at the end of the last period = A's retained share of its own customers it had at the end of the last period = .8 × .234 = .187

+

A's propensity to gain customers from B × B's share of market at the end of the last period = A's gain of the customers B had at the end of the last period = .070 × .483 = .034

+

A's propensity to gain customers from C × C's share of market at the end of the last period = A's gain of the customers B had at the end of the last period = .083 × .283 = .023

.187
.034
.023
$\overline{.244}$ = A's probable share of market on Sept. 1

Method 1 has some natural advantage over method 2. If we want to go from the initial period to the third period, for instance, we do not have to go through the intermediate steps if we use method 1. We simply proceed as follows.

Market shares after 3 periods:

$$
\begin{pmatrix}
.800 & .070 & .083 \\
.100 & .900 & .067 \\
.100 & .030 & .850
\end{pmatrix}^3
\times
\begin{pmatrix}
.22 \\
.49 \\
.29
\end{pmatrix}
=
\begin{array}{l}
\text{probable market shares} \\
\text{on Oct. 1}
\end{array}
$$

Matrix of transition probabilities cubed $\quad \times \quad$ July 1 market shares

And, of course, if we want the market shares which will obtain after 6 periods, we would set up the problem as follows.

Market shares after 6 periods:

$$
\begin{pmatrix}
.800 & .070 & .083 \\
.100 & .900 & .067 \\
.100 & .030 & .850
\end{pmatrix}^6
\times
\begin{pmatrix}
.22 \\
.49 \\
.29
\end{pmatrix}
=
\begin{array}{l}
\text{probable market shares} \\
\text{next Jan. 1}
\end{array}
$$

Matrix of transition probabilities to the sixth power $\quad \times \quad$ July 1 market shares

Of course, raising a matrix to the sixth or an even higher power is no easy job if you must do the calculations by hand. Computer programs are available, however, which will perform this otherwise onerous task in a matter of a few seconds.

To summarize the uses of the two alternative methods of computing market shares for future periods, we would obviously employ method 1 if we simply wanted the market shares for the specified future period, while we would choose method 2 if we wanted to observe the changes which were occurring in the market shares during all the intervening periods.

EQUILIBRIUM CONDITIONS

It is quite reasonable to assume in our dairy problems that a state of equilibrium might be reached in the future regarding market shares; that is, the exchange of customers under equilibrium would be such as to continue—to freeze—the three market shares which obtained at the moment equilibrium was reached. Of course, equilibrium can result *only* if no dairy takes action which alters the matrix of transition probabilities. From a marketing point of view, we would want the answer to this question: What would the three final or equilibrium shares of the market be?

To illustrate equilibrium, assume a new matrix of transition probabilities:

$$
\begin{array}{c}
 \\
A \\
B \\
C
\end{array}
\begin{array}{ccc}
A & B & C \\
\left(\begin{array}{ccc}
.90 & .15 & 0 \\
.05 & .75 & 0 \\
.05 & .10 & 1.0
\end{array}\right)
\end{array}
\qquad \text{Retention and loss} \Big| \quad \text{Retention and gain} \longrightarrow \qquad (11\text{-}5)
$$

Because C never loses any customers and because both other dairies do lose customers to C, it is only a question of time until C has all the customers. In Markov terminology this would be called a *sink* or *basin* of one state, meaning that one of our dairies (C) eventually gets all the customers.

A second type of equilibrium might occur. To illustrate this, assume another new matrix of transition probabilities:

$$
\begin{array}{c}
 \\
A \\
B \\
C
\end{array}
\begin{array}{ccc}
A & B & C \\
\left(\begin{array}{ccc}
.90 & 0 & 0 \\
.05 & .50 & .50 \\
.05 & .50 & .50
\end{array}\right)
\end{array}
\qquad\qquad\qquad (11\text{-}6)
$$

One can easily see that in time, dairy B and dairy C capture all A's customers. Why is this true? Because A loses .05 of its customers to B and .05 to C and does not regain any new customers from either B or C. As B and C both have the same probability of retaining customers (.50), they must eventually divide up the market. This would be referred to as a sink or basin of two states. That is, two dairies, B and C, eventually share all the customers in the whole market.

We could, of course, have a type of equilibrium where no sink or basin exists. Here no one dairy gets all the customers—no two dairies capture the entire market. But some final or equilibrium condition develops and continues in which the market shares will not change *so long as the matrix of transition probabilities remains the same.* Our original three-dairy problem illustrates this third type of equilibrium. To find out what the final or equilibrium shares of the market will be with our original problem, let us proceed as follows:

$$
\begin{array}{c}
\quad A \quad\; B \quad\; C \\
\begin{array}{c} A \\ B \\ C \end{array}
\begin{pmatrix}
.800 & .070 & .083 \\
.100 & .900 & .067 \\
.100 & .030 & .850
\end{pmatrix}
\end{array}
= \;
\begin{array}{l}
\text{original matrix of} \\
\text{transition} \\
\text{probabilities}
\end{array}
\qquad (11\text{-}1)
$$

Now, A's share of the market in the equilibrium period (let us label this unspecified future period the eq. period) equals

.800 × the share A had in the eq. −1 period (the period immediately preceding equilibrium)

+

.070 × the share B had in the eq. −1 period

+

.083 × the share C had in the eq. −1 period

We can write this relationship as an equation:

$$
A_{\text{eq.}} = .800 A_{\text{eq.}-1} + .070 B_{\text{eq.}-1} + .083 C_{\text{eq.}-1} \qquad (11\text{-}7)
$$

And, of course, we can write two more equations illustrating the shares of market B and C will have in the equilibrium period.

$$
B_{\text{eq.}} = .100 A_{\text{eq.}-1} + .900 B_{\text{eq.}-1} + .067 C_{\text{eq.}-1} \qquad (11\text{-}8)
$$

$$
C_{\text{eq.}} = .100 A_{\text{eq.}-1} + .030 B_{\text{eq.}-1} + .850 C_{\text{eq.}-1} \qquad (11\text{-}9)
$$

In the early periods, the gains and losses from dairy to dairy are usually of fairly high magnitude. But as equilibrium is approached, the gains and losses become smaller and smaller until just before equilibrium they are infinitesimally small. This concept is not a unique one; many phenomena behave in this manner. For instance, Figure 11-1 shows the graph of a number (100) being divided in half at several stages. In the case of our Markov process, the changes in market shares between the equilibrium period and the period just preceding it are so slight that they may for mathematical purposes be treated as equal; that is, eq. = eq. -1. This allows us to rewrite our three equations as follows:

$$A = .800A + .070B + .083C \tag{11-10}$$

$$B = .100A + .900B + .067C \tag{11-11}$$

$$C = .100A + .030B + .850C \tag{11-12}$$

Because the sum of the three market shares equals 1.0 we can add another equation illustrating this:

$$1.0 = A + B + C \tag{11-13}$$

In Eqs. (11-10) to (11-12) we have similar terms on both sides of the equality sign, so that we can reduce these equations to

$$0 = -.200A + .070B + .083C \tag{11-14}$$

$$0 = .100A - .100B + .067C \tag{11-15}$$

$$0 = .100A + .030B - .150C \tag{11-16}$$

$$1.0 = A + B + C \tag{11-13}$$

Figure 11-1 **Dividing a number in half by stages. As equilibrium is approached, the changes become smaller and smaller.**

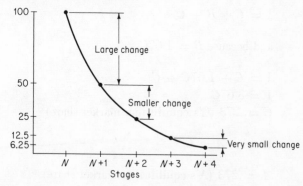

As we have four equations and only three unknowns, we can drop one equation [we drop Eq. (11-16)] and solve the remaining three equations simultaneously for the equilibrium market shares.

$$0 = -.200A + .070B + .083C \qquad (11\text{-}14)$$

$$0 = .100A - .100B + .067C \qquad (11\text{-}15)$$

$$1 = A + B + C \qquad (11\text{-}13)$$

Step 1.   Multiply Eq. (11-15) by .7 and add it to Eq. (11-14):

$$
\begin{array}{ll}
0 = -.200A + .070B + .083C & (11\text{-}14) \\
0 = .070A - .070B + .047C & (11\text{-}15) \times .7 \\
\hline
0 = -.130A + .130C & \\
.130A = .130C & \\
A = C &
\end{array}
$$

Step 2.   Multiply Eq. (11-15) by 2 and add it to Eq. (11-14):

$$
\begin{array}{ll}
0 = -.200A + .070B + .083C & (11\text{-}14) \\
0 = .200A - .200B + .134C & (11\text{-}15) \times 2 \\
\hline
0 = - .130B + .217C & \\
.13B = .217C & \\
B = 1.67C &
\end{array}
$$

Step 3.   Repeat Eq. (11-13):

$$1 = A + B + C$$

Because $A = C$, then

$$1 = C + B + C$$

and because $B = 1.67C$,

$$1 = C + 1.67C + C$$
$$1 = 3.67C$$
$$C = .273 \text{ (C's equilibrium market share)}$$

Because $A = C$,

$$A = .273 \text{ (A's equilibrium market share)}$$

and because $1 = A + B + C$,

$1 = .273 + B + .273$
$1 = B + .546$
$B = .454$ (B's equilibrium market share)

     Are you skeptical that an equilibrium has actually been reached? If so, let us prove it. Multiply the equilibrium market shares (A .273, B .454, C .273) by the matrix of transition probabilities:

$$
\begin{array}{c}
 \\
A \\
B \\
C
\end{array}
\begin{array}{ccc}
A & B & C \\
\end{array}
\begin{pmatrix}
.800 & .070 & .083 \\
.100 & .900 & .067 \\
.100 & .030 & .850
\end{pmatrix}
\times
\begin{pmatrix}
.273 \\
.454 \\
.273
\end{pmatrix}
=
\begin{pmatrix}
.273 \\
.454 \\
.273
\end{pmatrix}
$$

There is no change; therefore we are in an equilibrium position. Of course, if we had wanted to save a little time, we could have used determinants to solve Eqs. (11-14), (11-15), and (11-13) as follows:

$$
A = \frac{\begin{vmatrix} 0 & .07 & .083 \\ 0 & -.1 & .067 \\ 1 & 1 & 1 \end{vmatrix}}{\begin{vmatrix} -.2 & .07 & .083 \\ .1 & -.1 & .067 \\ 1 & 1 & 1 \end{vmatrix}} = .273
$$

$$
B = \frac{\begin{vmatrix} -.2 & 0 & .083 \\ .1 & 0 & .067 \\ 1 & 1 & 1 \end{vmatrix}}{\begin{vmatrix} -.2 & .07 & .083 \\ .1 & -.1 & .067 \\ 1 & 1 & 1 \end{vmatrix}} = .454
$$

$$
C = \frac{\begin{vmatrix} -.2 & .07 & 0 \\ .1 & -.1 & 0 \\ 1 & 1 & 1 \end{vmatrix}}{\begin{vmatrix} -.2 & .07 & .083 \\ .1 & -.1 & .067 \\ 1 & 1 & 1 \end{vmatrix}} = .273
$$

with, of course, the same answer.

Just a word about the equilibrium market shares we have calculated. They are based upon the assumption that the matrix of transition probabilities remains fixed—that the propensities of all three dairies to retain, gain, and lose customers do not change over time. In many cases this may be somewhat invalid, but no harm is done even so. For the period during which the transition probabilities are stable, we can calculate an equilibrium which will result. Then, if we have good reason to believe that the transition probabilities are indeed changing because of some action by management, we can use the new transition probabilities and calculate the equilibrium market shares which will result. In that manner, we are essentially using the Markov process as a short- or intermediate-run tool.

Relationship of market shares and equilibrium

An interesting fact about Markov analysis is that the final equilibrium will be the same (provided the transition probabilities remain fixed) regardless of the initial market shares held by various producers or suppliers, so long as no share is zero. That is to say, we will always end with the same final proportion of customers no matter what the original shares were. For example, if three suppliers have as their current shares of market

A   30%
B   60%
C   10%

and the matrix of transition probabilities is

$$
\begin{array}{c c c c}
 & A & B & C \\
A & .90 & .05 & .20 \\
B & .10 & .80 & .20 \\
C & 0 & .15 & .60
\end{array}
$$

then by using the technique for determining the equilibrium market shares discussed in the previous section, we can determine that the equilibrium market shares would be A .476, B .381, C .143.

If, on the other hand, the initial market shares were

A 20%
B 45%
C 35%

the equilibrium market shares for the three firms would still be the same (A .476, B .381, C .143), as long as the matrix of transition probabilities did not change. You can satisfy yourself that this is true by noting that the market shares were not used in explaining the equilibrium process; only the matrix of transition probabilities enters into the determination of equilibrium.

Of course, the nearer the initial market shares happen to be to the final or equilibrium market shares, the faster equilibrium will be reached. If the beginning shares for three firms are

A 35%
B 40%
C 25%

and the final or equilibrium shares will be

A 30%
B 35%
C 35%

we can see that the process will reach equilibrium much faster than if the initial market shares are

A 10%
B 75%
C 15%

—simply because in the former case, less change needs to occur to reach the final equilibrium. In the latter case, for instance, firm A needs to acquire sufficient customers to bring its market share from 10 per cent to its equilibrium share of 30 per cent, whereas in the former case, A would move only from 35 to 30 per cent before equilibrium is reached.

If this concept that the initial market shares have no bearing on the final equilibrium shares still appears a bit difficult to accept, consider the following example:

$$
\begin{array}{c c c c}
 & A & B & C \\
A & \begin{pmatrix} 1.0 & .3 & .1 \\ 0 & .6 & .2 \\ 0 & .1 & .7 \end{pmatrix} \\
B \\
C
\end{array}
$$

One can immediately see that *regardless of the initial market shares held by these three firms,* as long as none is zero, firm A will eventually get all the customers—A does not lose any of the customers he gains from B and C. Thus, if A begins with only 5 per cent of the customers, he will eventually have 100 per cent of the customers. Of course, the higher the initial percentage of customers held by firm A, the faster equilibrium will be reached.

USE OF MARKOV PROCESS IN MARKETING STRATEGY

To illustrate how Markov analysis is helpful in determining marketing strategy, consider the following situation. For three competing sellers the matrix of transition probabilities is as follows:

$$
\begin{array}{c c c c}
 & A & B & C \\
A & \begin{pmatrix} .2 & .1 & .2 \\ .6 & .5 & .3 \\ .2 & .4 & .5 \end{pmatrix} \\
B \\
C
\end{array}
\qquad
\begin{array}{c}
\text{Retention} \\
\text{and loss} \downarrow
\end{array}
\qquad
\begin{array}{c}
\text{Retention and gain} \\
\longrightarrow
\end{array}
$$

If the marketing strategies of these three firms do not change so as to affect the matrix of transition probabilities, we could reasonably expect equilibrium market shares of A .156, B .434, C .410.

In an effort to better his rather poor showing, seller A might consider two new marketing strategies.

Strategy 1. Seller A might try to retain more of his own customers. Assume that strategy 1 increases retention from 20 to 40 per cent, and assume that this change consists in A's reducing his loss of customers to seller B.

The new matrix of transition probabilities is

$$
\begin{array}{c}
\quad A \quad B \quad C \\
\begin{array}{c} A \\ B \\ C \end{array}
\begin{pmatrix}
.4 & .1 & .2 \\
.4 & .5 & .3 \\
.2 & .4 & .5
\end{pmatrix}
\end{array}
$$

The new equilibrium market shares work out to be A .2, B .4, and C .4. A's showing now is better; but even though A's campaign was specifically directed against B, note that firm C suffered somewhat. Why? C gains new customers from A and B—but more from B than from A. Now that B gets fewer of A's customers as a result of A's strategy, C's gain from B (.4) will represent a smaller number. We should not be too surprised that C's fortunes are not more drastically affected as a result of A's action; C does get back from A some of the customers A takes from B.

Strategy 2. As an alternative, seller A might direct his marketing efforts at capturing a greater share of the buyers who switch from C. Suppose that A's campaign is designed to induce .4 of those who switch from C to move to A, instead of the .2 who now do.

The matrix of transition probabilities now becomes

$$
\begin{array}{c}
\quad A \quad B \quad C \\
\begin{array}{c} A \\ B \\ C \end{array}
\begin{pmatrix}
.2 & .1 & .4 \\
.6 & .5 & .1 \\
.2 & .4 & .5
\end{pmatrix}
\end{array}
$$

If we calculate the equilibrium market shares which would result from this type of strategy, we find them to be A .233, B .391, and C .376.

We infer from this example that if the costs of the two programs are the same, clearly strategy 2 is the better one. Again in the case of strategy 2, notice that even though A's encroachment efforts were not directed against B at all, B suffers loss of customers as a result of A's marketing program directed against C. Why? B used to get .3 of C's customers each month. Now that A's efforts have been successful in getting .4 of C's customers, B's share of switchers is reduced to .1. Again, we should not be too surprised at seeing that B's share does not shrink drastically;

B will eventually get back from A some of the new customers A was successful in taking away from C.

In setting up our dairy problem at the beginning of this chapter, we assumed, in order to simplify the mathematics, that no old customers leave the market and no new customers enter the market during the time period involved. We know that this is seldom the case. What, then, about the more realistic experience, one in which new customers do move in and begin patronizing dairies and old customers do disappear from or drop out of the market? In these circumstances, the effects of the additions and the losses on (*a*) the market shares obtaining in immediately future periods and (*b*) the market shares at equilibrium would depend on three variables:

1. The dairy from which each newcomer begins to buy
2. The dairy from which each consumer was buying at the moment he ceased to be a customer
3. The extent to which the brand loyalty of each newcomer differs from the brand loyalty pattern obtaining at the time of his entry into the market as a customer

Source of information

Perhaps you have been wondering how the firms we have been referring to can get the data needed for application of the Markov process to their marketing problems. One solution is for a firm to buy the services of a marketing research organization. Some of these organizations collect information about brand loyalty and brand switching for clients. For example, the Market Research Corporation of America has established a sample of United States families who record and report all purchases of certain branded products to MRCA. Because the buying units comprising this consumer panel reveal which brands they buy, MRCA data can be used in Markov analysis. Some individual sellers ought to be in a position to collect the brand preference information each would need in order to make use of the Markov process.

PROBLEMS

11-1 Analyze the following matrix of transition probabilities and determine the equilibrium market shares for each firm. Give your reasons.

$$
\begin{array}{cccc}
 & \text{Firm X} & \text{Firm Y} & \text{Firm Z} \\
\text{Firm X} & \begin{pmatrix} 1.0 & .10 & .10 \\ \text{Firm Y} \quad 0 & .75 & .05 \\ \text{Firm Z} \quad 0 & .15 & .85 \end{pmatrix}
\end{array}
$$

11-2 On January 1, each of three dairies has one-third of the local market. Over the past year, dairy A retained .90 of its customers while losing .05 to dairy B and .05 to dairy C. Dairy B retained .85 of its customers while losing .10 to A and .05 to C. Dairy C retained .80 of its customers while losing .10 to A and .10 to B. If the same pattern of customer gains and losses continues for the coming year, what per cent of the market will each dairy have on next January 1?

11-3 On June 1 bakery A has 40 per cent of the local market, and bakeries B and C each have 30 per cent of the market. A marketing research firm has found that bakery A retains 85 per cent of its customers each month while gaining 5 per cent of B's customers and 10 per cent of C's customers. Bakery B retains 90 per cent of its customers while gaining 5 per cent of A's customers and 5 per cent of C's customers. Bakery C retains 85 per cent of its customers and gains 10 per cent of A's customers and 5 per cent of B's customers. What will each firm's share of the market be on August 1, and what will each firm's market share be at equilibrium?

11-4 At the end of last year, company A had 20 per cent of the market. Each of its competitors, company B and company C, had 40 per cent of the market. During last year, industry sales were $100 million, and company A had a net income of 5 per cent on its sales. Both of these figures are expected to remain the same for next year. Company A's advertising agency suggests that if A would spend an additional $100,000 during next year for advertising, A would retain 85 per cent of its customers while gaining 8 per cent of B's customers and 7 per cent of C's. Company B is expected to retain 85 per cent of its customers while gaining 10 per cent from A and 3 per cent from C. Company C is expected to retain 90 per cent of its customers while gaining 5 per cent from A and 7 per cent from B. Should company A make the additional expenditure for advertising?

11-5 Assume that instant mashed potatoes were introduced on the market simultaneously by three companies. The three firms, F, B, and C, launched their respective brands in January. At the start, each company had approximately one-third of the market. During the year, these developments took place:

Company F retained 80 per cent of its customers, lost 12 per cent to B, lost 8 per cent to C.

Company B retained 70 per cent of its customers, lost 20 per cent to F, lost 10 per cent to C.

Company C retained 90 per cent of its customers, lost 5 per cent to F, lost 5 per cent to B.

Assume that the market does not expand.
a. What share of the total market is likely to be held by each company at the end of next year?
b. Predict what the long-run market shares will be at the equilibrium state if buying habits do not change.

BIBLIOGRAPHY

W. Feller, *Introduction to Probability Theory and Its Application* (New York: John Wiley & Sons, Inc., 1957).

A. Kaufmann, *Methods and Models of Operations Research* (Englewood Cliffs, N.J.: Prentice-Hall, Inc., 1963).

J. G. Kemeny and J. L. Snell, *Finite Markov Chains* (Princeton, N.J.: D. Van Nostrand Company, Inc., 1960).

J. G. Kemeny, J. L. Snell, and G. L. Thompson, *Introduction to Finite Mathematics* (Englewood Cliffs, N.J.: Prentice-Hall, Inc., 1957).

chapter **QUEUING**
twelve

In industry there are many examples of processes which generate *waiting lines,* often referred to as queues. Such waiting lines occur when some employee, part, machine, or unit must wait for service because the servicing facility, operating at capacity, is temporarily unable to provide that service.

The pioneering work in the field of queuing theory was done by A. K. Erlang, a Danish engineer associated with the telephone industry. Early in this century Erlang was doing experiments involving the fluctuating demand for telephone facilities and its effect upon automatic dialing equipment. It was not until the end of World War II that this early work was extended to other more general problems involving queues or waiting lines.

We often see a very simple queuing problem at the checkout counters in a supermarket. The problem can be illustrated in this manner:

Queue or waiting line

This situation is referred to in queuing theory as the *single-channel* case; the arrivals (customers desiring to be checked out) form a single line which is serviced by the single processing station (the checker, in this instance). Queuing problems of the single-channel type can be solved without any additional mathematics beyond what we have already covered.

In the supermarket checkout problem, if the supermarket manager wants to minimize the length of the waiting line that would normally form at the single checkout counter, he can add another cash register and another checker. If the queues that form are still too long, he can add more counters. Each addition, of course, adds to expense, but at the same time, each further reduces the time customers have to wait for service. The manager tries to hit a happy medium. He wants waiting lines short enough to minimize customer ill will, but at the same time, he knows he cannot afford to provide enough service facilities to guarantee that no waiting line or queue can ever develop. In effect, our manager balances the increased cost of additional facilities against the customer ill will which increases as the average length of the queue increases.

There are many industrial applications of queuing theory in which the cost of time lost by the personnel in the waiting line *and* the cost of additional facilities can be determined accurately. In most of these

problems, one can arrive at the exact mathematical solution which provides the lowest total cost of (1) the lost time of persons waiting for
service plus (2) the wages of persons who provide the service. Let us
look at such a situation.

In the typical production machine shop, the expensive cutting tools
required in the machining processes are kept in a central location often
referred to as a tool crib. This crib is manned by one or more persons
who check out the tools required by the machinists in the shop. Adequate records for control purposes must be kept. When a machinist requires a certain tool, he proceeds to the tool crib, presents his tool
authorization to the attendant, and is issued the required tool. He returns to his machine, performs the work, and then goes back to the tool
crib, where he checks in the tool; if required, he draws another for the
next job to be performed. Because some of the tools involved in work
of this kind are very expensive, this procedure is necessary to ensure
adequate control of the tool inventory.

During the time the machinist has to wait in line at the tool crib for
service, he is idle; a labor loss is incurred by his company. This type of
loss is measurable because it is simply the amount of time he is required
to wait multiplied by the wage he receives per hour. By the same token,
when the employees who staff the tool crib are idle because no machinist
is requiring service, their wages represent a labor loss to the company.

One way to reduce the waiting time of the machinists is to provide
sufficient tool crib employees so that no queue is allowed to form. Because the arrival of the machinists is on a random basis, a large number
of tool crib operators would be required. During the time when no
machinists arrived for service, the entire combined wages of this large
group of attendants would be a loss. What we need is the mathematical
solution which takes into account all the factors in the problem *and* determines the ratio of tool crib attendants to machinists which will guarantee the lowest total cost. This type of situation can best be illustrated by
using some figures representing what might be a real experience, as in
Table 12-1.

From Table 12-1 it is apparent that *two* crib attendants will minimize the total cost of (1) the machinists' lost time plus (2) the crib attendants' wages. Having fewer *or* more than two attendants will raise this
total cost.

In a real industrial situation, of course, no one wants to observe the
operation for the extended period of time necessary to acquire these
figures. That would be an unnecessary waste of time and money when

Table 12-1

Simulated behavior at tool crib				
	Number of attendants			
	1	2	3	4
Average arrival of machinists during 8-hr shift	100	100	100	100
Average time each machinist spends waiting for service	10 min	6 min	4 min	1 min
Total time lost by machinists during 8-hr shift	1,000 min	600 min	400 min	100 min
Machinists' average pay	$3/hr	$3/hr	$3/hr	$3/hr
Value of machinists' lost time	$50	$30	$20	$5
Tool crib attendants' average pay	$2/hr	$2/hr	$2/hr	$2/hr
Total pay of tool crib attendants for 8-hr shift	$16	$32	$48	$64
Machinists' lost time plus tool crib attendants' pay	$66	$62	$68	$69

↑
Optimum no.
of tool crib
attendants = 2

Table 12-2

Uses of queuing theory		
Situation	Queue or waiting line	Service facility
Food service	Patrons waiting to eat	Waiters
Gasoline station	Motorists waiting for service	Attendants
Dentist's office	Patients	Dentist
Textile mill	Loom waiting for repairs	Loom fixer
Parts warehouse	Mechanics drawing out parts	Parts attendants
Assembly line	Employees waiting for the unfinished assembly	Employees currently processing the assembly

the same solution to the problem can be obtained using some mathematical techniques associated with queuing theory. These we will develop and discuss later.

The problem of the tool crib attendants and the machinists represents, of course, only one application of queuing theory. Consider the illustrations in Table 12-2, which lists cases where application of this useful technique can provide optimum solutions to common managerial problems. These are just a few of the many opportunities for the application of the theory of queues or waiting lines. Let us now proceed to the derivation of the basic ideas behind this management tool.

ARRIVAL RATES AND SERVICING RATES

As in the case of other disciplines, queuing theory has its own set of terms. We must learn them before we can proceed to a study of the mathematical methods which determine the optimum allocation of personnel to servicing facilities. Among these terms are the arrival rate and the servicing rate.

The *arrival* rate represents the average rate at which persons or items appear at a servicing facility for service. It could, for instance, take the form of the number of employees arriving at the company cafeteria for lunch; in another case it could represent the number of cars arriving at a toll gate on a particular bridge. The arrival rate is generally expressed as a rate of arrival per unit of time; this could be 60 employees per hour or 180 cars per hour.

The *servicing* rate refers to the rate at which the servicing facility can handle the incoming calls for service. It too would be expressed as a rate per unit of time and might take the form of the number of applications that could be processed per hour in a personnel office (75 per hour, for instance), or the number of inventory requests that could be handled in a warehouse (65 per day, for example).

The term *queue discipline* refers to the manner in which the arriving customers are selected for service. There are several possibilities here. Arriving customers usually take their places in the waiting line on a first-come–first-in-line basis. By the same token, customers in line are usually serviced on a next-in-line–next-served basis. There are, however, cases in which this is not the pattern. For instance, some priority other than the previously mentioned common ones could be observed. Priorities could recognize the urgency of the servicing required; some customers would have preference over others and perhaps would not be required to join the queue at all. In the queuing problems that we shall treat in this chapter, the normal arrangement of first-come–first-in-line and first-in-line–first-served will be followed.

The manner in which arrivals and servicing times are distributed has considerable bearing on the solution to queuing problems. For instance, arrivals can be random over time *or* the arrival rate can be uniform in that it does not vary. A *random* arrival case would be the one in which customers desiring service arrive in no logical pattern or order over time; in the first five minutes of the day, 95 customers may arrive, whereas in another similar five-minute period, only 4 customers would arrive. The opposite, the *uniform* arrival rate, would be the case where the arrivals were always at the same frequency; for example, 5 customers arrive each minute throughout the entire working period. In the normal business situation, the arrivals usually are randomly distributed.

Even though the arrivals are randomly distributed, their average can be calculated if a long enough period of time is used. If we observe the process for a sufficient period of time, we can calculate the total number of customers who arrived for service and the total time over which they arrived. By dividing the two magnitudes, we establish an average rate of arrivals over time.

Servicing time may also be randomly distributed or uniform. In the case of randomly distributed servicing times, we might find a situation in which the first customer could be serviced in five minutes, but the servicing facility would need one hour to handle the next customer. The existence of random servicing times is generally attributable to the nature of the service required. For instance, in the case of a repair facility handling small motors, one motor arriving for service might require only a minor soldering job on one of the terminal wires, but the next motor arriving might well require a complete rewinding job.

Servicing times may, of course, be uniform; each item which arrives for service may take the same time as each other item. This might be the case where an inspector measures one dimension of a finished part and signs an inspection form. If all the finished parts are identical, there is no reason why it should take any longer to perform one inspection than any other inspection. Although in the simple examples below we assume that arrival rates and servicing times are uniform rather than random, we shall soon get to the point where we can treat randomly distributed arrival and servicing rates.

The case in which both the arrival rate and the servicing rate are uniform can be illustrated with the following examples.

1. No queue, idle time.   Assume that arrivals occur at the uniform rate of 10 per hour, 10 arrivals each hour and every hour, occurring precisely every 6 minutes.   Assume also that services can be performed at a uniform rate of 12 per hour every hour.   With this situation, a queue will not form because the servicing facility can handle with ease the entire arrival workload.   In fact, we may easily calculate that the servicing facility will be idle $2/12$, or 16.67 per cent, of the time because arrivals are only $10/12$ of servicing capacity.

2. No queue, no idle time.   Assume now that arrivals occur at the uniform rate of 10 per hour, 10 arrivals each hour and every hour, occurring at 6-minute intervals during that hour.   Assume also that services can and are performed at a uniform rate of 10 per hour every hour. With this situation, a queue cannot form because arrivals are serviced at the same rate at which they arrive.   Also in this situation, there will be no idle time in the servicing facility because it must operate at full capacity to handle the arrivals.

3. Queue forms, no idle time.   Assume now that arrivals occur at the uniform rate of 10 per hour, occurring every 6 minutes during that hour.   Assume also that services are performed at a uniform rate of 8 per hour every hour.   With this situation, a queue will form and grow because the input rate is higher than the ability of the servicing facility to handle it.   The queue of unserviced arrivals builds up at the rate of 2 units per hour, the excess of arrivals over serviced items.   At the end of 7 hours, for instance, we would normally expect to see 14 units in the queue.

Thus the assumption of uniform arrivals and service times makes quite easy the calculation of whether a queue will form and what its length will be after any period of time.   If, however, we move to the more usual case in which both arrivals and services are randomly distributed, in which they happen at other than precise intervals, the problem and the calculations become more difficult.   For instance, if we allow arrivals and services to be randomly distributed, even though the servicing facility has a capacity greater than the average arrivals, a group of items arriving at the same time for service may form a temporary queue.   And, of course, by the same token, a temporary reduction in arrivals may enable the service facility to catch up, to remove a queue that had previously formed.

SIMULATION METHOD OF SOLVING QUEUING PROBLEMS

How can we treat queuing problems with randomly distributed arrival and service times? One of the better methods is to simulate the entire problem—to design an experiment which will duplicate as nearly as possible the real situation and then watch what does happen. This method of simulation is one of the more effective methods of treating queuing problems of this type.

Now, what would simulate random arrivals at a servicing facility? We could use a table of random numbers (see Appendix Table 3). A table of random numbers is a group of numbers which occur in no order; that is, they are all mixed up, and no one number is more likely to occur next than any other number. With random numbers it is possible without complicated mathematics to simulate the operation of a service facility and to determine the optimum assignment of service personnel in relation to the arrivals at the facility.

Let us suppose, for example, that a manufacturing plant operates an inventory warehouse which issues raw materials to shop foremen who arrive at the warehouse with properly certified requests. Currently, 2 persons are assigned to operate the warehouse. The number of shop foremen who use the warehouse from time to time is 10. The plant manager notices that a waiting line (shop foremen waiting for service) occasionally develops at the warehouse. He wonders if the assignment of 2 persons to the warehouse service counter is sufficient; he assigns this problem to his assistant for solution and recommendations.

The assistant observed the operation of the warehouse for one-hour periods spread over a month. These one-hour periods were scheduled at random during the day in order to get a reasonable cross section of activity. The assistant gathered the following data during his observations.

Average time between requests: 5 minutes
Total number of requests for service observed: 150
Different lengths of service time and number of each:

8 minutes	15
9 minutes	30
10 minutes	45
11 minutes	60
Total requests	150

In addition to recording the above data, the assistant divided his observed time into five-minute intervals and recorded the number of shop foremen who arrived during each interval. He found that there was a 100 per cent chance of one or more arrivals within any given five minutes.

At the completion of the observation period, the assistant tabulated the results of his observations as follows:

Percentage distribution of service times	$^{15}\!/_{150} = 10\%$ (8 min)
	$^{30}\!/_{150} = 20\%$ (9 min)
	$^{45}\!/_{150} = 30\%$ (10 min)
	$^{60}\!/_{150} = 40\%$ (11 min)
Weighted average of service times	$10\% \times$ 8 min $=$ 0.8 min
	$20\% \times$ 9 min $=$ 1.8 min
	$30\% \times 10$ min $=$ 3.0 min
	$40\% \times 11$ min $=$ $\underline{4.4 \text{ min}}$
Average service time	10.0 min

With this information, the assistant is ready to simulate the operation of the materials warehouse using a table of random digits such as Appendix Table 3. These digits run from 0 through 9. As we have previously noted, they occur in no particular order, although over long periods of time each digit occurs the same number of times.

We first consider the task of simulating the arrivals of shop foremen at the materials warehouse. We know that their arrivals are random but that there *is* a 100 per cent chance of one or more arrivals within any given five-minute period. Because we are dealing with 10 digits (with 0, 1, 2, 3, 4, 5, 6, 7, 8, 9), we could select one of these (perhaps 7) and let it represent an arrival. Since the digit 7 appears on the average once in each group of 10 digits, it represents the 100 per cent chance of an arrival.

Now if we break our simulation down into a number of five-minute periods of operation and if we go through a different list of random 10-digit numbers for each simulated period, the number of 7s we find in each 10-digit random number will represent the number of arrivals during that period.

We have simulated arrivals at the materials warehouse for a total of 24 five-minute periods. This is not necessarily the optimum period of simulation, but because the procedure is identical whether the number of periods is 10, 20, or even 100, we have elected to keep the number of simulated periods to a reasonable minimum to simplify the explanation.

To illustrate the procedure of simulating arrivals, let us reproduce the first 12 random 10-digit numbers and note the number of 7s appearing in each. We will read from left to right on the first 3 rows of random digits in Appendix Table 3.

1581922396	(none)
2068577984	2
8262130892	(none)
8374856049	1
4637567488	2
0928105582	(none)
7295088579	2
9586111652	(none)
7055508767	3
6472382934	1
4112077556	2
3440672486	1

Using the number of arrivals we have just computed for the first 12 five-minute periods and using the same technique to compute the number of arrivals during the *next* 12 five-minute periods, we have simulated the arrival of shop foremen at the warehouse. Results for all 24 periods of simulation are shown in Table 12-3.

Having simulated the arrivals at the warehouse, we now turn our attention to a simulation of the service times that would be required by each of the above arrivals. We know from a statement of the problem that these service times are randomly distributed, but we have gathered sufficient data to enable us to utilize a table of random numbers to represent or simulate this random distribution.

Recall the distribution of service times observed:

8 minutes	10%
9 minutes	20%
10 minutes	30%
11 minutes	40%

Table 12-3

Simulated arrivals for 24 periods			
Period number	Number of arrivals	Period number	Number of arrivals
1	0	13	0
2	2	14	0
3	0	15	1
4	1	16	4
5	2	17	1
6	0	18	1
7	2	19	1
8	0	20	0
9	3	21	0
10	1	22	1
11	2	23	0
12	1	24	2

Because we are still working with the same random digits (0, 1, 2, 3, 4, 5, 6, 7, 8, 9), we could divide them up in this sequence:

Let 0 represent the probability of a service time of 8 minutes.

Let 1 and 2 represent the probabilities of a service time of 9 minutes.

Let 3, 4, and 5 represent the probabilities of a service time of 10 minutes.

Let 6, 7, 8, and 9 represent the probabilities of a service time of 11 minutes.

Because we have 1 chance in 10 of getting a 0, it represents a .1 probability. Because we have 2 chances in 10 of getting either a 1 or a 2, they represent together a .2 probability. Because we have 3 chances in 10 of getting 3, 4, or 5, they represent together a .3 probability. Because we have 4 chances in 10 of getting a 6, 7, 8, or 9, they represent together a .4 probability. In this manner we are able to simulate the behavior of randomly distributed service times using a table of random numbers.

To illustrate this procedure, let us turn back to the first five-minute period of simulation in Table 12-3 and look at the arrivals. There were no arrivals during the first five-minute period.

Looking at the second five-minute period of simulated activity, we see that there were 2 arrivals. To simulate their service times, we turn to the table of random numbers. For arrival simulation we have elected to use the random digits beginning at the left-hand side of the fourth from bottom row of the table. The first two random digits on this row are 9 and 8. According to our representations on page 343, the first two arrivals require 11 minutes each for servicing.

To repeat this process for clarity, we turn to the third five-minute period and notice from Table 12-3 that there were no arrivals during this time; so on we go to the fourth period, when there was 1 arrival. The third random digit in our row is 4, signifying that this particular arrival required 10 minutes for servicing. If there are no arrivals, we do *not* skip a number. We have completed Table 12-4 by working through the above process for all 24 periods of simulation. Each arrival has been assigned a circled number.

Table 12-4

Simulated service times for 24 periods		
Period number	Number of arrivals	Service time of each
1	0	
2	2	① ② 11 min, 11 min
3	0	
4	1	③ 10 min
5	2	④ ⑤ 11 min, 10 min
6	0	
7	2	⑥ ⑦ 9 min, 10 min
8	0	

Table 12-4 (continued)

Period number	Number of arrivals	Service time of each
		⑧ ⑨ ⑩
9	3	10 min, 10 min, 11 min
		⑪
10	1	11 min
		⑫ ⑬
11	2	10 min, 8 min
		⑭
12	1	11 min
13	0	
14	0	
		⑮
15	1	11 min
		⑯ ⑰ ⑱ ⑲
16	4	10 min, 11 min, 11 min, 11 min
		⑳
17	1	9 min
		㉑
18	1	8 min
		㉒
19	1	11 min
20	0	
21	0	
		㉓
22	1	11 min
23	0	
		㉔ ㉕
24	2	9 min, 11 min

Now that we have simulated both the arrivals at the warehouse and the service time required for each arrival, we are ready to simulate the entire operation of the warehouse. We want to determine the optimum number of servicemen in the warehouse in order to minimize the total cost of warehouse operation *plus* time lost by waiting on the part of the foremen.

We use as our basic rule for service the first-come–first-served rule —the foremen are served as they arrive. The best method to illustrate the overall operation is to use a time scale covering the entire period of simulation. Since the 24 simulated 5-minute periods are so long as to require a pull-out page if placed end to end, we shall get around this by using time scales placed under each other on a single page, each unit or segment representing 15 minutes; eight such representative scales will be required. We begin the simulation at, let us say, 9 A.M. To make it easier to refer to arrivals, we use the circled numbers assigned to them in Table 12-4. Directly above each arrival is its service time.

To establish a routine for arrivals within each 5-minute period of simulation, we shall use the following assumptions:

1. If there is one arrival, it will be assumed to occur at the beginning of the 5-minute period.

2. If there are two arrivals, one will be assumed to arrive at the beginning of the period and the other to arrive at the beginning of the third minute during the period.

3. If there are three arrivals, one will be assumed to arrive at the beginning of the period, the second to arrive at the beginning of the third minute, and the third to arrive at the beginning of the fifth minute.

4. If there are four arrivals, they will be assumed to arrive at the beginning of the second, third, fourth, and fifth minutes.

To avoid dealing with fractional minutes, we elected to set up the pattern assumed above. To be sure, the power of simulation lies in its ability to treat situations and events as they actually happen—to avoid forcing them into arbitrary distributions or behavior patterns. Ideally, the distribution of arrivals within the 5-minute period should be based on *observed* patterns of behavior.

Figure 12-1 illustrates the arrival of all the foremen who used the service facility during the 2-hour period of simulated activity. We first try to operate the warehouse with two servicemen.

To illustrate the actual behavior of the system, let us use a diagram in which each minute of time is represented in the left-hand mar-

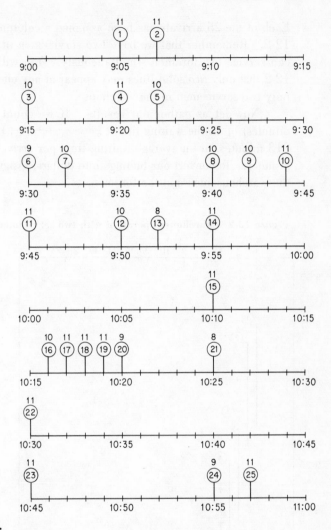

Figure 12-1 **Arrivals.**

gin. Beside each minute we can show each arrival, the time it is serviced, its service time, and the time it waits if waiting is necessary. This diagram is shown in Figure 12-2.

The following symbols make the diagram easy to follow:

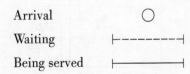

Each of the 25 arrivals has been assigned a column at the top of Figure 12-2. Remember that we have two servicemen in the warehouse; they can service two foremen simultaneously. You will notice from Figure 12-2 that only *two* solid lines may appear at any one time, since we have only two servicemen in the warehouse.

Now let us gather our results. If we count the total length (in minutes) of all the waiting time (⊢----------⊣), we see that it totals 213 minutes, or an average waiting time per arrival of 213/25 = 8.52 minutes. To convert our findings into dollars, assign a wage rate to both the warehousemen and the foremen:

Figure 12-2 **Warehouse operation with two servicemen.**

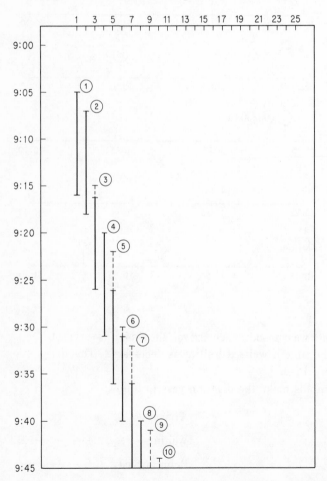

Wage rate for warehouse attendant	$3/hour
Wage rate for foremen	$4/hour

Now, if the average time between arrivals was 5 minutes (page 340), the foremen must make 96 trips to the warehouse daily (8 hours per day × 12 trips per hour). And if the average waiting time is 8.52 minutes per trip, total waiting time is 8.52 × 96 = 817.9 minutes, or 13.63 hours of lost time daily.

Figure 12-2   **(continued)**

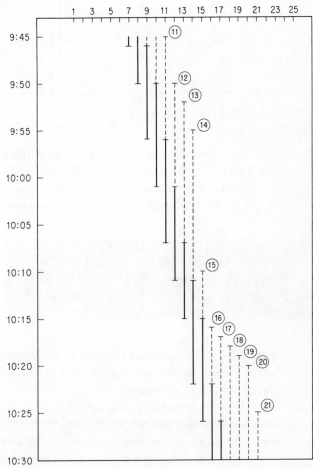

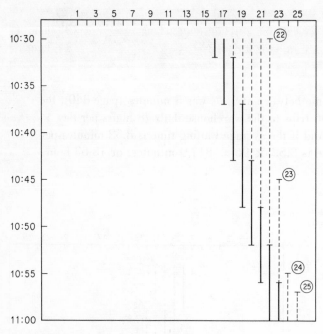

Figure 12-2 **(continued)**

The foremen's time costs \$4 per hour; therefore, the daily cost of lost time is 13.63 hours $\times$ \$4 = \$54.52. Add to this the cost of the two warehouse attendants (8 hours $\times$ \$3 per hour $\times$ 2 men = \$48) and we get, as the total cost of operating the warehouse in this manner,

Cost of lost time of foremen	\$ 54.52
Wages of attendants	48.00
Total daily cost	\$102.52

Is two, then, the optimum number of attendants to assign to the warehouse? There is only one way we can be sure—that is to simulate the system with *three* attendants.

We have done this in Figure 12-3 in exactly the same manner as before, except that now we have allowed three solid lines to exist simultaneously because three foremen can now be serviced at the same time.

Again we will count the total number of minutes of lost waiting time, which in this case totals 47 minutes. This is equivalent to 47/25, or 1.88 minutes lost per arrival. With 96 arrivals per day, the total time lost is 96 × 1.88, or 180.48 minutes, which equals about 3 hours per day.

Cost of lost time of foremen	3 × $4	= $12
Wages of attendants	8 × $3 × 3	= $72
Total daily cost		$84

Figure 12-3 **Warehouse operation with three servicemen.**

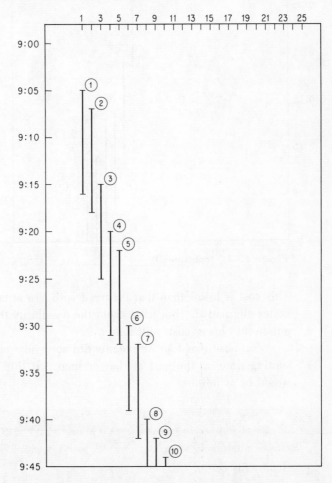

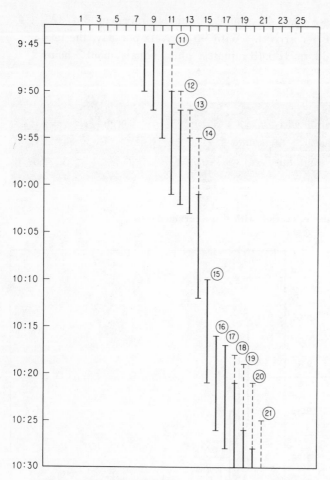

Figure 12-3 **(continued)**

This cost is lower than that incurred with two attendants; thus it is the better alternative. But what about the possibility that using four attendants would lower costs still more?

Suppose that four attendants did somehow manage to remove *all* waiting time on the part of the foremen. If this were the case, costs would be as follows:

Cost of lost time of foremen	0 hours $\times$ \$4 $=$ \$ 0
Wages of attendants	8 $\times$ \$3 $\times$ 4 $=$ \$96
Total daily cost	\$96

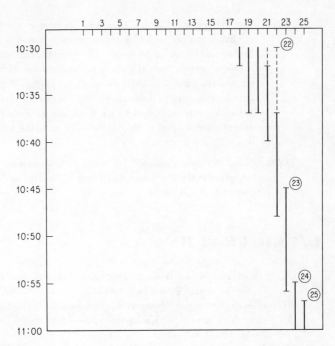

Figure 12-3 (continued)

This clearly results in an alternative not as attractive financially as having three attendants.

PROBLEMS

12-1 The Ajax Company operates a toolroom in one of its manufacturing plants. Currently the toolroom is staffed by one attendant. The arrival of machinists for service is observed to follow a uniform rate of 20 per hour, and the toolroom attendant is observed to handle these requests for service at the uniform rate of 18 per hour. Calculate the waiting line which is likely to be generated after 4 hours of operation.

12-2 If the toolroom attendant (problem 1 above) is paid $2.50 per hour and the machinists are paid $3.50 per hour, would it be profitable for the Ajax Company to increase the number of attendants?

12-3 Using the data from problems 1 and 2, calculate the optimum number of attendants the Ajax Company should assign to the toolroom to minimize the total cost of the operation.

12-4 Suppose the uniform arrival rate increases to 24 per hour. What changes, if any, would this cause in the answer to problem 3?

12-5 The Mastercraft Machine Company operates a warehouse which services its mechanics. The mechanics are observed to arrive at the warehouse at the random arrival rate of 10 per hour. The one warehouse attendant currently assigned is able to service these arrivals at the uniform rate of 8 per hour. The observer has also recorded data which indicate that there is a .2 probability of 1 or more arrivals during any 10-minute period. If the attendant is paid $2.50 per hour and each mechanic is paid $4 per hour, use the simulation method to determine the optimum number of attendants to assign to the warehouse to minimize total cost.

12-6 Using the data presented in problem 5, determine to what extent, if any, the optimum solution would be affected if the attendant's wage rate were to be increased to $3.50 per hour.

BIBLIOGRAPHY

R. H. Bock and W. K. Holstein, *Production Planning and Control* (Columbus, Ohio: Charles E. Merrill Books, Inc., 1963).

H. N. Broom, *Production Management* (Homewood, Ill.: Richard D. Irwin, Inc., 1962).

B. Hanes, *Mathematics for Management Science* (Columbus, Ohio: Charles E. Merrill Books, Inc., 1962).

J. E. Howell and D. Teichroew, *Mathematical Analysis for Business Decisions* (Homewood, Ill.: Richard D. Irwin, Inc., 1963).

A. Kaufmann, *Methods and Models of Operations Research* (Englewood Cliffs, N.J.: Prentice-Hall, Inc., New Jersey, 1963).

W. T. Morris, *Analysis for Materials Handling Management* (Homewood, Ill.: Richard D. Irwin, Inc., 1962).

A. Shuchman, *Scientific Decision Making in Business* (New York: Holt, Rinehart and Winston, Inc., 1963).

APPENDIXES

Appendix 1

Areas under the curve

	.00	.01	.02	.03	.04	.05	.06	.07	.08	.09
0.0	.50000	.50399	.50798	.51197	.51595	.51994	.52392	.52790	.53188	.53586
0.1	.53983	.54380	.54776	.55172	.55567	.55962	.56356	.56749	.57142	.57535
0.2	.57926	.58317	.58706	.59095	.59483	.59871	.60257	.60642	.61026	.61409
0.3	.61791	.62172	.62552	.62930	.63307	.63683	.64058	.64431	.64803	.65173
0.4	.65542	.65910	.66276	.66640	.67003	.67364	.67724	.68082	.68439	.68793
0.5	.69146	.69497	.69847	.70194	.70540	.70884	.71226	.71566	.71904	.72240
0.6	.72575	.72907	.73237	.73536	.73891	.74215	.74537	.74857	.75175	.75490
0.7	.75804	.76115	.76424	.76730	.77035	.77337	.77637	.77935	.78230	.78524
0.8	.78814	.79103	.79389	.79673	.79955	.80234	.80511	.80785	.81057	.81327
0.9	.81594	.81859	.82121	.82381	.82639	.82894	.83147	.83398	.83646	.83891
1.0	.84134	.84375	.84614	.84849	.85083	.85314	.85543	.85769	.85993	.86214
1.1	.86433	.86650	.86864	.87076	.87286	.87493	.87698	.87900	.88100	.88298
1.2	.88493	.88686	.88877	.89065	.89251	.89435	.89617	.89796	.89973	.90147
1.3	.90320	.90490	.90658	.90824	.90988	.91149	.91309	.91466	.91621	.91774
1.4	.91924	.92073	.92220	.92364	.92507	.92647	.92785	.92922	.93056	.93189
1.5	.93319	.93448	.93574	.93699	.93822	.93943	.94062	.94179	.94295	.94408
1.6	.94520	.94630	.94738	.94845	.94950	.95053	.95154	.95254	.95352	.95449
1.7	.95543	.95637	.95728	.95818	.95907	.95994	.96080	.96164	.96246	.96327
1.8	.96407	.96485	.96562	.96638	.96712	.96784	.96856	.96926	.96995	.97062
1.9	.97128	.97193	.97257	.97320	.97381	.97441	.97500	.97558	.97615	.97670

	.00	.01	.02	.03	.04	.05	.06	.07	.08	.09
2.0	.97725	.97784	.97831	.97882	.97932	.97982	.98030	.98077	.98124	.98169
2.1	.98214	.98257	.98300	.98341	.98382	.98422	.98461	.98500	.98537	.98574
2.2	.98610	.98645	.98679	.98713	.98745	.98778	.98809	.98840	.98870	.98899
2.3	.98928	.98956	.98983	.99010	.99036	.99061	.99086	.99111	.99134	.99158
2.4	.99180	.99202	.99224	.99245	.99266	.99286	.99305	.99324	.99343	.99361
2.5	.99379	.99396	.99413	.99430	.99446	.99461	.99477	.99492	.99506	.99520
2.6	.99534	.99547	.99560	.99573	.99585	.99598	.99609	.99621	.99632	.99643
2.7	.99653	.99664	.99674	.99683	.99693	.99702	.99711	.99720	.99728	.99736
2.8	.99744	.99752	.99760	.99767	.99774	.99781	.99788	.99795	.99801	.99807
2.9	.99813	.99819	.99825	.99831	.99836	.99841	.99846	.99851	.99856	.99861
3.0	.99865	.99869	.99874	.99878	.99882	.99886	.99899	.99893	.99896	.99900
3.1	.99903	.99906	.99910	.99913	.99916	.99918	.99921	.99924	.99926	.99929
3.2	.99931	.99934	.99936	.99938	.99940	.99942	.99944	.99946	.99948	.99950
3.3	.99952	.99953	.99955	.99957	.99958	.99960	.99961	.99962	.99964	.99965
3.4	.99966	.99968	.99969	.99970	.99971	.99972	.99973	.99974	.99975	.99976
3.5	.99977	.99978	.99978	.99979	.99980	.99981	.99981	.99982	.99983	.99983
3.6	.99984	.99985	.99985	.99986	.99986	.99987	.99987	.99988	.99988	.99989
3.7	.99989	.99990	.99990	.99990	.99991	.99991	.99992	.99992	.99992	.99992
3.8	.99993	.99993	.99993	.99994	.99994	.99994	.99994	.99995	.99995	.99995
3.9	.99995	.99995	.99996	.99996	.99996	.99996	.99996	.99996	.99997	.99997

Directions: To find the area under the curve between the left-hand end and any point, determine how many standard deviations that point is to the right of the average, then read the area directly from the body of the table. *Example:* The area under the curve from the left-hand end and a point 1.81 standard deviations to the right of the average is .96485 of the total area under the curve.

Appendix 2

Square roots (1-400)

1	1.00	41	6.40	81	9.00	121	11.00	161	12.69
2	1.41	42	6.48	82	9.06	122	11.05	162	12.73
3	1.73	43	6.56	83	9.11	123	11.09	163	12.77
4	2.00	44	6.63	84	9.17	124	11.14	164	12.81
5	2.24	45	6.71	85	9.22	125	11.18	165	12.85
6	2.45	46	6.78	86	9.27	126	11.23	166	12.88
7	2.65	47	6.86	87	9.33	127	11.27	167	12.92
8	2.83	48	6.93	88	9.38	128	11.31	168	12.96
9	3.00	49	7.00	89	9.43	129	11.36	169	13.00
10	3.16	50	7.07	90	9.49	130	11.40	170	13.04
11	3.32	51	7.14	91	9.54	131	11.45	171	13.08
12	3.46	52	7.21	92	9.59	132	11.49	172	13.11
13	3.61	53	7.28	93	9.64	133	11.53	173	13.15
14	3.74	54	7.35	94	9.70	134	11.58	174	13.19
15	3.87	55	7.42	95	9.75	135	11.62	175	13.23
16	4.00	56	7.48	96	9.80	136	11.66	176	13.27
17	4.12	57	7.55	97	9.85	137	11.70	177	13.30
18	4.24	58	7.62	98	9.90	138	11.74	178	13.34
19	4.36	59	7.68	99	9.95	139	11.79	179	13.38
20	4.47	60	7.75	100	10.00	140	11.83	180	13.42
21	4.58	61	7.81	101	10.05	141	11.87	181	13.45
22	4.69	62	7.87	102	10.10	142	11.92	182	13.49
23	4.80	63	7.94	103	10.15	143	11.96	183	13.53
24	4.90	64	8.00	104	10.20	144	12.00	184	13.56
25	5.00	65	8.06	105	10.25	145	12.04	185	13.60
26	5.10	66	8.12	106	10.30	146	12.08	186	13.64
27	5.20	67	8.19	107	10.34	147	12.12	187	13.67
28	5.29	68	8.25	108	10.39	148	12.17	188	13.71
29	5.39	69	8.31	109	10.44	149	12.21	189	13.75
30	5.48	70	8.37	110	10.49	150	12.25	190	13.78
31	5.57	71	8.43	111	10.54	151	12.29	191	13.82
32	5.66	72	8.49	112	10.58	152	12.33	192	13.86
33	5.74	73	8.54	113	10.63	153	12.37	193	13.89
34	5.83	74	8.60	114	10.68	154	12.41	194	13.93
35	5.92	75	8.66	115	10.72	155	12.45	195	13.96
36	6.00	76	8.72	116	10.77	156	12.49	196	14.00
37	6.08	77	8.77	117	10.82	157	12.53	197	14.04
38	6.16	78	8.83	118	10.86	158	12.57	198	14.07
39	6.25	79	8.89	119	10.91	159	12.61	199	14.11
40	6.32	80	8.94	120	10.95	160	12.65	200	14.14

201	14.18	241	15.52	281	16.76	321	17.92	361	19.00
202	14.21	242	15.56	282	16.79	322	17.94	362	19.03
203	14.25	243	15.59	283	16.82	323	17.97	363	19.05
204	14.28	244	15.62	284	16.85	324	18.00	364	19.08
205	14.32	245	15.65	285	16.88	325	18.03	365	19.11
206	14.35	246	15.68	286	16.91	326	18.06	366	19.13
207	14.39	247	15.72	287	16.94	327	18.08	367	19.16
208	14.42	248	15.75	288	16.97	328	18.11	368	19.18
209	14.46	249	15.78	289	17.00	329	18.14	369	19.21
210	14.49	250	15.81	290	17.03	330	18.17	370	19.24
211	14.53	251	15.84	291	17.06	331	18.19	371	19.26
212	14.56	252	15.87	292	17.09	332	18.22	372	19.29
213	14.59	253	15.91	293	17.12	333	18.25	373	19.31
214	14.63	254	15.94	294	17.15	334	18.28	374	19.34
215	14.66	255	15.97	295	17.18	335	18.30	375	19.36
216	14.70	256	16.00	296	17.20	336	18.33	376	19.39
217	14.73	257	16.03	297	17.23	337	18.36	377	19.42
218	14.76	258	16.06	298	17.26	338	18.38	378	19.44
219	14.80	259	16.09	299	17.29	339	18.41	379	19.47
220	14.83	260	16.12	300	17.32	340	18.44	380	19.49
221	14.87	261	16.16	301	17.35	341	18.47	381	19.52
222	14.90	262	16.19	302	17.38	342	18.49	382	19.54
223	14.93	263	16.22	303	17.41	343	18.52	383	19.57
224	14.97	264	16.25	304	17.44	344	18.55	384	19.60
225	15.00	265	16.28	305	17.46	345	18.57	385	19.62
226	15.03	266	16.31	306	17.49	346	18.60	386	19.65
227	15.07	267	16.34	307	17.52	347	18.63	387	19.67
228	15.10	268	16.37	308	17.55	348	18.65	388	19.70
229	15.13	269	16.40	309	17.58	349	18.68	389	19.72
230	15.17	270	16.43	310	17.61	350	18.71	390	19.75
231	15.20	271	16.46	311	17.64	351	18.74	391	19.77
232	15.23	272	16.49	312	17.66	352	18.76	392	19.80
233	15.26	273	16.52	313	17.69	353	18.79	393	19.82
234	15.30	274	16.55	314	17.72	354	18.81	394	19.85
235	15.33	275	16.58	315	17.75	355	18.84	395	19.87
236	15.36	276	16.61	316	17.78	356	18.87	396	19.90
237	15.39	277	16.64	317	17.80	357	18.89	397	19.92
238	15.43	278	16.67	318	17.83	358	18.92	398	19.95
239	15.46	279	16.70	319	17.86	359	18.95	399	19.98
240	15.49	280	16.73	320	17.89	360	18.97	400	20.00

Appendix 3

2,500 random digits

1581922396	2068577984	8262130892	8374856049	4637567488
0928105582	7295088579	9586111652	7055508767	6472382934
4112077556	3440672486	1882412963	0684012006	0933147914
7457477468	5435810788	9670852913	1291265730	4890031305
0099520858	3090908872	2039593181	5973470495	9776135501
7245174840	2275698645	8416549348	4676463101	2229367983
6749420382	4832630032	5670984959	5432114610	2966095680
5503161011	7413686599	1198757695	0414294470	0140121598
7164238934	7666127259	5263097712	5133648980	4011966963
3593969525	0272759769	0385998136	9999089966	7544056852
4192054466	0700014629	5169439659	8408705169	1074373131
9697426117	6488888550	4031652526	8123543276	0927534537
2007950579	9564268448	3457416988	1531027886	7016633739
4584768758	2389278610	3859431781	3643768456	4141314518
3840145867	9120831830	7228567652	1267173884	4020651657
0190453442	4800088084	1165628559	5407921254	3768932478
6766554338	5585265145	5089052204	9780623691	2195448096
6315116284	9172824179	5544814339	0016943666	3828538786
3908771938	4035554324	0840126299	4942059208	1475623997
5570024586	9324732596	1186563397	4425143189	3216653251
2999997185	0135968938	7678931194	1351031403	6002561840
7864375912	8383232768	1892857070	2323673751	3188881718
7065492027	6349104233	3382569662	4579426926	1513082455
0654683246	4765104877	8149224168	5468631609	6474393896
7830555058	5255147182	3519287786	2481675649	8907598697
7626984369	4725370390	9641916289	5049082870	7463807244
4785048453	3646121751	8436077768	2928794356	9956043516
4627791048	5765558107	8762592043	6185670830	6363845920
9376470693	0441608934	8749472723	2202271078	5897002653
1227991661	7936797054	9527542791	4711871173	8300978148
5582095589	5535798279	4764439855	6279247618	4446895088
4959397698	1056981450	8416606706	8234013222	6426813469
1824779358	1333750468	9434074212	5273692238	5902177065
7041092295	5726289716	3420847871	1820481234	0318831723
3555104281	0903099163	6827824899	6383872737	5901682626
9717595534	1634107293	8521057472	1471300754	3044151557
5571564123	7344613447	1129117244	3208461091	1699403490
4674262892	2809456764	5806554509	8224980942	5738031833
8461228715	0746980892	9285305274	6331989646	8764467686
1838538678	3049068967	6955157269	5482964330	2161984904
1834182305	6203476893	5937802079	3445280195	3694915658
1884227732	2923727501	8044389132	4611203081	6072112445
6791857341	6696243386	2219599137	3193884236	8224729718
3007929946	4031562749	5570757297	6273785046	1455349704
6085440624	2875556938	5496629750	4841817356	1443167141
7005051056	3496332071	5054070890	7303867953	6255181190
9846413446	8306646692	0661684251	8875127201	6251533454
0625457703	4229164694	7321363715	7051128285	1108468072
5457593922	9751489574	1799906380	1989141062	5595364247
4076486653	8950826528	4934582003	4071187742	1456207629

Dudley J. Cowden and Mercedes S. Cowden, *Practical Problems in Business Statistics*, 2d ed., © 1963, by permission of Prentice-Hall, Inc., Englewood Cliffs, N.J.

INDEX